ELEMENTARY CONTEMPORARY MATHEMATICS

A Blaisdell Book in Pure and Applied Mathematics

Consulting Editor
J O H N K E M E N Y, *Dartmouth College*

Elementary
Contemporary Mathematics

MERLIN M. OHMER
The University of Southwestern Louisiana

CLAYTON V. AUCOIN
Clemson University

MARION J. CORTEZ
Northside School

Blaisdell Publishing Company
A Division of Ginn and Company

WALTHAM, MASSACHUSETTS · TORONTO · LONDON

TO

our wives and children

PREFACE

The Committee on the Undergraduate Program in Mathematics of the Mathematical Association of America has recommended two semesters of the structure of the number system, one semester of algebra, and one semester of geometry for all prospective elementary school teachers (Level I). We have written this book for the two-semester sequence on the structure of the number system, and have used it in the two-semester course at the University of Southwestern Louisiana where we have taught the entire text as indicated in the following table.

Chapter	*Number of Lessons*	
1. Logic	12	
2. Sets	9	1st Semester
3. The Set of Counting Numbers	11	(45 lessons)
4. Numeration Systems	8	
TESTING	5	
5. Subtraction and the Set of Integers	6	
6. Elementary Number Theory	9	
7. The Rational Numbers	10	2nd Semester
8. Decimals and the Real Number System	9	(45 lessons)
9. Finite Number Systems	6	
TESTING	5	

The text is suitable either for training of prospective elementary teachers or for in-service or summer institute training of experienced teachers and has been used successfully in both pre-service and institute courses.

We have included many theorems and proofs in the text with the hope that the students will read and understand both the statements of the theorems given in the text and also those proofs presented in class by the teacher. At the University of Southwestern Louisiana we have proved approximately one-third of the theorems each semester, and over a period of several semesters, have proved each theorem at least once. The teachers have found it beneficial to inform the students of the particular theorems which they were going to prove in a given semester, thus enabling the students to read ahead with more proficiency. The end of each proof is indicated by the symbol "$/\!/$."

Some problems call for proofs of theorems. Although the teacher may wish to omit these problems, we hope that the student will at least read and understand the theorems on which they are based as well as those included in the body of the text.

The text is comprehensible and clear without the proofs of the theorems because each theorem is sufficiently motivated and explained by examples—some preceding and some following the theorem. Moreover, difficult definitions are also well motivated by examples.

We are indebted to many persons, especially to the many students and elementary school teachers who studied this text in mimeographed form. In particular, we express our gratitude to Dr. John G. Kemeny, Chairman of the Mathematics Department of Dartmouth College and former Chairman of the CUPM panel on Teacher Training, for his candid and valuable suggestions, comments, and criticisms. He followed and read the entire manuscript as it was being developed and re-read it after it was completed. We are grateful also to Dr. Z. L. Loflin, Chairman of the Mathematics Department at the University of Southwestern Louisiana; to Miss Jessie May Hoag, Dr. David R. Andrew, Mrs. Claire Aucoin, and Mr. Duane D. Blumberg, all of the University of Southwestern Louisiana, for their valuable comments and criticisms during the development of the manuscript; to Dr. Katherine C. Mires, Chairman of the Mathematics Department at Northwestern State College, Alva, Oklahoma, for her valuable comments and criticisms on the manuscript; to Dr. Robert J. Wisner, former Executive Director of the Committee on the Undergraduate Program in Mathematics, for his encouragement during the development of the manuscript; and to Mrs. Sidney Delhomme for typing most of the manuscript.

Finally, we thank our wives for their patience, understanding, and encouragement during the preparation of the manuscript.

MERLIN M. OHMER
CLAYTON V. AUCOIN
MARION J. CORTEZ

Lafayette, Louisiana
June 1, 1964

CONTENTS

Contents

ELEMENTARY CONTEMPORARY MATHEMATICS

Chapter 1

LOGIC

1.1 Introduction to Logic

Logical reasoning plays an important role in everybody's life today. Every day one must make decisions based on his ability to reason. As the rules employed by the average person in his daily reasoning are more subconscious than conscious, he occasionally reasons incorrectly. The following example illustrates the need for a systematic study of the language of logic and logical inference.

> If Toby wins the contest, then he will travel to Europe.
> If he travels to Europe, then he will visit Rome.
> If he does not visit Paris, then he will not visit Rome.
> Toby just won the contest.
> Conclusion: Toby will visit Paris.

It is not easy to see that the stated conclusion is actually *valid*; that is, the conclusion actually follows logically from the three given statements. Later you will learn how to derive the conclusion from the given statements.

The purpose of this chapter is to present a brief introduction to the elementary concepts of logic. An understanding of these principles is extremely valuable in the study of mathematics. As this text is not a treatise on logic, we do not attempt to build a complete logical system but only to include the fundamental ideas of logic. The student who wishes to pursue the study of logic per se should consult any of the well-known texts on logic.

In any discussion, we must *agree* on the definitions of the terms used, or else we must leave certain terms *undefined.* You have probably witnessed heated arguments between friends. Usually such an argument ends where it begins; each person leaves still convinced of his own point of view. Actually, the debaters may have been in almost complete agreement. This apparent paradox has a simple explanation—the two persons did not agree beforehand on the definitions of the words used. Each attached his own special meanings to the words. For example, a United States official may have a definition of the word *democracy* far different from that of a USSR official. Your experience tells you that the two officials probably cannot agree on an issue involving democracy. In order to avoid ambiguity and contradictions in mathematics, we must agree, in advance, on the definitions of all technical words used or else we must state which words are undefined. The reason for not defining certain mathematical words is that it is impossible to define all mathematical words without permitting our definitions to form circular chains. As simple as this fact may seem, many great mathematicians and philosophers of the past did not realize this. If you look up the definition of an unfamiliar word in a standard dictionary, you discover that this unfamiliar word is defined in terms of other words. If you look up these other words, you find that they are defined in terms of other words. Eventually one of the new words is the original word whose definition you were seeking. For example, we might find the following:

> set—group
> group—assemblage
> assemblage—collection
> collection—set

Once we have selected the relatively small number of undefined words in the mathematical system under investigation, we strive to have the definitions obey the following properties:

(1) Any definition of a new word must be expressed in terms of the undefined words and/or the previously defined words and common nontechnical English words.
(2) Any definition must be consistent with itself and with other definitions.
(3) Any definition must be meaningful.
(4) Any definition must be expressed in such a manner that it includes all desired cases and excludes all undesired cases.

Just as we begin with certain undefined words, we also begin with certain statements which we assume to be true. These assumed statements are called *postulates.* Other names for the assumed statements are *axioms* and *assumptions.* Among other things, the postulates describe the undefined words. For example, the words *point* and *line* are left undefined in Euclidean Geometry. However, they are described in the postulates: two different points determine exactly one line; two different lines which are not parallel intersect in exactly one point.

Just as we define the new words in terms of the undefined words and/or the previously defined words, we prove new statements called *theorems* from the postulates, definitions, and previously proved theorems. The reasoning process which we employ in proving theorems is controlled by the laws of logic of rules of inference. The laws of logic control the combination of given sentences (called the *hypotheses*) into one or more new sentences (called the *conclusion*).

Since our use of the word *sentence* is different from the English usage, we begin with its definition.

DEFINITION 1. A *sentence* is any declarative statement which is either true or false, but not both true and false.

From Definition 1 we see that a sentence must be meaningful and unambiguous. The following are examples of sentences.

Example 1.   My mother has blue eyes.

Example 2.   All dogs are quadrupeds.

Example 3.   Some dogs are quadrupeds.

Example 4.   No dogs are quadrupeds.

Example 5.   Benjamin Franklin wore glasses.

Example 6. $14 + 2 = 16$.

Example 7. $6 + 3 = 3 + 6$.

Example 8.   5 is equal to 6.

Example 9.   All ninth grade algebra students study mathematics and some ninth grade students study English.

Example 10.   If John comes home, then his wife will cook dinner.

Although we could refuse to admit that Examples 1, 5, and 10 are sentences on the grounds that one cannot determine, for example, whether Example 10 is true until he knows who *John* is, we prefer to agree that any name appearing in a sentence specifies a particular person, object, and so on. In everyday conversation when one of your acquaintances tells you that Jack Jones is ill, you know that he is referring to a particular Jack Jones, in spite of the fact that, in reality, there are numerous persons named Jack Jones. Actually, although one would ordinarily say that the sentence of Example 6 is true, it is similar to Examples 1, 5, and 10. When we write "14 + 2 = 16," we mean "fourteen plus two is equal to sixteen." The symbols 14, 2, and 16 are similar to the names John, Ben, et cetera. They symbolize or represent the numbers just as the name *John* symbolizes or represents the person. You will learn in Chapter 4 that the symbol 14 may represent some number other than fourteen. However, when we write 14 + 2 = 16, you know that we are referring to particular numbers. Thus we agree to visualize a sentence as stated by a specific person at a specific time and place. In this way any possible ambiguities are clarified by the context.

The similar statement "$x + 2 = 16$" is *not* a sentence because the symbol x does not specify a particular number. Until we know that the symbol x specifies a particular number, we cannot determine whether "$x + 2$" $= 16$ is true or not. For example, if $x = 14$, we can say that "$x + 2 = 16$" is true; whereas, if $x = 23$, we can say that "$x + 2 = 16$" is false. A nonspecific symbol (such as x, y, z, $\triangle$, $\square$, et cetera) for a number or person or object is called a *variable*. Since replacement of the variable x by a specific number converts the statement "$x + 2 = 16$" into a sentence, we say that the statement "$x + 2 = 16$" is an *open sentence*. In a similar manner the open sentence "x wears glasses" can be converted to a sentence by the replacement of the variable x by a particular or specific person. Later you will learn a more formal definition of *variable*. In the meantime, the intuitive concept of variable is sufficient.

DEFINITION 2. A statement which contains a variable is called an *open sentence* if and only if it is not a sentence but becomes a sentence upon replacement of the variable by a specific number, person, or object.

Notice that an open sentence may contain more than one variable. Throughout this chapter, the word *number* means *counting number*; that is, 0, 1, 2, 3, and so on.* The following are examples of open sentences.

Example 11. $x + 2 = 5 \times 7$

* Many texts consider 1, 2, 3, . . . as counting numbers, and 0, 1, 2, 3, . . . as whole numbers. See page 72 for further discussion of this.

Example 12. $x + 7 = 7 + 2x$

Example 13. $4x = 4 + x$

Example 14. $x^2 + 3x + 2 = 0$

Example 15. $a + 2 = 2x$

Example 16. $6 + 3x = a + by$

Example 17. $ax^2 + bx + c = 0$

Some examples of nonsentences which are not open sentences are:

Example 18.   Study mathematics while you are young.

Example 19.   Why are you wearing sunglasses?

Example 20.   The tallest man in the class.

Exercise 1.1

I. Classify the following as sentence, open sentence, or neither.

(1) Mary went to the movie.
(2) All the students in this class did their homework.
(3) $3 + 4 = 11 - 4$.
(4) No men live forever.
(5) $x - y = a + b$.
(6) All men are mortal.
(7) Adam dates a freshman.
(8) $2/3 + 3/5$.
(9) If x is less than 7.
(10) There is a number y greater than 11 and less than 17.
(11) If the sum of two numbers is zero, then both of the numbers are zero or neither is zero.
(12) $100 - 4 + 13$.
(13) 11 is greater than y.
(14) $5 + 4 = 9$ and $3 + 4 = 8$.
(15) $x - 2 = 7$.
(16) $x + 5$ is larger than 8.
(17) $2x - 3 = 2 + 3$.
(18) $2x - 1 = 5$.

(19) $x/5 = 10$.
(20) $x/5 + 3/5$ is larger than.
(21) $x/5 + 3/5$.
(22) $x/5 + 3/5$ is larger than $7/5$.
(23) $a + 0 = a$.
(24) $b \times 1 = b$.
(25) How are you?
(26) $24 + 4 = 14 + 10$.
(27) Go away.
(28) $0/6 = 0$.
(29) $0 + a = 0$.
(30) $24/3 = 9$.

1.2   Quantifiers

Recall that an open sentence is not really a sentence. However, an open sentence can be converted to a sentence by the replacement of the variable with a specific number, person, or object. For example, the open sentence $x + 2 = 7$ is converted to the true sentence $5 + 2 = 7$ by replacing the variable *x* with the number 5. Replacement of the variable x by the number 3 converts the open sentence $x + 2 = 7$ to the false sentence $3 + 2 = 7$. The replacement method is not the only method of converting an open sentence to a sentence. For example, we could assert that there is a number x such that $x + 2 = 7$. The assertion "there is a number x such that $x + 2 = 7$" is a sentence; in fact, it is a true sentence. Similarly, the assertion "for all numbers x, $x + 2 = 7$" is a sentence; but it is a false sentence. The open sentence $x + 3 = 3 + x$ becomes a sentence if we prefix the phrase "for all x." Thus "for all numbers x, $x + 3 = 3 + x$" is a sentence, and, in fact, is a true sentence. Note that "there is a number x such that $x + 3 = 3 + x$" is also a true sentence. Although "$x + 3 \neq x$" is not a sentence, the statement "for any number x, $x + 3 \neq x$" is a true sentence. You may notice that the latter sentence has the same meaning as the sentence "there is no number x such that $x + 3 = x$."

Observe that we have converted an open sentence by prefixing the phrase "for all numbers x" or the phrase "there exists a number x such that." As both of these phrases convey the idea of quantity, the words *all* and *there exist* are called *quantifiers*. An alternate expression for the quantifier *there exists* is *some*. The third quantifier is *no* or *none*. The sentences "*all* dogs are quadrupeds," "*some* dogs are quadrupeds," and "*no* dogs are quadrupeds" illustrate the use of the quantifiers *all*, *some*, and *no*. Recall that the word *number* in this chapter means *counting number*. Thus the sentence "for some number x, $x + 3 = 1$" is false. If we included the negative numbers, the sentence "for some number x,

$x + 3 = 1$" would be true. Thus we realize that a quantifier refers to a specific collection of numbers, persons, or objects. The sentence "the base angles of an isosceles triangle are equal" means "for all isosceles triangles t, the base angles of t are equal." Hence the quantifier here is *all* and refers to the collection of isosceles triangles. Whenever the quantifier is omitted by the writer and supplied by the reader, we say that the quantifier is *implied* rather than *expressed*. Thus, in the foregoing, the quantifier *all* is implied. If we supply a quantifier to an open sentence, we convert that open sentence to a sentence.

The quantifier *all* is called the *universal quantifier*, and the quantifier *some* (there exists) is called the *existential quantifier*. As the quantifier *no* (none) may be expressed in terms of the universal or existential quantifier, it is not given a special name. For example, the sentence "no odd number is divisible by two" may be expressed as either "there does not exist an odd number which is divisible by two" or "for all x, if x is an odd number, then x is not divisible by two."

In summary we list the two methods of converting an open sentence to a sentence.

(1) Replace the variable by the name of a specific number, person, or object.
(2) Quantify the variable.

Exercise 1.2

I. Identify the quantifier or quantifiers in each of the following sentences, as *all, some* (*there exists*), or *no* (*none*).

(1) All birds fly.
(2) Some birds fly.
(3) Some students will become teachers.
(4) No reptiles can fly.
(5) Some numbers are odd.
(6) There is a smallest number.
(7) For every number, there is a larger one.
(8) There is no largest number.
(9) For all numbers x, $x + 5 = 8$.
(10) There exists a number x such that $x + 5 = 8$.
(11) Some birds fly and no monkeys fly.
(12) For all numbers x, if x is positive, then $x + 2$ is positive.
(13) For all numbers x, either x is even or x is odd.
(14) Any even number is divisible by two.
(15) There is a man x such that x has blue eyes.

II. State whether a quantifier is expressed or implied in each of the following.

(1) $4 + 3 = 9$.
(2) For all x, $x + 5 = 5 + x$.
(3) Men are mortal.
(4) There is no x such that $x = x + 1$.
(5) $5 + 4 = 4 + 5$.
(6) A rectangle has four sides.
(7) Socrates is mortal.
(8) A rose is a flower.
(9) 5 is a counting number.
(10) An equilateral triangle has equal angles.

III. Identify the quantifier (expressed or implied) in each of the statements in Exercise II.

IV. Classify each statement in Exercise II as a sentence or an open sentence.

V. Quantify each of the following open sentences by use of each of the three quantifiers (all, some, none). Determine whether each of the resulting sentences is true or false.

(1) $x + x = 2x$
(2) $x + 3 = 7$
(3) $t + 5 = 5$
(4) $6 + y = 6$
(5) $7 + y = y$
(6) $t + 5 = t$
(7) $t + 6 = 6$
(8) $2t + 3t = 5t$
(9) $a + 7 = 3$
(10) $5 + b = 2$

1.3 Connectives, Compound Sentences, and Simple Sentences

In English grammar, you study simple sentences and compound sentences and use words such as *or* and *and*. In mathematics, also, we study simple sentences and compound sentences. However, our definitions differ slightly from those in grammar. In order to define these terms, we first give a name to the undefined words *not, or, and, if ... then ...* , and *if and only if*.

DEFINITION 3. The words *not, or, and, if ... then ...* , and *if and only if* are called *connectives*.

DEFINITION 4. A sentence is said to be a *compound sentence* if and only if it contains a connective.

DEFINITION 5. A sentence is said to be a *simple sentence* if and only if it does not contain a connective.

Similar definitions are made for open sentences.

Since any sentence either does or does not contain a connective, we see that every sentence can be classified as either compound or simple. However, you should realize that the connective may not appear explicitly; a substitute may appear in its place or the connective may be implied. For example, the sentence "Mary is enrolled in Mathematics, but Mary is not enrolled in Greek" is a compound sentence. Although the connective *and* does not appear explicitly in that sentence, the English substitute *but* does appear.

The dots in the notation *if ... then ...* mean that some words have not been written. For example, in the sentence "*if* it rains today, *then* the game will be postponed," the connective consists of only the two words *if* and *then* and is written *if ... then ....* . The omitted words are "it rains today" and "the game will be postponed."

The following are examples of simple sentences.

Example 1. Betty went to college.

Example 2. Betty was early for her mathematics class today.

Example 3. $10 + 5 = 5 + 10$.

Example 4. Page's father is a mathematics teacher.

Example 5. $4 + 5 = 9$.

Example 6. $4 + 5 = 10$.

Example 7. This bird can fly.

Example 8. $2 + 5 = 5 + 2$.

Example 9. The sum of these two numbers is eight.

Example 10. 5 is smaller than 8.

The following are examples of compound sentences.

Example 11. Some birds can fly, and no monkeys fly.

Example 12.   Betty did not go to college.

Example 13.   Betty went to college and passed all her subjects.

Example 14.   Betty was early for her mathematics class today but late for her Greek class.

Example 15. $4 + 5 \neq 10$ and $4 + 5 = 9$.

Example 16.   If it rains tomorrow, then I will read a book.

Example 17.   Ronnie will score twenty points in a basketball game if and only if he plays four quarters.

Example 18.   It did not rain yesterday.

Example 19.   Tom will attend Harvard or Yale.

Example 20. $2 = 5$ or $2 + 3 = 5$.

A comment on the words "if and only if" used in the definitions may be in order. You are familiar with the definition of equilateral triangle, namely, triangle ABC is said to be equilateral if and only if the lengths of its sides are equal. This definition is really a statement of *two* facts. First, any triangle whose sides are of equal length is an equilateral triangle. Second, the sides of any equilateral triangle are of equal length.

Exercise 1.3

I. Classify each of the following sentences as simple or compound. Name the connectives of each compound sentence.

(1) $6 + 5 = 5 + 6$.
(2) $6 + 5 \neq 5 + 6$.
(3) $4 + 3$ is not equal to 6.
(4) $(4 + 3 = 3 + 4)$ or $(4 + 3 = 3)$.
(5) $(4 + 3 = 3 + 4)$ or $(4 + 3 \neq 3 + 4)$.
(6) $(5 + 0 = 5)$ and $(0 + 5 = 5)$.
(7) $(6 + 0 = 6)$ and $(6 \times 1 = 6)$.
(8) $(7 \times 0 = 0)$ and $(0 \times 7 = 0)$.
(9) $(1 \times 5 = 5)$ and $(2 \times 5 \neq 5)$.
(10) If $1 + 5 = 6$, then $5 + 1 = 6$.
(11) $7 + 7 = 7$.
(12) If $3 \times 3 = 9$, then $3 + 3 = 9$.

(13) If all monkeys are quadrupeds, then some birds fly.
(14) All birds fly if and only if all fish swim.
(15) If there exists a number x such that $x + 1 = 5$, then there exists a number y such that $y + 3 = 5$.
(16) There does not exist a number x such that $2 + x = 1$, and for all numbers x, $1 + x = x + 1$.
(17) For all numbers a, $a + 2 = 2 + a$ if and only if $a \times 2 = 2 \times a$.
(18) For all numbers x, $x + 2 \neq 1$.
(19) For all numbers x, $x = x$ or $x \neq x$.
(20) If $2 = 3$ and $5 = 7$, then $4 \neq 9$.

1.4   Symbols and Form

In the preceding section you learned that a compound sentence contains one or more of the connectives *not, or, and, if ... then ...* , and *if and only if.* Thus any compound sentence may be constructed from simple sentences and the connectives. For example, the *compound* sentence "Carol went home, and Susan studied French" may be constructed from the *simple* sentence "Carol went home," the *simple* sentence "Susan studied French," and the connective *and.* Similarly the *compound* sentence "$2 + 3 = 3 + 2$, and $5 + 4 = 9$" may be constructed from the *simple* sentence "$2 + 3 = 3 + 2$," the *simple* sentence "$5 + 4 = 9$," and the connective *and.* Since the connective is *and* in both sentences, it seems natural to make an exhaustive study of any sentence of the form "... *and* .... ." In the following sections we study compound sentences involving each of the five connectives. In this section we introduce symbols for sentences and the connectives and define certain words which will facilitate our study of compound sentences.

The following symbolic notation is used throughout this text. The lower-case letters p, q, r, and so forth represent *sentences.*

The symbol $\sim$ represents the connective *not.*
The symbol $\vee$ represents the connective *or.*
The symbol $\wedge$ represents the connective *and.*
The symbol $\rightarrow$ represents the connective *if ... then ....* .
The symbol $\rightleftarrows$ represents the connective *if and only if.*

Example 1.   Let p represent the sentence "Carol went home," let q represent the sentence "Susan studied French," and let r represent the sentence "Beverly washed the dishes." Then $\sim q$ (read not-q) represents the sentence "Susan did not study French."

$p \lor r$ represents the sentence "Carol went home or Beverly washed the dishes;"

$p \land q$ represents the sentence "Carol went home and Susan studied French;"

$p \to q$ represents the sentence "If Carol went home, then Susan studied French;"

$q \rightleftarrows r$ represents the sentence "Susan studied French if and only if Beverly washed the dishes."

If p, q, and r represented any other sentences, the *meanings* of the resulting compound sentences would be different from those above. However, the *forms* would be unchanged. In succeeding sections we learn methods of determining whether a given compound sentence is true or false. The truth or falsity of some compound sentences depends on the truth or falsity of the constituent sentences composing the compound sentences. However, there are some compound sentences which are true regardless of the truth or falsity of their constituent parts.

Since the connective $\sim$ does not connect *two* sentences, no ambiguity results when another connective is used with it. For example, we agree that $p \lor \sim q$ means $p \lor (\sim q)$, $p \land \sim q$ means $p \land (\sim q)$, $\sim p \lor q$ means $(\sim p) \lor q$, $p \to \sim q$ means $p \to (\sim q)$, $p \rightleftarrows \sim q$ means $p \rightleftarrows (\sim q)$, and similarly, $\sim p \to q$ means $(\sim p) \to q$. We agree that the notation $\sim \sim p$ *means* $\sim (\sim p)$. This agreement eliminates the excessive use of parentheses.

Example 2. Symbolize the sentence "Paul will attend Harvard but not Tulane."

Let p represent "Paul will attend Harvard" and q represent "Paul will attend Tulane." Then $\sim q$ represents "Paul will not attend Tulane." By recalling that *but* is an English substitute for *and*, we may write $p \land \sim q$.

Example 3. Symbolize the sentence "Ralph will attend the basketball game, but Leslie will not."

Let p represent "Ralph will attend the basketball game" and q represent "Leslie will attend the basketball game." Then $\sim q$ represents "Leslie will not attend the basketball game." Hence we may write $p \land \sim q$.

Example 4. Symbolize the sentence "If Marcia does not take a nap, then Claire will not go shopping."

Let p represent "Marcia takes a nap" and q represent "Claire will go shopping." Then $\sim p$ represents "Marcia does not take a nap" and $\sim q$ represents "Claire will not go shopping." Thus we may write $\sim p \rightarrow \sim q$.

Notice that the form of the compound sentence in Example 2 is identical with the form of the compound sentence in Example 3.

In the following definitions we assign *names* to compound sentences of the five basic forms.

DEFINITION 6.   The sentence $\sim p$ (read *not-p*) is called the *negation of p*.

DEFINITION 7.   The sentence $p \vee q$ (read *p or q*) is called the *disjunction of p and q*.

DEFINITION 8.   The sentence $p \wedge q$ (read *p and q*) is called the *conjunction of p and q*.

DEFINITION 9.   The sentence $p \rightarrow q$ (read *if p, then q*) is called a *conditional sentence*.

An alternative way to read $p \rightarrow q$ is *p only if q*.

DEFINITION 10.   The sentence $p \rightleftarrows q$ (read *p if and only if q*) is called a *biconditional sentence*.

In this section, we are interested in writing compound sentences in the forms just introduced.

Exercise 1.4

Check each of the following to determine if it is a sentence. If it is a sentence, state whether it is a simple or compound sentence. Let p, q, r represent simple sentences and represent each *sentence* in terms of p, q, r, and the connectives.

(1) If Bill is in jail, then he is not a nuisance to his family.
(2) $42 - 23 = 16 - 1$, and $5 = 4 + 1$.
(3) $(2 + 3) + 7 = 2 + (3 + 7)$.
(4) $x - y$ is less than $y - x$.
(5) 7 is larger than 3 or 3 is smaller than 7.
(6) If $1/2 + 1/2 = 1$, then $1/4 + 1/4 + 1/4 + 1/4 = 1$.
(7) 2 is smaller than 2×3.
(8) 5 is smaller than $4 + 3$, or $2 + 1$ is not equal to 4.
(9) 8 is larger than 1, and $8 + 3$ is smaller than 5.

(10) John, open your book or leave the room.
(11) $(4 \times 2) \times 5 = 4 \times (2 \times 5)$.
(12) It is false that Lane is not present today.
(13) $(2 + 3 = 3 + 4)$, or $(2 + 3 = 3 + 2)$.
(14) $4 \times 1 = 0$ or $4 \times 1 = 4$.
(15) If Toby passes this course, then Toby will have learned Algebra.
(16) $m \times 0 = m$ or $m + 0 = 0$.
(17) $3 + 0 = 3$ or $3 + 0 = 0$.
(18) $7(3 + 5) = 7(3) + 7(5)$.
(19) Either logic is mathematics or logic is not mathematics.
(20) Mathematics is the queen of the sciences and mathematics is not the queen of the sciences.
(21) $2 \times 3 + 5 = 15$ and $3 \times 3 + 4 \times 5 = 15$.
(22) $1 + 7 = 8$ and $3 + 8 \neq 15$.

1.5 Truth Values of the Negation, Truth Tables

In the previous section we devoted our attention to the study of the five basic forms of compound sentences. In this section we shall study the first of these types with regard to its truth values. That is, we shall investigate the conditions under which the negation of a given sentence is true. We say that the *truth value* of any true sentence is *true*, and the *truth value* of any false sentence is *false*. For example, the truth value of the sentence $3 + 8 = 8 + 3$ is true, whereas the truth value of the sentence $3 + 8 = 8 + 1$ is false.

The following definition gives the conditions under which the negation is true.

DEFINITION 11.   The *negation of p* (written $\sim p$) *is a true sentence* if and only if p is a false sentence.

The following examples illustrate Definition 11.

Example 1. $\sim(5 = 7)$ is *true* because $5 = 7$ is *false*.

Example 2. $\sim(2 + 3 = 1)$ is *true* because $2 + 3 = 1$ is *false*.

Example 3. $\sim(4 + 3 = 3 + 4)$ is *false* because $4 + 3 = 3 + 4$ is *true*.

Example 4. $\sim(5 + 0 = 5)$ is *false* because $5 + 0 = 5$ is *true*.

Example 5. ~(All men are mortal) is *false* because "all men are mortal" is *true*.

Unless the forms of the negations in the Examples 1 through 5 are desired for emphasis, they are usually written Example 1: $5 \neq 7$ (read 5 is not equal to 7); Example 2: $2 + 3 \neq 1$; Example 3: $4 + 3 \neq 3 + 4$; Example 4: $5 + 0 \neq 5$; and Example 5: some men are not mortal. Whenever you are asked to *negate* (compute the negation or denial of) a given sentence, it is understood that you will negate as explained in this paragraph (that is, without merely placing $\sim$ in front of the sentence to be negated). Thus the negation of "some ducks fly" is "no ducks fly;" the negation of "all birds fly" is "some birds do not fly;" the negation of "$2 + 3 = 6$" is "$2 + 3 \neq 6$;" the negation of "no birds swim" is "some birds swim."

The truth value of $\sim p$ is true if the truth value of p is false, and the truth value of $\sim p$ is false if the truth value of p is true. If we use the capital letters T (for true) and F (for false), we may tabulate the truth values of the negation of p in a device known as a *truth table*. To compute the truth table for $\sim p$, we note first that p has two possible truth values T and F. For each of these we wish to know whether $\sim p$ is true or false. From Definition 11, we know that $\sim p$ is false if p is true and that $\sim p$ is true if p is false. The truth table for $\sim p$ is shown in Figure 1.1.

p	$\sim p$
T	F
F	T

FIGURE 1.1

The truth table exhibits all the information we need to know about $\sim p$; that is, it exhibits all the information contained in Definition 11 and no extraneous information. Thus we could have defined the negation by its truth table.

Exercise 1.5

I. Negate each of the following sentences in two ways—first as in Examples 1 through 5—and then in the usual manner as described after the examples.

(1) Uranus is a star.
(2) The earth is not a planet.
(3) George Washington lived before Abraham Lincoln.
(4) $5 + 4 = 9$.
(5) $6 + 2 = 9$.
(6) $4 + 5 = 5 + 4$.

(7) $2 + 3 = 3$.

(8) $0 + 0 = 20$.

(9) Some numbers are odd.

(10) Some numbers are even.

(11) Some numbers are not odd.

(12) Some numbers are not even.

(13) No numbers are perfect squares.

(14) No numbers are even.

(15) All numbers are primes.

(16) All numbers are composites.

(17) There is at least one number larger than 100.

(18) There is no largest number.

(19) Not all numbers are divisible by 2.

(20) For some x, $x + 5 = 3$.

II. Decide whether each sentence in Exercise I is true or false, and then use the truth table for negation (in Figure 1.1) to decide whether the negation of each of these sentences is true or false.

1.6   Truth Values of the Disjunction and Conjunction, Truth Tables

In this section we shall study the truth values of the disjunction $p \lor q$ and of the conjunction $p \land q$. In many ways they are similar to the common usage. However, we shall discover one important difference in the case of the disjunction. The following definition gives the conditions under which the disjunction is false.

DEFINITION 12.   The *disjunction of p and q* (written $p \lor q$) *is a false sentence* if and only if p is a false sentence and q is a false sentence.

The following examples illustrate Definition 12.

Example 1. $(5 + 7 = 15) \lor (6 + 0 = 0)$ is *false* because $5 + 7 = 15$ is false and $6 + 0 = 0$ is false.

Example 2. $(5 + 7 = 15) \lor (6 + 0 = 6)$ is *true* because $6 + 0 = 6$ is true.

Example 3. $(5 + 7 = 12) \lor (6 + 0 = 0)$ is *true* because $5 + 7 = 12$ is true.

Example 4. $(5 + 7 = 12) \lor (6 + 0 = 6)$ is *true* because $5 + 7 = 12$ is true (or because $6 + 0 = 6$ is true).

The definition states that $p \vee q$ is false whenever p is false and q is false and that $p \vee q$ is true otherwise. Thus $p \vee q$ is true whenever both p and q are true sentences. This may surprise you somewhat. In common English usage the disjunction of two true sentences is usually, but not always, considered false. For example, the sentence "Tomorrow I will read *Peter Pan* or I will go to a movie" is usually considered to mean I will do one or the other but not both. Likewise, the sentence "Page will have tea or coffee with her meal" is usually considered to mean that Page will take tea or coffee but not both. However, the sentence "Beverly will buy a movie camera or (Beverly will buy) a movie projector" is usually considered true if she buys a movie camera, or if she buys a projector, or if she buys both. The disjunction $p \vee q$ in the English language has a double meaning; sometimes it means "p or q but not both p and q," and sometimes it means "p or q or both p and q." In the latter sense, it has the meaning of *and/or* sometimes seen in legal documents. This ambiguity is avoided in mathematics by the adoption of Definition 12. That is, in mathematics, $p \vee q$ means either p or q (or both). Thus the mathematical meaning of $p \vee q$ is the legal meaning of p and/or q. If a mathematician should need to consider the sentence "p or q but not both," he could introduce a special symbol, such as $\underline{\vee}$. However, in this text we shall not need such a special symbol for "p or q but not both."

To compute the truth table for $p \vee q$ we note that p has two possible truth-values T and F. For each of these, q has, independently, two possible truth-values T and F. Hence there are four possible truth-value combinations. For each of these combinations we wish to know the truth-value of the disjunction $p \vee q$. From Definition 12 we know that $p \vee q$ is false whenever p is false and q is false and that $p \vee q$ is true in the remaining three cases. The truth table for $p \vee q$ is shown in Figure 1.2.

p	q	$p \vee q$
T	T	T
T	F	T
F	T	T
F	F	F

Figure 1.2

The truth table exhibits all the information we need to know about $p \vee q$; that is, it exhibits the fact that $p \vee q$ is true whenever either p is true or q is true (or both) and that $p \vee q$ is false whenever p is false and q is false. Thus it exhibits all the information contained in Definition 12 and no extraneous information. Hence we could have defined the disjunction by its truth table.

The following definition gives the condition under which the conjunction is true.

DEFINITION 13. The *conjunction of p and q (written p ∧ q) is a true sentence* if and only if *p* is a true sentence and *q* is a true sentence.

The following examples illustrate Definition 13 and show that the conjunction in mathematics is exactly as in English.

Example 5. $(2 + 3 = 5) \wedge (5 + 0 = 5)$ is *true* because $2 + 3 = 5$ is true and $5 + 0 = 5$ is true.

Example 6. $(2 + 3 = 5) \wedge (5 + 0 = 0)$ is *false* because $5 + 0 = 0$ is false.

Example 7. $(2 + 3 = 3) \wedge (5 + 0 = 5)$ is *false* because $2 + 3 = 3$ is false.

Example 8. $(2 + 3 = 3) \wedge (5 + 0 = 0)$ is *false* because $2 + 3 = 3$ is false (or $5 + 0 = 0$ is false).

Definition 13 states (and Examples 5 through 8 illustrate) that the conjunction $p \wedge q$ is true whenever both p and q are true sentences and is false in the remaining cases. To compute the truth table for $p \wedge q$ we note, as in the disjunction $p \vee q$, that p has two possible truth values T and F and that, for each of these, q has independently two possible truth values T and F. For each of the four possible truth-value combinations we wish to know the truth value of the conjunction $p \wedge q$. The truth table for $p \wedge q$ is shown in Figure 1.3.

p	q	$p \wedge q$
T	T	T
T	F	F
F	T	F
F	F	F

FIGURE 1.3

The truth table exhibits all the information we need about $p \wedge q$; that is, it exhibits the fact that $p \wedge q$ is true whenever both p and q are true sentences and that $p \wedge q$ is false whenever either p is false or q is false or both p and q are false. Thus it exhibits all the information contained in Definition 13 and no extraneous information. Hence we could have defined the conjunction by its truth table.

Example 9.   Compute the truth table of $\sim(p \wedge q)$.

p	q	$p \wedge q$	$\sim(p \wedge q)$
T	T	T	F
T	F	F	T
F	T	F	T
F	F	F	T

Example 10.   Compute the truth table of $\sim p \vee \sim q$.

p	q	$\sim p$	$\sim q$	$\sim p \vee \sim q$
T	T	F	F	F
T	F	F	T	T
F	T	T	F	T
F	F	T	T	T

Exercise 1.6

I. Compute the truth value of each of the following sentences.

(1) $4 + 5 = 9$.

(2) $7 + 8 = 8 + 7$.

(3) $(4 + 5 = 9) \wedge (7 + 8 = 8 + 7)$.

(4) $(4 + 5 = 9) \vee (7 + 8 = 8 + 7)$.

(5) $\sim(4 + 5 = 9)$.

(6) $4 + 5 \neq 9$.

(7) $(3 \times 1 = 3) \wedge (3 + 0 = 3)$.

(8) $(8 + 0 = 8) \wedge (0 + 2 = 3)$.

(9) $(8 + 0 = 0) \wedge (0 + 2 = 2)$.

(10) $(1 + 5 = 5 + 1) \vee (7 = 13)$.

(11) $(2 + 5 = 5) \vee (2 + 5 = 7)$.

(12) $(5 + 4 = 4 + 6) \vee (1 + 3 = 3 + 10)$.

(13) $\sim(3 + 2 = 2 + 3) \vee (4 + 0 = 4)$.

(14) (Some numbers are divisible by 2) $\vee$ (no numbers are divisible by 2).

(15) (Some numbers are divisible by 2) $\wedge$ (no numbers are divisible by 2).

(16) All numbers are equal to each other.

(17) There are at least two numbers which are not equal to each other.

(18) (Some numbers are divisible by 2) $\wedge$ (some numbers are divisible by 3).

(19) Some numbers are greater than 3.

(20) (Some numbers are not divisible by two) $\wedge$ (some numbers are not divisible by 3).

II. Compute the truth table for each of the following.

(1) $p \vee \sim p$

(2) $p \wedge \sim p$

(3) $\sim (p \vee q)$

(4) $\sim p \wedge \sim q$

(5) $\sim\sim p$

(6) $p \wedge p$

(7) $p \vee p$

(8) $\sim (p \wedge \sim p)$

(9) $\sim (p \vee \sim p)$

(10) $p \vee \sim q$

(11) $\sim p \vee q$

(12) $\sim (\sim p \vee q)$

(13) $\sim (\sim p \vee \sim q)$

III. (1) Let p be the sentence "$2 + 3 = 5$" and q be the sentence "$2 \times 3 = 6$." Write each sentence in Exercise II and compute its truth value.

(2) Let p be the sentence "$2 + 3 = 5$" and q be the sentence "$2 \times 3 = 5$." Write each sentence in Exercise II and compute its truth value.

(3) Let p be the sentence "$2 + 3 = 6$" and q be the sentence "$2 \times 3 = 6$." Write each sentence in Exercise II and compute its truth value.

(4) Let p be the sentence "$2 + 3 = 6$" and q be the sentence "$2 \times 3 = 5$." Write each sentence in Exercise II and compute its truth value.

IV. Use the results of Exercise III to verify the results of Exercise II.

1.7 Truth Values of the Conditional, Truth Tables

In this section we shall study the truth values of the conditional sentence $p \rightarrow q$ and shall illustrate its application to the proving of theorems in mathematics. The following definition gives the condition under which the conditional sentence $p \rightarrow q$ is false.

DEFINITION 14. The *conditional sentence* $p \rightarrow q$ *is a false sentence* if and only if p is a true sentence and q is a false sentence.

The following examples illustrate Definition 14.

Example 1. $(2 + 3 = 5) \rightarrow (2 + 0 = 2)$ is *true*, because $2 + 3 = 5$ is true and $2 + 0 = 2$ is true.

Example 2. $(2 + 3 = 5) \rightarrow (2 + 0 = 0)$ is *false*, because $2 + 3 = 5$ is true and $2 + 0 = 0$ is false.

Example 3. $(2 + 3 = 3) \rightarrow (2 + 0 = 2)$ is *true*, because $2 + 3 = 3$ is false.

Example 4. $(2 + 3 = 3) \rightarrow (2 + 0 = 0)$ is *true*, because $2 + 3 = 3$ is false.

There should be no difficulty with Examples 1 and 2; their truth values follow from Definition 14. However, questions may arise about the truth values of Examples 3 and 4. It may seem strange to say that $p \rightarrow q$ is true when p is false. The reason for this is probably that we are accustomed to assuming that p is true in any sentence of the form $p \rightarrow q$. This natural assumption is usually made in any mathematical theorem of the form $p \rightarrow q$. Thus, when we state a theorem "If p, then q," we usually *prove* the theorem by *assuming* that p is true and then *proving* that q is true. We do not say what the truth value of q is, in the event that p happens to be false. Remember that Definition 14 says that $p \rightarrow q$ is false if and only if p is true and q is false; that is, the only case in which $p \rightarrow q$ is false is the case in which p is true and q is false. The conditional is true in the three remaining cases.

Another example should clarify the problem.

Example 5.   Your mother makes the following statement to you: "If it rains all night tonight, then Lafayette will be flooded in the morning."

We wish to compute the truth values of her statement (sentence of the form $p \rightarrow q$) in all cases. The following are the only cases which can occur:

(a) rain all night, flood next morning,
(b) rain all night, no flood next morning,
(c) no rain all night, flood next morning,
(d) no rain all night, no flood next morning.

In case (a), we would certainly say that your mother told us the truth and hence that $p \rightarrow q$ is true. In case (b), we would have to admit that your mother did not tell the truth and hence that $p \rightarrow q$ is false. In case (c), we would certainly give your mother the benefit of the doubt and say that she told the truth and hence that $p \rightarrow q$ is true. She made no assertion about what would happen if it did not rain. After all, the city can flood from causes other than rain; for example, the main water line can break and flood the city. In case (d), we would have to give your mother the benefit of the doubt and say that she told the truth and hence that $p \rightarrow q$ is true.

Recall that your mother promised a flood if it rained. She did not say what would happen if it did not rain. Thus if it does not rain, she told the truth whether the city floods or not. The only case in which she could have erred is case (b), rain and no flood.

Definition 14 tells us that $p \rightarrow q$ is false whenever p is true and q is false and that $p \rightarrow q$ is true in the remaining three cases. The truth table for $p \rightarrow q$ is shown in Figure 1.4.

p	q	$p \rightarrow q$
T	T	T
T	F	F
F	T	T
F	F	T

FIGURE 1.4

The truth table exhibits all the information we need to know about $p \rightarrow q$; that is, it exhibits all the information contained in Definition 14 and no extraneous information. Thus we could have defined the conditional $p \rightarrow q$ by its truth table.

In the conditional $p \rightarrow q$, the sentence p is called the *antecedent* or *hypothesis* and the sentence q is called the *consequent* or *conclusion*. In mathematical theorems of the form $p \rightarrow q$, the hypothesis p and the conclusion q are so related that $p \rightarrow q$ cannot be false; that is, it is impossible for the hypothesis to be true and the conclusion to be false simultaneously.

Example 6.   Compute the truth table of $\sim(p \lor q) \rightarrow (\sim p \land \sim q)$.

p	q	$\sim p$	$\sim q$	$p \lor q$	$\sim(p \lor q)$	$\sim p \land \sim q$	$\sim(p \lor q) \rightarrow (\sim p \land \sim q)$
T	T	F	F	T	F	F	T
T	F	F	T	T	F	F	T
F	T	T	F	T	F	F	T
F	F	T	T	F	T	T	T

Example 7.   Compute the truth table of $(\sim p \wedge \sim q) \to \sim(p \vee q)$.

p	q	$\sim p$	$\sim q$	$\sim p \wedge \sim q$	$p \vee q$	$\sim(p \vee q)$	$(\sim p \wedge \sim q) \to \sim(p \vee q)$
T	T	F	F	F	T	F	T
T	F	F	T	F	T	F	T
F	T	T	F	F	T	F	T
F	F	T	T	T	F	T	T

Exercise 1.7

I. Compute the truth value of each of the following sentences.

  (1) $\sim(4 + 5 = 9)$.
  (2) $(4 + 5 = 9) \wedge (6 + 1 = 9)$.
  (3) $(4 + 5 = 9) \vee (6 + 1 = 9)$.
  (4) $(7 + 0 = 7) \to (2 + 0 = 2)$.
  (5) $(2 + 3 = 3 + 2) \to (2 + 0 = 0)$.
  (6) $(2 + 3 = 6) \to (2 + 0 = 2)$.
  (7) $(2 + 1 = 0) \to (1 + 2 = 0)$.
  (8) $(4 \neq 3) \to \sim(2 = 1)$.
  (9) $(4 \neq 3) \to (2 = 1)$.
(10) $(4 = 3) \to \sim(2 = 1)$.
(11) $(4 = 3) \to (2 = 1)$.
(12) $p \to p$.
(13) $p \to \sim p$.
(14) $p \to (p \vee p)$.
(15) $(p \wedge q) \to (p \vee q)$.
(16) $(p \wedge q) \to p$.
(17) $(q \wedge r) \to (q \vee r)$.
(18) $\sim(p \vee q) \to (\sim p \wedge \sim q)$.
(19) $\sim(p \wedge q) \to (\sim p \vee \sim q)$.
(20) $\sim p \vee \sim q \to \sim(p \wedge q)$.

II. Compute the truth table of each of the following.

  (1) $p \to (p \vee q)$.
  (2) $q \to (p \vee q)$.
  (3) $p \to p$.
  (4) $(p \wedge q) \to p$.
  (5) $(p \wedge q) \to q$.
  (6) $p \to (p \wedge q)$.
  (7) $(p \wedge q) \to (p \vee q)$.
  (8) $\sim p \to p$.
  (9) $p \to \sim p$.
(10) $p \wedge \sim p$.

(11) $p \lor \sim p$.

(12) $\sim(p \to q) \to (p \land \sim q)$.

(13) $[p \land (p \to q)] \to q$.

(14) $[\sim q \land (p \to q)] \to \sim p$.

(15) $\sim(p \land q) \to (\sim p \lor \sim q)$.

(16) $(p \to q) \to (\sim q \to \sim p)$.

(17) $[\sim p \land (p \to q)] \to \sim q$.

(18) $(p \to q) \to (q \to p)$.

(19) $(p \lor q) \to (q \lor p)$.

(20) $(p \land q) \to (q \land p)$.

III. Determine whether each of the following conditional sentences is true for all p and q.

(1) $p \to (p \lor q)$.

(2) $q \to (p \lor q)$.

(3) $(p \lor q) \to p$.

(4) $p \to (p \land q)$.

(5) $p \to \sim p$.

(6) $(p \lor q) \to (\sim p \land \sim q)$.

(7) $(p \land q) \to (q \land p)$.

(8) $[p \land (p \to q)] \to q$.

(9) $(p \to q) \to (q \to p)$.

(10) $(p \land \sim p) \to q$.

1.8 Truth Values of the Biconditional Sentence, Truth Tables

The previous discussion has revealed that $p \to q$ may be true when $q \to p$ is false. For example, $2 + 3 = 4 \to 5 + 1 = 6$ is true; however, $5 + 1 = 6 \to 2 + 3 = 4$ is false. Whenever $p \to q$ is true and $q \to p$ is true, we may state that the biconditional sentence $p \rightleftarrows q$ is true.

DEFINITION 15. The *biconditional sentence* $p \rightleftarrows q$ *is a true sentence* if and only if $p \to q$ is true and $q \to p$ is true.

The following examples illustrate Definition 15.

Example 1. $(2 + 3 = 5) \rightleftarrows (6 + 0 = 6)$ is true.

Example 2. $(2 + 3 = 5) \rightleftarrows (6 + 0 = 0)$ is false.

Example 3. $(2 + 3 = 3) \rightleftarrows (6 + 0 = 6)$ is false.

Example 4. $(2 + 3 = 3) \rightleftarrows (6 + 0 = 0)$ is true.

Definition 15 tells us that $p \rightleftarrows q$ is true whenever both $p \rightarrow q$ and $q \rightarrow p$ are true sentences and is false in the remaining two cases. The truth table for $p \rightleftarrows q$ is shown in Figure 1.5.

p	q	$p \rightarrow q$	$q \rightarrow p$	$(p \rightarrow q) \wedge (q \rightarrow p)$	$p \rightleftarrows q$
T	T	T	T	T	T
T	F	F	T	F	F
F	T	T	F	F	F
F	F	T	T	T	T

Figure 1.5

The truth table exhibits all the information we need to know about $p \rightleftarrows q$; that is, it exhibits all the information contained in Definition 15 and no extraneous information. Thus we could have defined the biconditional sentence by its truth table. From Figure 1.5, we see that $p \rightleftarrows q$ is true whenever both p and q are true or both are false, and that $p \rightleftarrows q$ is false otherwise.

Example 5. Exhibit the truth table for the sentence $\sim(p \vee q) \rightleftarrows (\sim p \wedge \sim q)$.

p	q	$\sim p$	$\sim q$	$(p \vee q)$	$\sim(p \vee q)$	$\sim p \wedge \sim q$	$\sim(p \vee q) \rightleftarrows (\sim p \wedge \sim q)$
T	T	F	F	T	F	F	T
T	F	F	T	T	F	F	T
F	T	T	F	T	F	F	T
F	F	T	T	F	T	T	T

Note. The headings in this example are more numerous than in the previous examples. In order to determine the truth values of the sentence $\sim(p \vee q) \rightleftarrows (\sim p \wedge \sim q)$, we need to know the truth values of $\sim(p \vee q)$ and of $(\sim p \wedge \sim q)$. To determine the truth values of $\sim(p \vee q)$ we determine the truth values of $p \vee q$. We compute the truth values of the sentence $p \vee q$ from the assigned truth values of the sentences p and q. Similarly, for the sentence $\sim p \wedge \sim q$, we determine the truth values of the sentence $\sim p$ and $\sim q$. We compute the truth values of the sentences $\sim p$ and $\sim q$ from the assigned truth values of the sentences p and q.

In the last column of the truth table of Example 5 notice that $\sim(p \vee q) \rightleftarrows (\sim p \wedge \sim q)$ is true regardless of the truth values of the constituent sentences p and q.

DEFINITION 16. Any compound sentence which is true regardless of the truth values of its constituent sentences is called a *logical truth,* or *tautology,* and is said to be *logically true.*

The biconditional sentence of Example 5 is a logical truth whereas the biconditional sentence of Figure 1.5 is not. The biconditional sentence $p \rightleftarrows q$ is called an *equivalence* if and only if it is a logical truth.

DEFINITION 17. The sentence p is said to be *equivalent* to the sentence q if and only if $p \rightleftarrows q$ is a logical truth.

Mathematicians are especially interested in logical truths since every logical truth is true in all cases.

Exercise 1.8

I. Compute the truth table for each of the following.

(1) $p \rightleftarrows (p \vee p)$.
(2) $(p \wedge q) \rightleftarrows (p \vee q)$.
(3) $p \rightleftarrows p$.
(4) $(p \vee {\sim}p) \rightleftarrows (p \wedge {\sim}p)$.
(5) ${\sim}(p \wedge q) \rightleftarrows ({\sim}p \vee {\sim}q)$.
(6) ${\sim}(p \wedge {\sim}q) \rightleftarrows ({\sim}p \vee q)$.
(7) ${\sim}(p \vee {\sim}q) \rightleftarrows (p \rightarrow q)$.
(8) $({\sim}p \vee q) \rightleftarrows (p \rightarrow q)$.
(9) ${\sim}(p \vee {\sim}q) \rightleftarrows ({\sim}p \wedge q)$.
(10) $(p \rightarrow q) \rightleftarrows (q \rightarrow p)$.
(11) $(p \rightarrow q) \rightleftarrows ({\sim}q \rightarrow {\sim}p)$.
(12) $(p \rightarrow q) \rightleftarrows ({\sim}p \rightarrow {\sim}q)$.

II. Determine which of the above sentences are logical truths.

1.9 Algebra of Sentences

In the preceding sections we studied truth tables of compound sentences formed from two sentences. In this section we shall study the truth tables of compound sentences formed from more than two sentences. We call $\vee$, $\wedge$, $\rightarrow$, and $\rightleftarrows$ *binary operators* because each of them connects exactly *two* sentences. As $p \wedge q \vee r$ is ambiguous, it is really not a sentence. However, if we mean the disjunction of the sentence $p \wedge q$ and the sentence r, we must punctuate and write $(p \wedge q) \vee r$.

On the other hand, if we write $p \wedge (q \vee r)$, we mean the conjunction of the sentence p and the sentence $q \vee r$. The truth table corresponding to $(p \wedge q) \vee r$ is shown in Figure 1.6, and the truth table corresponding to $p \wedge (q \vee r)$ is shown in Figure 1.7.

p	q	r	$p \wedge q$	$(p \wedge q) \vee r$
T	T	T	T	T
T	T	F	T	T
T	F	T	F	T
T	F	F	F	F
F	T	T	F	T
F	T	F	F	F
F	F	T	F	T
F	F	F	F	F

FIGURE 1.6

p	q	r	$q \vee r$	$p \wedge (q \vee r)$
T	T	T	T	T
T	T	F	T	T
T	F	T	T	T
T	F	F	F	F
F	T	T	T	F
F	T	F	T	F
F	F	T	T	F
F	F	F	F	F

FIGURE 1.7

You will notice that there are eight lines in each of the above truth tables. For each of the two truth values of p there are two truth values of q. For each of these four combinations there are two truth values of r. Comparison of the truth values of $(p \wedge q) \vee r$ of Figure 1.6 with the truth values of $p \wedge (q \vee r)$ of Figure 1.7 reveals that the two sentences are *not* equivalent.

You may wonder whether there is another sentence which is equivalent to $(p \wedge q) \vee r$. The truth table in Figure 1.8 proves that the sentence $(p \vee r) \wedge (q \vee r)$ is equivalent to the sentence $(p \wedge q) \vee r$.

p	q	r	$(p \wedge q)$	$(p \wedge q) \vee r$	$p \vee r$	$q \vee r$	$(p \vee r) \wedge (q \vee r)$
T	T	T	T	T	T	T	T
T	T	F	T	T	T	T	T
T	F	T	F	T	T	T	T
T	F	F	F	F	T	F	F
F	T	T	F	T	T	T	T
F	T	F	F	F	F	T	F
F	F	T	F	T	T	T	T
F	F	F	F	F	F	F	F

FIGURE 1.8

Comparison of column 5 with column 8 of Figure 1.8 shows that $(p \wedge q) \vee r$ is true whenever $(p \vee r) \wedge (q \vee r)$ is true, and $(p \wedge q) \vee r$ is false whenever $(p \vee r) \wedge (q \vee r)$ is false. Thus $(p \wedge q) \vee r$ is true if and only if $(p \lor r) \land (q \lor r)$ is true. Hence $(p \land q) \lor r$ $\rightleftarrows (p \lor r) \land (q \lor r)$ is logically true; that is, the two sentences are equivalent. Moreover, the truth table in Figure 1.9 proves that the sentence $(p \land q) \lor (p \land r)$ is equivalent to the sentence $p \land (q \lor r)$.

p	q	r	$q \lor r$	$p \land (q \lor r)$	$p \land q$	$p \land r$	$(p \land q) \lor (p \land r)$
T	T	T	T	T	T	T	T
T	T	F	T	T	T	F	T
T	F	T	T	T	F	T	T
T	F	F	F	F	F	F	F
F	T	T	T	F	F	F	F
F	T	F	T	F	F	F	F
F	F	T	T	F	F	F	F
F	F	F	F	F	F	F	F

FIGURE 1.9

We have used the truth tables to prove some of the important logical truths involving sentences p, q, and r. For future reference, we list below some basic properties of sentences which we shall use to prove the basic properties of sets in Chapter 2. Later the basic properties of numbers will be derived from the properties of sets. In the exercises you are asked to prove those which you have not proved previously in this text.

For any sentences p, q, and r

(1) $p \lor q$ is a sentence.
(2) $(p \lor q) \rightleftarrows (q \lor p)$ is logically true.
(3) $[(p \lor q) \lor r] \rightleftarrows [p \lor (q \lor r)]$ is logically true.
(4) $(p \lor p) \rightleftarrows p$ is logically true.
(5) $p \lor \sim p$ is logically true. (*Law of the excluded middle*)
(6) $p \land q$ is a sentence.
(7) $(p \land q) \rightleftarrows (q \land p)$ is logically true.
(8) $[(p \land q) \land r] \rightleftarrows [p \land (q \land r)]$ is logically true.
(9) $(p \land p) \rightleftarrows p$ is logically true.
(10) $p \land \sim p$ is logically false. (*Law of contradiction*)
(11) $[p \land (q \lor r)] \rightleftarrows [(p \land q) \lor (p \land r)]$ is logically true.
(12) $[p \lor (q \land r)] \rightleftarrows [(p \lor q) \land (p \lor r)]$ is logically true.
(13) $\sim(p \lor q) \rightleftarrows [\sim p \land \sim q]$ is logically true.   (*De Morgan's*
(14) $\sim(p \land q) \rightleftarrows [\sim p \lor \sim q]$ is logically true.   *laws*)
(15) $\sim\sim p \rightleftarrows p$ is logically true. (*Double negation law*)
(16) $\sim(p \rightarrow q) \rightleftarrows (p \land \sim q)$.
(17) $(p \rightarrow q) \rightleftarrows (\sim p \lor q)$.

Henceforth, whenever a sentence is written without qualification, it will be considered true. For example, we may write $(p \wedge q) \rightleftarrows (q \wedge p)$ and say that $p \wedge q$ is equivalent to $q \wedge p$.

Exercise 1.9

I. Prove the basic properties listed above which you have not proved previously.

II. (1) Let p be the sentence "$2 + 3 = 5$," q be the sentence "$1 + 5 = 6$," and r be the sentence "$4 + 0 = 4$." Illustrate each of the basic properties above.

(2) Let p be the sentence "$2 + 3 = 6$," q be the sentence "$1 + 5 = 6$," and r be the sentence "$4 + 1 = 4$." Illustrate each of the basic properties above.

III. Negate each of the following sentences in two ways.

(1) p (7) $\sim(p \wedge \sim q)$

(2) $p \wedge q$ (8) $\sim p \wedge \sim q$

(3) $p \vee q$ (9) $p \rightarrow q$

(4) $\sim p \vee q$ (10) $\sim(p \rightarrow q)$

(5) $\sim(p \vee q)$ (11) $p \rightarrow (q \wedge r)$

(6) $p \wedge \sim q$ (12) $p \rightarrow (q \vee r)$

1.10 Converse, Inverse, and Contrapositive

In Section 1.9 we found that some compound sentences are logical truths and some are not. In Exercise 1.9 we were asked to determine which of the given sentences are logical truths. Some basic logical truths were listed in Section 1.9. In this section we investigate some of these in more detail. It is important that the student understand these to formulate correct mathematical proofs and valid arguments. A discussion of mathematical proof will be given in the next section.

In the truth table of Figure 1.5 we saw that the truth values of $p \rightarrow q$ were not the same as the truth values of $q \rightarrow p$. Thus $p \rightarrow q$ is *not* equivalent to $q \rightarrow p$. Actually, we can illustrate this by an example. Let p be the sentence "Mr. Jones can see" and q be the sentence "Mr. Jones is alive." Obviously $p \rightarrow q$ is a true sentence; however, $q \rightarrow p$ may be false. For any sentence $p \rightarrow q$, the sentence $q \rightarrow p$ is called the *converse* of $p \rightarrow q$. We see that $p \rightarrow q$ is the converse of $q \rightarrow p$. Thus the converse of a true sentence may be false. Many students commit errors in mathematical proofs by assuming that $q \rightarrow p$ is true whenever $p \rightarrow q$ is true.

By truth table analysis (see Section 1.8), we can prove that the sentence $p \to q$ is equivalent to the sentence $\sim q \to \sim p$. The sentence $\sim q \to \sim p$ is called the *contrapositive* of $p \to q$. The contrapositive of $\sim q \to \sim p$ is $\sim\sim p \to \sim\sim q$; that is, $p \to q$. Thus $\sim q \to \sim p$ is true whenever $p \to q$ is true, and $\sim q \to \sim p$ is false whenever $p \to q$ is false.

Similarly (see Exercise 1.8) the sentence $\sim p \to \sim q$ may be false even if the sentence $p \to q$ is true. For any sentence $p \to q$, the sentence $\sim p \to \sim q$ is called the *inverse* of $p \to q$. Thus $\sim p \to \sim q$ is not equivalent to $p \to q$. In the following section we illustrate how students make invalid arguments by assuming these two sentences are equivalent. You may prove by the truth table method that the inverse of $p \to q$ is equivalent to the converse of $p \to q$; that is, $(\sim p \to \sim q) \rightleftarrows (q \to p)$ is logically true.

Example 1. The converse of the sentence "if triangle ABC is equilateral, then triangle ABC is isosceles" is the sentence "if triangle ABC is isosceles, then triangle ABC is equilateral." Obviously the first sentence $p \to q$ is true. However, the converse $q \to p$ may be false. The inverse of $p \to q$ is $\sim p \to \sim q$; that is, the inverse is the sentence "if triangle ABC is *not* equilateral, then triangle ABC is *not* isosceles." The inverse may be false, because triangle ABC may be isosceles but not equilateral. The contrapositive of $p \to q$ is $\sim q \to \sim p$; that is, the contrapositive is the sentence "if triangle ABC is not isosceles, then triangle ABC is not equilateral." The contrapositive is obviously true; of course, the original sentence is true also.

Example 2. Let p be the sentence "triangle ABC is congruent to triangle DEF" and let q be the sentence "triangle ABC is similar to triangle DEF." Then $p \to q$ is a true sentence. However, the converse $q \to p$ is not necessarily true; that is, two triangles may be similar without being congruent. Moreover, the inverse $\sim p \to \sim q$ may also be false. However, the contrapositive $\sim q \to \sim p$ is true; that is, if two triangles are not similar, then they are not congruent.

Example 3. The sentence "if August earns less than \$5,000 per year, then August earns less than \$8,000 per year" is true. The converse "if August earns less than \$8,000 per year, then August earns less than \$5,000 per year" is not necessarily true. The inverse "if August does not earn less than \$5,000 per year, then August does not earn less than \$8,000 per year" is not necessarily true. The contrapositive "if August does not earn less than \$8,000 per year, then August does not earn less than \$5,000 per year" is true.

Example 4.   The converse of $p \rightarrow (r \wedge q)$ is $(r \wedge q) \rightarrow p$. The inverse is $\sim p \rightarrow \sim(r \wedge q)$. Since $\sim(r \wedge q) \rightleftarrows (\sim r \vee \sim q)$, we see that the inverse may be written $\sim p \rightarrow (\sim r \vee \sim q)$. The contrapositive of $p \rightarrow (r \wedge q)$ is $\sim(r \wedge q) \rightarrow \sim p$. We may write the contrapositive as $(\sim r \vee \sim q) \rightarrow \sim p$.

Example 5.   The converse of $(p \vee q) \rightarrow r$ is $r \rightarrow (p \vee q)$. The inverse of $(p \vee q) \rightarrow r$ is $\sim(p \vee q) \rightarrow \sim r$, which may be written $(\sim p \wedge \sim q) \rightarrow \sim r$. The contrapositive of $(p \vee q) \rightarrow r$ is $\sim r \rightarrow \sim(p \vee q)$, which may be written $\sim r \rightarrow (\sim p \wedge \sim q)$.

The relationship between a sentence and its contrapositive and the relationship between the inverse and the converse are illustrated in Figure 1.10 and Figure 1.11.

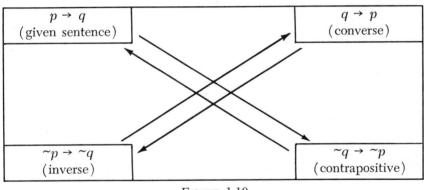

FIGURE 1.10

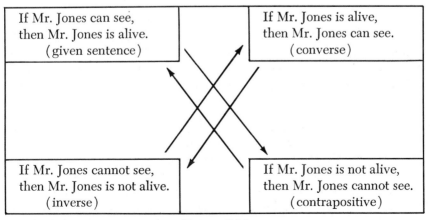

FIGURE 1.11

Exercise 1.10

I. State the converse of each of the following sentences.

(1) If John and Mary are twins, then John and Mary have the same birthday.
(2) If John is Mary's brother, then Mary is John's sister.
(3) If John does Mary's homework, then Mary makes an A.
(4) If John and Mary are not twins, and John and Mary are brother and sister, then John and Mary are not the same age.
(5) If John has exactly 5 apples and Mary has exactly 4 apples, then John and Mary have exactly 9 apples.
(6) If John forgets to wake Mary, then Mary will miss breakfast or Mary will be late for school.
(7) $p \to (q \land r)$.
(8) $(p \land q) \to r$.
(9) $(p \lor q) \to r$.
(10) $\sim p \to r$.
(11) $(p \lor q) \to (p \land q)$.
(12) $p \to \sim q$.
(13) $(p \lor q) \to p$.
(14) $\sim p \to \sim q$.
(15) $(\sim p \lor q) \to (q \lor \sim p)$.
(16) $(p \lor \sim q) \to (q \lor \sim p)$.

II. State the inverse of each of the sentences in Exercise I.

III. State the contrapositive of each of the sentences in Exercise I.

IV. Analyze Example 3. In particular, explain why the converse and inverse *may* be false, while the contrapositive *must* be true.

1.11 Deductive Inference

In the study of mathematics we need to know how to make *valid arguments;* that is, to derive certain sentences from one or more given sentences. The given sentences are called the *premises,* or *hypotheses,* and the derived sentence is called the *conclusion.*

DEFINITION 18. An argument with premises $p_1, p_2 \ldots p_k$ and conclusion q is said to be *valid* if and only if the sentence $(p_1 \land p_2 \land \ldots \land p_k) \to q$ is logically true.

Notice that the validity of an argument depends on the *form* rather than the *meaning.* The following examples illustrate valid arguments.

Example 1.   P1: If it rains, the grass will grow.
                  P2: It is raining now.
                   C: The grass will grow.

This argument is of the form:

P1: $p \rightarrow q$
P2: p
  C: q

Example 2.   P1: If Jones wins the election, the taxes will decrease.
                  P2: Jones won the election today.
                   C: The taxes will decrease.

Notice that this argument also is of the form:

P1: $p \rightarrow q$
P2: p
  C: q

Since both arguments are of the same form, we check their validity by determining whether the sentence $[p \wedge (p \rightarrow q)] \rightarrow q$ is logically true. In fact, after we have checked the validity of this argument form, we need not check the validity of any other argument of this form. The meanings of the sentences p and q will have no effect on the validity of the argument. By Definition 18, this argument is valid if and only if $[(p \rightarrow q) \wedge p] \rightarrow q$ is logically true. The truth table in Figure 1.12 proves that the argument form is valid.

p	q	$p \rightarrow q$	$(p \rightarrow q) \wedge p$	$[(p \rightarrow q) \wedge p] \rightarrow q$
T	T	T	T	T
T	F	F	F	T
F	T	T	F	T
F	F	T	F	T

Figure 1.12

Since the truth values in the last column are all T, we conclude that the sentence $[(p \rightarrow q) \wedge p] \rightarrow q$ is logically true. Hence the argument is valid.

As the following example illustrates, the *truth* of the conclusion of an argument does not guarantee that the argument is *valid;* that is, an invalid argument may have either a true conclusion or a false conclusion. Similarly, a valid argument may have either a true conclusion or a false conclusion.

Example 3. P1: If wages are higher than in 1940, then prices are higher than in 1940.

P2: Prices are higher than in 1940.

C: Wages are higher than in 1940.

This argument is of the form:

P1: $p \rightarrow q$

P2: q

C: p

The truth table in Figure 1.13 proves that the argument is invalid.

p	q	$p \rightarrow q$	$(p \rightarrow q) \wedge q$	$[(p \rightarrow q) \wedge q] \rightarrow p$
T	T	T	T	T
T	F	F	F	T
F	T	T	T	F
F	F	T	F	T

FIGURE 1.13

Since the truth value in the third line of the last column is F, we conclude that the argument is invalid. If the argument were valid, all truth values in the last column would be T. An invalid argument is called a *fallacy*.

The above fallacy is important because some people confuse the converse of $p \rightarrow q$ with the sentence itself and reason as follows:

P1: $p \rightarrow q$ $q \rightarrow p$

P2: q q

C: p

As we learned in Section 1.10 the converse of a conditional is not equivalent to the conditional.

Another common fallacy is illustrated in the following example.

Example 4. P1: $p \rightarrow q$ If Mr. Jones can see, then Mr. Jones is alive.

P2: $\sim p$ Mr. Jones cannot see.

C: $\sim q$ Mr. Jones is not alive.

As in Example 3, we can prove by truth table analysis that this argument is invalid. Some people confuse the inverse of a conditional sentence with the sentence itself and reason as follows:

P1:	$p \to q$	$\sim p \to \sim q$	If Mr. Jones cannot see, then Mr. Jones is not alive.
P2:	$\sim p$	$\sim p$	Mr. Jones cannot see.
C:		$\sim q$	Mr. Jones is not alive.

As we learned in Section 1.10, the inverse of a conditional is not equivalent to the conditional.

The following example illustrates an argument which is valid.

Example 5.   P1:   If Smith committed the burglary, then he was at the scene of the crime.

P2:   Smith was not at the scene of the crime.

C: Smith did not commit the burglary.

Arguments of this type are used extensively in courts of law and are universally recognized as valid. This argument is of the form:

P1: $p \to q$
P2: $\sim q$
C : $\sim p$

Since $p \to q$ is equivalent to $\sim q \to \sim p$, we see that an equivalent form is

P1: $\sim q \to \sim p$
P2: $\sim q$
C: $\sim p$

The validity of this last argument follows from the valid argument in Examples 1 and 2.

We may prove by the truth table method that

$$[(p \to q) \wedge (q \to r)] \to [p \to r] \text{ is a logical truth.}$$

Thus any argument of the following form is valid.

P1: $p \to q$
P2: $q \to r$
C: $p \to r$

Repeated application of the above argument enables us to make the following valid argument.

P1: $p \to q$
P2: $q \to r$
P3: $r \to s$
P4: p
C: s

Many mathematical proofs are based on this form of argument. The following example illustrates this form of argument.

Example 6.   P1:   If the contract is legal, then Lane is liable.
                 P2:   If Lane is liable, then he must go to jail.
                 P3:   If he goes to jail, then he will lose his job.
                 P4:   The contract is legal.
                  C: Lane will lose his job.

Since we have discussed valid arguments, we are prepared to derive the conclusion of the argument in Section 1.1.

P1:   If Toby wins the contest, then he will travel to Europe.
P2:   If he travels to Europe, then he will visit Rome.
P3:   If he doesn't visit Paris, then he won't visit Rome.
P4:   Toby just won the contest.
 C: Toby will visit Paris.

We may symbolize the argument as follows:

P1: $p \to q$ $p \to q$
P2: $q \to r$ $q \to r$
P3: $\sim s \to \sim r$ $r \to s$
P4: p p
 C: s

Hence the conclusion "Toby will visit Paris" follows from the conjunction of the premises. Thus the argument is valid.

A valid argument is called a *proof.* A sentence which may be proved true is called a *theorem.* Many theorems are of the form $p \to q$. Although a theorem should be stated in unambiguous language, mathematicians frequently state theorems involving quantifiers without actually expressing the quantifiers. This is permissible whenever the quantifier is understood from the context. For example, the open sentence "if x is less than 5, then x is less than 6" may be stated in lieu of the sentence "for all numbers x, if x is less than 5, then x is less than 6." Since the context makes it clear that the quantifier "all" is intended, we may, in fact, refer to the open sentence as a sentence. When we do this, we *say* the sentence "if x is less than 5, then x is less than 6," *but* we *mean* the sentence "for all numbers x, if x is less than 5, then x is less than 6." As another example of the omission of the quantifier, we frequently *state* "if x is a counting number, then $x \cdot 1 = x$" but mean "for all x, if x is a counting number, then $x \cdot 1 = x$."

In order to prove a theorem, we should devise a plan of attack. Random manipulation of the symbols seldom produces the required proof. We should know *first* exactly what theorem is to be proved and *then* we should devise a plan of attack. When all direct methods fail, we should try the *indirect* method of proof. In some cases, even if the direct method does not fail, the indirect method is more convenient than the direct method. In the indirect method, frequently called *reductio ad absurdum,* or *proof by contradiction,* we assume that the desired conclusion is false and use the negation of the desired conclusion as another premise. Then we derive a sentence of the form $r \wedge \sim r$. Since $r \wedge \sim r$ is logically false (*Law of contradiction*) we assert that the desired conclusion follows logically from the given premises. Proof by contradiction is a valid method of proof because the following argument is valid.

P1: p
P2: $(p \wedge \sim q) \rightarrow (r \wedge \sim r)$
C: q

Later, when we prove mathematical theorems by contradiction, we shall elaborate on the method of proof.

Another form of the indirect method of proof involves the contrapositive. To prove that $p \rightarrow q$ is true, we may prove that $\sim q \rightarrow \sim p$ is true. Suppose we are given the premise p and wish to derive the conclusion q. If we can prove that $p \rightarrow q$ is true, we can then use the sentence $[p \wedge (p \rightarrow q)] \rightarrow q$ to derive q. The argument may be arranged as follows:

P1: p
P2: $p \rightarrow q$
C: q

It is sometimes more convenient to prove that the contrapositive $\sim q \rightarrow \sim p$ is true. Since $\sim q \rightarrow \sim p$ is equivalent to $p \rightarrow q$, the following argument is valid.

P1: p
P2: $\sim q \rightarrow \sim p$
C: q

For example, if we are given that a^2 is an odd number and wish to conclude that a is an odd number, we may prove that either of the following equivalent sentences is true.

(1) If a^2 is an odd number, then a is an odd number.
(2) If a is not an odd number, then a^2 is not an odd number.

As the proof of the second sentence is easier than of the first, we employ the following valid argument.

P1: p a^2 is an odd number.

P2: $\sim q \rightarrow \sim p$ If a is not an odd number, then a^2 is not an odd number.

C: q a is an odd number.

We summarize this section by tabulating the two basic valid arguments and the two most common fallacies.

P1: p P2: $p \rightarrow q$ C: q valid argument (direct reasoning)		P1: q P2: $p \rightarrow q$ C: p invalid argument (converse reasoning)
P1: $\sim p$ P2: $p \rightarrow q$ C: $\sim q$ invalid argument (inverse reasoning)		P1: $\sim q$ P2: $p \rightarrow q$ C: $\sim p$ valid argument (contrapositive reasoning)

FIGURE 1.14

Exercise 1.11

I. Test each of the following arguments for validity.

(1) P1: If the international situation is tense, then the stock market will fall.
   P2: The stock market fell today.
   C: The international situation is tense.

(2) P1: If the international situation is tense, then the stock market will fall.
   P2: The international situation is tense.
   C: The stock market will fall.

(3) P1: If the international situation is tense, then the stock market will fall.
   P2: The international situation is not tense.
   C: The stock market will not fall.

(4) P1: If the international situation is tense, then the stock market will fall.

P2: The stock market is not falling.

C: The international situation is not tense.

(5) P1: If Dave goes bowling, then he watches television.

P2: If he watches television, he falls asleep.

P3: Dave fell asleep.

C: Dave went bowling.

(6) P1: If a number is odd, then twice the number is even.

P2: Twice this number is even.

C: This number is odd.

II. Prove that each of the following arguments is valid.

(1) P1: $p \lor q$
P2: $\sim p$
C: q

(2) P1: $p \lor q$
P2: $\sim q$
C: p

(3) P1: $\sim p \lor q$
P2: p
C: q

(4) P1: $p \lor \sim q$
P2: $\sim p$
C: $\sim q$

(5) P1: $\sim(p \to q)$
P2: p
C: $\sim q$

(6) P1: $p \rightleftarrows q$
P2: q
C: p

(7) P1: $p \rightleftarrows q$
P2: $\sim p$
C: $\sim q$

(8) P1: $p \to q$
P2: $q \to r$
P3: $r \to s$
P4: $\sim s$
C: $\sim p$

(9) P1: $\sim(p \land q)$
P2: p
C: $\sim q$

(10) P1: $\sim(p \land q)$
P2: q
C: $\sim p$

(11) P1: $\sim p \lor \sim q$
P2: p
C: $\sim q$

(12) P1: $\sim p \lor \sim q$
P2: q
C: $\sim p$

(13) P1: $p \land q$
P2: $p \to q$
P3: $q \to s$
C: $r \lor s$

(14) P1: $p \lor q$
P2: $\sim p$
P3: r
C: $q \to r$

(15) P1: $p \to q$
P2: $p \lor r$
P3: $\sim r$
C: q

(16) P1: $p \rightleftarrows q$
P2: $p \to r$
P3: q
C: r

(17) P1: $p \lor q$
P2: $p \rightleftarrows r$
P3: $\sim q$
C: r

(18) P1: $p \rightarrow q$
　　P2: $q \rightarrow r$
　　P3: $\sim s \rightarrow \sim r$
　　P4: 　p
　　 C: 　s

(19) P1: $\sim p \rightarrow \sim q$
　　P2: $r \rightarrow q$
　　P3: 　r
　　 C: 　p

(20) P1: $p \rightleftarrows q$
　　P2: $q \rightleftarrows r$
　　P3: $r \rightleftarrows s$
　　P4: $\sim s \rightleftarrows \sim t$
　　 C: $p \rightleftarrows t$

III. State whether a quantifier is implied in each of the following. If a quantifier is implied, identify it.

(1) $x + x = 2x$.
(2) $2y + y = 3y$.
(3) $1 + 1 = 2$.
(4) $2 + 1 = 1 + 2$.
(5) $a + b = b + a$.
(6) $ab = ba$.
(7) $a + 1 = 1 + a$.
(8) $x \cdot 1 = x$.
(9) $xy = yx$.
(10) $x + 2y = 2y + x$.
(11) An equilateral triangle is equiangular.
(12) $6 = 6$.
(13) $x = x + 5$.
(14) $x = x$.
(15) $x + y = x + y$.
(16) Violets are blue.
(17) $x(a + t) = xa + xt$.
(18) $a(x + y + z) = ax + ay + az$.
(19) Whales are mammals.
(20) $2 + 3x = 3x$.
(21) A counting number is never negative.
(22) The base angles of an isosceles triangle are congruent.
(23) $c + 0 = 0$.
(24) $c \cdot 0 = 0$.
(25) This counting number is not 0.
(26) A rooster does not lay eggs.
(27) $a + c + b + 7 = 7 + a + b + c$.
(28) Jim's rooster does not lay eggs.
(29) A circle has a center and a radius.
(30) A square is a parallelogram.

Chapter 2

SETS

2.1 Introduction to Sets

The idea of *set* is one of the most widely used concepts in mathematics. There are several reasons for making a systematic study of sets. First, the system of real numbers can be developed systematically and logically from the theory of sets. Second, the terminology of modern mathematics is laden with the language of sets. For these reasons the language of sets is being introduced into the elementary curriculum. In particular, the School Mathematics Study Group have introduced sets into their fourth grade texts. In this text the words *set, class, collection,* and *aggregate* will be considered synonymous. As you learned in Chapter 1, it is not possible to define every word used. However, sufficient description is given (usually in the postulates) of each mathematical concept or word used. In this text, the word *set* is taken as undefined, and the concept of set is described by the following examples.

Example 1.   All students in this room.

Example 2.   All chairs in this room.

Example 3.   All boys in this room.

Example 4.   All girls in this room.

Example 5.   All mathematics books in this room.

Example 6.   All books in this room.

Example 7.   All Latin books in this room.

Example 8.   The counting numbers from 1 to 10 (1, 2, 3, 4, 5, 6, 7, 8, 9, 10)

Example 9.   All teachers in this room.

Example 10.   The counting numbers greater than 5 and less than 8.

Example 11.   The counting numbers 1, 2, 3, . . . , 100.

Example 12.   The even counting numbers 0, 2, 4, ...

Example 13.   The golf clubs in Arnold Palmer's golf bag.

Example 14.   The set of dishes in your mother's cabinet.

The three dots . . . in Examples 11 and 12 indicate that we have not *written* all of the elements of the set and that the indicated pattern is followed throughout. This is the approximate meaning of et cetera (etc.) in English. Throughout this text, the set of counting numbers (the numbers 0, 1, 2, 3, . . .) will be denoted by C_0.

We see that a *set* consists of a collection of objects. These objects (or members) are called *elements* of the set. One necessary property of a *well-defined* set is that it be determinable whether a given object is a member of the set. It is easy to see that all of the examples above have this property. The set of interesting numbers and the set of pretty girls are not well-defined sets because there is no universal agreement on the meanings of interesting numbers and pretty girls. Hereafter in this text the word *set* shall mean *well-defined set*.

We say that the elements of a set *belong* to the set. In Example 8, 1 belongs to the set, 2 belongs to the set, . . ., and 10 belongs to the set. Every boy in this room belongs to the set described in Example 3.

We usually designate a set by a capital letter A, B, C, . . . and the elements of a set by lower-case letters a, b, c, ... The symbol $\in$ means *is an element of* or *is a member of*. For example, $a \in A$ means *a is an element of A.* We may describe a set by listing each of its elements exactly once in braces. Thus the sets A and B of Examples 8 and 12, respectively, may be described as follows:

$$A = \{1, 2, 3, . . ., 10\}$$
$$B = \{0, 2, 4, . . .\}.$$

The number 0 is an element of B; in the notation we write $0 \in B$. However, 0 is not an element of A; we write $0 \notin A$. Similarly, $3 \notin B$ but $3 \in A$.

Exercise 2.1

I. Use English sentences and give five examples of sets.

II. Use set notation and give five examples of sets.

III. Let $A = \{0, 2, 4, \ldots\}$, $B = \{1, 3, 5, \ldots\}$, $C = \{3, 6, 9, \ldots\}$, $D = \{1, 5, 9, 13\}$, $E = \{8, 24\}$, $F = \{3, 9, 15\}$, $G = \{0, 5, 10, 15, 20\}$.

To what sets does each of the following belong? Write your answer in the form $a \in K$ or $a \notin K$; for example, $4 \in A$, $4 \notin B$, et cetera.

(1)	0	(6)	15
(2)	3	(7)	5/2
(3)	5	(8)	999
(4)	24	(9)	24600000
(5)	9	(10)	1000.1

IV. In what way is F related to C?

V. In what way is E related to A?

VI. In what way is A related to B?

VII. In what way is D related to F?

VIII. In what way is G related to A?

IX. In what way is F related to B?

2.2 Subsets

DEFINITION 1. The set A is said to be a *subset* of the set B (written $A \subset B$) if and only if each element of A is an element of B.

Thus if $A = \{2, 3, 7\}$ and $B = \{2, 3, 5, 6, 7, 8, 9\}$, then A is a subset of B. We note that any set A is a subset of A. The notation $\subset$ means *is a subset of*, or *is contained in*, whereas the notation $\not\subset$ means *is not a subset of* or *is not contained in*. Thus in the example above $A \subset B$ but $B \not\subset A$. However $X \subset X$ for any set X. In particular, $A \subset A$ and $B \subset B$. If $S = \{1, 3, 5, 7\}$ and $T = \{1, 3, 5, 9\}$, then $S \not\subset T$ and $T \not\subset S$. Even though *some* elements of S belong to T, there is *one* element of S which does not belong to T. Which one? In order that $A \not\subset B$ there must be at least one element $a \in A$ such that $a \notin B$. Why does this follow from the definition of $A \subset B$?

DEFINITION 2. *The sets A and B are equal* (written $A = B$) if and only if $A \subset B$ and $B \subset A$.

By this definition, we see that $A = A$ for any set A. If $C = \{1, 3, 5, 7\}$ and $D = \{1, 5, 7, 3\}$, then $C \subset D$ and $D \subset C$ and hence $C = D$. The order in which the elements are listed is unimportant.

DEFINITION 3.   The set A is said to be a *proper subset* of the set B if and only if $A \subset B$ and $B \not\subset A$.

For example, $\{1, 2, 3, 4\}$ is a proper subset of $\{1, 2, 3, 4, 5\}$. Although any set is contained in itself, no set is a proper subset of itself.

You may have wondered if there is another way to describe a set without specifically *listing* each of its elements. If we wish to describe the set of all boys in this room, we may write $B = \{b{:}b$ is a boy in this room$\}$, which is read *B is the set of all b such that b is a boy in this room*. The colon $(:)$ is read *such that*. If $E = \{x{:}x$ is an even counting number$\}$, then $E = \{0, 2, 4, 6, \ldots\}$. This same set E could have been written $E = \{y{:}y$ is an even counting number$\}$. The set $A = \{10, 12, 14\}$ is a subset of E. We could have written $A = \{x{:}(x$ is an even counting number$) \wedge (x$ is greater than $8) \wedge (x$ is less than $16)\}$. However, in this case it is simpler to write $A = \{10, 12, 14\}$. In some cases, the former notation is simpler.

Exercise 2.2

I. Write three subsets of $\{10, 12, 14\}$.

II. Write four subsets of $\{$red, white, blue$\}$.

III. (1) Write five subsets of $\{$Tom, Dick, Harry$\}$.
    (2) Write 15 subsets of $\{1, 2, 3, 4\}$.

IV. Write each of the following sets notationally in two ways.

   (1) The set of all counting numbers.
   (2) The set of all even counting numbers.
   (3) The set of all odd counting numbers.
   (4) The set of all multiples of 5 which are counting numbers.
   (5) The set of all counting numbers greater than 9 and less than 100.
   (6) The set of all counting numbers greater than 5.
   (7) The set of all counting numbers less than 10.
   (8) The set of all numbers equal to 15.
   (9) The set of all counting numbers between 15 and 16.

V. Describe in words each of the following sets.

   (1) $\{x{:}x$ is a counting number $\wedge$ x is greater than $100\}$.
   (2) $\{101, 102, 103, \ldots\}$.

    (3) $\{x: 5x = 10\}$.

    (4) {Sunday, Monday, Tuesday, Wednesday, Thursday, Friday, Saturday}.

    (5) $\{11, 13, 15, \ldots\}$.

 VI. Let $A = \{1, 11, 21, \ldots\}$, $B = \{21, 22, 23, \ldots\}$, $C = \{0, 2, 4, \ldots\}$, $D = \{101, 111, 121, \ldots\}$, $E = \{1001, 1002\}$, and $F = \{1001, 1003, 1005\}$. Write $X \subset Y$ or $X \not\subset Y$ for $X = A, B, C, D, E, F$ and $Y = A, B, C, D, E, F$. (*Hint*. State whether $A \subset A$, $A \subset B$, $A \subset C$, $\ldots$, $A \subset F$, et cetera. There are 36 possible cases.)

2.3 Finite Sets, Infinite Sets, and One-to-One Correspondence

You have probably noticed that some of the sets in Exercise 2.2 contained limited numbers of elements, whereas other sets contained unlimited numbers of elements. In order to distinguish between these two types of sets, we shall introduce the concepts of *finite* set and *infinite* set. Intuitively, which sets of Exercise 2.2 do you think are finite? Before we state actual definitions of *finite* set and *infinite* set, we first consider the problem of *pairing* or *matching* sets.

DEFINITION 4. The set A is said to be *in one-to-one correspondence with* (or *equivalent to*) the set B if and only if there is a correspondence between A and B such that each element of A corresponds to exactly one element of B, and each element of B corresponds to exactly one element of A.

We employ the notation $\approx$ to indicate that two sets are equivalent. Thus we write $A \approx B$ and say A *is equivalent to* B (or A *is in one to one correspondence with* B); for example, $\{1, 2, 3\} \approx \{a, b, c\}$ and $\{4, 1, 7, 9\} \approx \{2, 4, 9, 10\}$. Observe that two equivalent sets are not necessarily equal. The double headed arrow $\leftrightarrow$ is employed in the actual pairing of the elements, as illustrated in the following examples.

Example 1. $\{1, 2, 3\}$ and $\{11, 12, 13\}$ are in a one-to-one correspondence. To show the pairing process, we sometimes exemplify this by the following scheme.

$1 \leftrightarrow 11$	$1 \leftrightarrow 13$	$1 \leftrightarrow 12$
$2 \leftrightarrow 12$	$2 \leftrightarrow 12$	$2 \leftrightarrow 11$
$3 \leftrightarrow 13$	$3 \leftrightarrow 11$	$3 \leftrightarrow 13$

Are there any other one-to-one correspondences between the given sets?

Example 2.   {11, 12, 13} is in one-to-one correspondence with {x, y, z}.

Example 3.   The set of counting numbers {0, 1, 2, 3, ...} is in one-to-one correspondence with the set of even counting numbers {0, 2, 4, 6, ...}. We can pair them as follows:

$$0 \quad 1 \quad 2 \quad 3 \quad ... \quad n \quad ...$$
$$\updownarrow \quad \updownarrow \quad \updownarrow \quad \updownarrow \quad ... \quad \updownarrow \quad ...$$
$$0 \quad 2 \quad 4 \quad 6 \quad ... \quad 2n \quad ...$$

What even counting number should be paired with the counting number 5, 25, 109?

Example 4.   The sets {1, 2, 3, 4, 5, ...} and {30, 31, 32, 33, 34, ...} are in one-to-one correspondence.

$$1 \quad 2 \quad 3 \quad 4 \quad 5 \quad ... \quad n \quad ...$$
$$\updownarrow \quad \updownarrow \quad \updownarrow \quad \updownarrow \quad \updownarrow \quad ... \quad \updownarrow \quad ...$$
$$30 \quad 31 \quad 32 \quad 33 \quad 34 \quad ... \quad n+29 \quad ...$$

Example 5.   The sets $A = \{0, 1, 2\}$ and $B = \{0, 2\}$ are not in one-to-one correspondence. To convince yourself of this fact, try to pair their elements. Is any proper subset of A in one-to-one correspondence with A?

DEFINITION 5.   Any set A is said to be *infinite* if and only if there is a proper subset of A which can be put into one-to-one correspondence with A.

From Example 3 we see that the set of counting numbers is an infinite set, since the set of even counting numbers and the set of counting numbers are in one-to-one correspondence. Set A from Example 5 is *not* infinite since no proper subset of A can be put into one-to-one correspondence with A.

DEFINITION 6.   Any set A is said to be a *finite* set if and only if it is not infinite.

Thus the sets in Examples 1, 2, and 5 are finite sets.

More intuitive but less precise definitions of finite set and infinite set are the following. If the members of a set A can be counted with the counting coming to an end, we say that A is finite. If the counting does not come to an end, we say that A is infinite.

This definition uses terms which have meaning in ordinary conversation but have not been defined mathematically. Notice that Definition 5 does not have this disadvantage. Precise definitions are pleasing and beautiful to mathematicians and eliminate the possibility for misconceptions. Definition 5 characterizes the essential properties of an infinite set, whereas the intuitive notion gives one only a feeling of the concept of infinite set. While these intuitive definitions could be made rigorous, we prefer not to develop the background necessary for this treatment.

Exercise 2.3

I. Put each of the following pairs of sets in one-to-one correspondence.

(1) $\{0, 5, 10, 15\}$ and $\{a, b, x, y\}$.

(2) $\{a, \#, t, \%\}$ and $\{100, 200, 400, 800\}$.

(3) $\{w\}$ and $\{11\}$.

(4) $\{10, 20, 30, 40, \ldots\}$ and $\{1, 2, 3, 4, \ldots\}$.

(5) $\{0, 4, 8, 12, 16, \ldots\}$ and $\{x : x$ is a counting number$\}$.

II. Determine which of the following sets can be placed in one-to-one correspondence with each other.

(1) $A = \{x, y, z\}$.

(2) $B = \{e, \#, \Sigma, \%\}$.

(3) $C = \{1, 2, 3, 4, \ldots\}$.

(4) $D = \{10, 20, 30, 40, \ldots\}$.

(5) $E = \{1, 2, 3, 8\}$.

(6) $F = \{w, x, y, z\}$.

(7) $G = \{1, 2, 4, 8\}$.

(8) $H = \{1, 2, 4, 8, \ldots\}$.

(9) $I = \{2, 4, \ldots, 20\}$.

(10) $J = \{1, 2, 3\}$.

(11) $K = \{x : (x$ is a counting number$) \wedge (x$ is odd$) \wedge (x$ is less than 20$)\}$.

(12) $L = \{x : (x$ is a counting number$) \wedge (x \neq 0)\}$.

III. (1) State, without proof, which of the sets of Exercise II are infinite.

(2) State, without proof, which of the sets of Exercise II are finite.

IV. (1) Prove that the set $\{1, 2, 3, 4, \ldots\}$ is infinite. (*Hint.* Use Example 4 and Definition 5.)

(2) Prove that the set $\{1, 2\}$ is finite. (*Hint.* Use Definition 6.)

V. Prove that $\{x : x$ is an even counting number$\}$ is infinite.

2.4   Universal Set, Complementation, and the Empty Set

DEFINITION 7.   The set U consisting of all elements under discussion is
called the *universal set* or *universe*.

The universal set U may change from one discussion to another. For
example, in one discussion the universal set may be the set of counting
numbers, whereas in another discussion the universal set may be the set
of fractions. In fact, in some discussions the universal set may be the set
of all human beings. In the study of first grade arithmetic, what is a
universal set? In any discussion of a set A, it is understood that $A \subset U$.
In cases of doubt, the universal set should be specified.

DEFINITION 8.   The *complement* of a set A (written $\tilde{A}$) is the set of all
elements of U which do not belong to A.

We see from Definition 8 that $\tilde{A} = \{x : x \in U \land x \notin A\}$.
An alternate notation for $\tilde{A}$ is $U \setminus A$; that is, $U \setminus A = \tilde{A}$.

Example 1.   If $U = \{0, 1, 2, 3, \ldots, 10\}$ and $A = \{1, 3, 5, 7, 9\}$, then
$\tilde{A} = \{0, 2, 4, 6, 8, 10\}$.

Example 2.   If $U = \{0, 1, 2, 3, \ldots\}$ and $A = \{1, 3, 5, 7, 9, \ldots\}$, then
$\tilde{A} = \{0, 2, 4, 6, \ldots\}$.

Example 3.   If $U = \{0, 1, 2, 3, \ldots\}$ and $A = \{1, 3, 5, 7, 9\}$, then
$\tilde{A} = \{0, 2, 4, 6, 8, 10, 11, 12, 13, \ldots\}$.

Example 4.   If $U = \{x : x$ is a student enrolled in this school$\}$ and A
$= \{x : x$ is a male student enrolled in this school$\}$, then
$\tilde{A} = \{x : x$ is a female student enrolled in this school$\}$.

Since the universal set U is a subset of itself, Definition 8 tells us
that $\tilde{U}$ is the set of all elements of U which do not belong to U. As U
contains all of the elements under discussion, $\tilde{U}$ contains no elements.
If we wish to consider $\tilde{U}$ to be a set, then we must introduce a new
concept.

DEFINITION 9.   The *empty* set or *null* set is the set which contains no
elements.

In this text the empty set will be denoted by the Greek letter phi ϕ
or the empty braces $\{\ \}$. From the definition of subset, it can be proved

that the empty set is a subset of every set and, in particular, of the universal set. As we shall see in the next section, the concept of the empty set is a useful and convenient one.

From the above discussion, it follows that $\widetilde{U} = \phi$ and $\widetilde{\phi} = U$.

Exercise 2.4

I. Let $A = \{1, 2, 3, 4\}$. Tell whether each of the following is an element of A or a subset of A.

(1) $\{2, 3\}$ (9) ϕ
(2) $\{4\}$ (10) $\{2\}$
(3) 4   (11) $\{3, 4\}$
(4) $\{1\}$ (12) 3
(5) 1   (13) $\{2, 4\}$
(6) $\{1, 2, 3, 4\}$ (14) 2
(7) $\{3\}$ (15) $\{2, 3, 4\}$
(8) $\{\ \}$ (16) $\{1, 2, 3\}$

II. The players of the New York Yankee baseball team constitute a set Y. Name three sets which contain Y as a subset and which may be considered universal sets.

III. Let $U = \{0, 2, 4, 6, 8, 10\}$. State the complement of each of the following sets.

(1) $\{0, 4, 8\}$ (6) $\{4, 8\}$
(2) $\{0, 6, 10\}$ (7) $\{0, 2, 4, 6, 8, 10\}$
(3) $\{2, 10\}$ (8) $\{0, 2, 8, 10\}$
(4) $\{2\}$ (9) $\{0, 4, 6, 8, 10\}$
(5) $\{0\}$ (10) $\{\ \}$

IV. Let $U = \{0, 1, 2, 3, \ldots\}$. State the complement of each of the following sets.

(1) $\{0, 2, 4, \ldots\}$ (4) $\{100, 101, 102, \ldots\}$
(2) $\{1, 3, 5, \ldots\}$ (5) $\{x : x \text{ is even}\}$
(3) $\{0, 1, 2, 3, \ldots\}$ (6) $\{x : x \text{ is odd}\}$

V. Given $U = \{x : x \text{ is a human being}\}$, state the complement of each of the following sets:

(1) $A = \{x : x \text{ is a female}\}$.
(2) $B = \{x : x \text{ is a human being and } x\text{'s age is less than or equal to } 5\}$.
(3) C is the set of all married persons.
(4) D is the set of all single persons.
(5) E is the set of all male human beings.

2.5 Union and Intersection

Analogous to the sentential connectives *or* and *and* are the set connectives *union* and *intersection*. A brief review of the definitions of the sentential connectives is recommended at this point.

DEFINITION 10. The *union* of two sets A and B is the set consisting of all elements which belong to A *or* to B. In symbols, $A \cup B = \{x : x \in A \lor x \in B\}$.

The symbol $\cup$, sometimes called *cup*, is used to indicate the union of two sets, and $A \cup B$ is read A *union* B.

Example 1. If $A = \{0, 1, 2, 3, 4\}$ and $B = \{2, 4, 6, 8\}$, then $A \cup B = \{0, 1, 2, 3, 4, 6, 8\}$. (*Note*. We do *not* write $A \cup B = \{0, 1, 2, 3, 4, 2, 4, 6, 8\}$.)

Example 2. If $A = \{0, 1\}$ and $B = \{0, 1, 2\}$, then $A \cup B = \{0, 1, 2\}$. (*Note*. In this case, $A \subset B$, and hence $A \cup B = B$.)

Example 3. If $A = \{2, 4, 6, 8\}$ and $B = \{3, 5, 7\}$, then $A \cup B = \{2, 3, 4, 5, 6, 7, 8\}$.

Example 4. If $A = \{$Tony, Jackie, Lorraine$\}$, $B = \{$Barbara, Sandra, Ed, Jackie, Lloyd$\}$, then $A \cup B = \{$Tony, Jackie, Lorraine, Barbara, Sandra, Ed, Lloyd$\}$.

DEFINITION 11. The *intersection* of two sets A and B is the set of all elements which belong to both A and B. In symbols, $A \cap B = \{x : x \in A \land x \in B\}$.

The symbol $\cap$, sometimes called *cap*, is used to indicate the intersection of two sets, and $A \cap B$ is read A *intersection* B.

Example 5. If $A = \{0, 1, 2, 3, 4\}$ and $B = \{2, 4, 6, 8\}$, then $A \cap B = \{2, 4\}$.

Example 6. If $A = \{0, 1\}$ and $B = \{0, 1, 2\}$, then $A \cap B = \{0, 1\}$. Note that in this case $A \subset B$ and hence $A \cap B = A$.

Example 7. If $A = \{2, 4, 6, 8\}$ and $B = \{3, 5, 7\}$, then $A \cap B = \{\ \} = \phi$.

Example 8.   If A is any set and $B = \phi$, then $A \cap B = A \cap \phi = \phi$.

Example 9.   If $A = \{\text{Angie, Ann, Alice, Anita}\}$ and $B = \{\text{Bizer, Bea, Butch}\}$, then $A \cap B = \phi$.

Examples 7 and 9 provide further illustrations of the necessity and usefulness of the concept of the empty set. In order that the intersection of any two sets always be a set, as required by Definition 11, it is necessary to have the concept of the empty set.

DEFINITION 12. Two sets A and B are said to be *disjoint* (from each other) if and only if $A \cap B = \phi$.

Thus A and B in Example 7 and A and B in Example 9 are disjoint sets. Since $A \cap \phi = \phi$, for any set A, we see that every set is disjoint from the null set.

As each of the operators $\cup$ and $\cap$ operates on *two* sets to form a third set, the operators $\cup$ and $\cap$ are called *binary* operators.

Exercise 2.5

I. Compute $A \cup B$ in each of the following.
  (1) $A = \{2, 4, 6, 8\}, B = \{2, 9\}$.
  (2) $A = \{2, 4, 6, 8\}, B = \{2, 8\}$.
  (3) $A = \{1, 3, 5\}, B = \{0, 2, 4\}$.
  (4) $A = \{1, 3, 5, \ldots\}, B = \{0, 2, 4, \ldots\}$.
  (5) $A = \{0, 1, 2, \ldots\}, B = \{1, 3, 5, \ldots\}$.
  (6) $A = \{0\}, B = \{0, 1, 2, 3, \ldots\}$.
  (7) $A = \{\ \}, B = \{0, 1, 2, 3, \ldots\}$.
  (8) $A = \{0\}, B = \{1, 2, 3, \ldots\}$.
  (9) $A = \{\text{Jessie, May, Bea}\}, B = \{\text{Janice, Craig, Lisa, Inez}\}$.
  (10) $A = \{\text{Doris, Fannie, Bea, Jo}\}, B = \{\text{Bea, Hazel, Erenze, Elvina, Louise, Toby}\}$.

II. Compute $A \cap B$ in each of the above.

III. Compute $A \cup B$ and $A \cap B$ in each of the following.
  (1) $A = \{0, 1\}, B = \{0, 1, 2\}$.
  (2) $A = \{1, 2, 3\}, B = \{3, 4, 5\}$.
  (3) $A = \{1, 2, 3\}, B = \{4, 5, 6\}$.
  (4) $A = \{0, 1\}, B = \{0\}$.
  (5) $A = \{1, 3, 5, \ldots\}, B = \{2, 4, 6, \ldots\}$.
  (6) $A = \phi, B = \{1, 2, 3, 4, 5\}$.
  (7) $A = \{\ \}, B = \{1, 2, 3, 4, 5\}$.

(8) $A = \{x{:}x$ is a counting number greater than 100$\}$, $B = \{x{:}x$ is a counting number less than or equal to 100$\}$.

(9) $A = \{x{:}x$ is a counting number greater than or equal to 100$\}$, $B = \{x{:}x$ is a counting number less than or equal to 100$\}$.

(10) $A = \{x{:}x$ is a counting number greater than 100$\}$, $B = \{x{:}x$ is a counting number less than 100$\}$.

(11) $A = \{x{:}x$ is a counting number greater than or equal to 100$\}$, $B = \{x{:}x$ is a counting number less than 100$\}$.

(12) A is the set of single persons, B is the set of married persons.

IV. What is the relationship of $A \cup B$ to $B \cup A$? Justify your answer.

V. What is the relationship of $A \cap B$ to $B \cap A$? Justify your answer.

2.6   Venn Diagrams

In the eighteenth century the Swiss mathematician Euler introduced the technique of the use of circles to indicate sets and relationships among sets. In the nineteenth century the British logician Venn refined and extended this idea to include other geometric figures. For this reason, these diagrams or figures are called Euler diagrams or Venn diagrams. In this text, we refer to them as *Venn diagrams*.

The elements of a set may be considered as points interior to a circle, square, rectangle, or other closed plane figure. To indicate that $A \subset B$, we may draw a circle interior to another circle or to a square or rectangle as indicated in Figure 2.1.

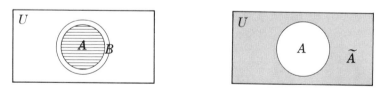

FIGURE 2.1   FIGURE 2.2

In Figure 2.1, you will notice that every point in the set A is also in the set B. As in Figure 2.1, throughout this text a rectangle will be used to indicate the universal set U. All sets in any discussion will be considered subsets of the universal set. You may wonder why we display the universal set. You will recall that the complement of a set B is defined if and only if the universal set is specified. The portrayal of the universal set makes it possible for us to indicate the complement of any set.

In Figure 2.2, the complement of A is indicated by the shaded region $\tilde{A}$. In Figure 2.1, what is the complement of B?

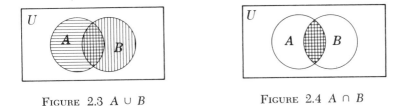

FIGURE 2.3 $A \cup B$ FIGURE 2.4 $A \cap B$

The shaded part of Figure 2.3 illustrates $A \cup B$. The shaded part of Figure 2.4 illustrates $A \cap B$. Note that the sets A and B illustrated in Figures 2.3 and 2.4 are not disjoint. The shaded parts of Figures 2.5 and 2.6 illustrate $A \cup B$ and $A \cap B$, respectively, when A and B are disjoint. The fact that $A \cap B = \phi$ is indicated in Figure 2.6 by the absence of shading.

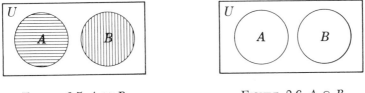

FIGURE 2.5 $A \cup B$ FIGURE 2.6 $A \cap B$

The shaded parts of Figures 2.7 and 2.8 illustrate $A \cup B$ and $A \cap B$ when $A \subset B$ and $A \neq B$. Note that $A \cup B = B$ and $A \cap B = A$.

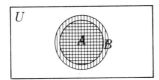

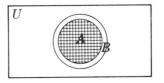

FIGURE 2.7 $A \cup B$ FIGURE 2.8 $A \cap B$

The following example illustrates an application of Venn diagrams.

Example.   Let $U =$ the set of all high school teachers, $A =$ the set of all high school mathematics teachers, and $B =$ the set of all high school coaches.

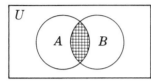

FIGURE 2.9 $A \cap B$

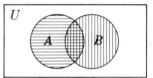

FIGURE 2.10 $A \cup B$

The shaded part of Figure 2.9 represents $A \cap B$; namely, the set of all high school coaches who are also high school mathematics teachers. The shaded part of Figure 2.10 represents $A \cup B$; namely, the set of all high school teachers who are mathematics teachers or who are coaches (or both). The unshaded part of Figure 2.10 represents $\widehat{A \cup B}$; namely, the set of all high school teachers who are neither mathematics teachers nor coaches.

Exercise 2.6

I. Let $U =$ the set of all human beings. Use Venn diagrams to illustrate each of the following.

(1) $A =$ the set of all students, $B =$ the set of all high school students.

(2) $A =$ the set of all high school teachers, $B =$ the set of all teachers.

(3) $A =$ set of all students, $B =$ set of all persons under 1 year old.

(4) $A =$ set of all teachers, $B =$ set of all parents.

(5) $A =$ set of all males over 21 years of age, $B =$ set of all females over 21 years of age, $C =$ set of all persons over 10 years of age.

II. Shade the union of A and B in each part of Exercise I.

III. Shade the intersection of A and B in each part of Exercise I.

IV. (1) Shade the union of A and C in Exercise I(5).
    (2) Shade the union of B and C in Exercise I(5).

(3) Shade the union of A, B, and C in Exercise I(5).
(4) Shade the intersection of A and C in Exercise I(5).
(5) Shade the intersection of B and C in Exercise I(5).
(6) Shade the intersection of A, B, and C in Exercise I(5).

V. In Figures 2.11, 2.12, 2.13, and 2.14, U = the set of all students. A = the set of all students of mathematics, B = the set of all students of chemistry, and C = the set of all students of speech.

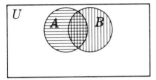

FIGURE 2.11

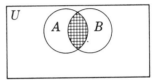

FIGURE 2.12

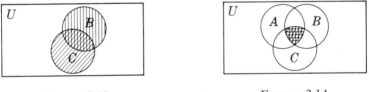

FIGURE 2.13   FIGURE 2.14

In terms of union, intersection, and complement (for example, A ∪ B, A ∩ B, or Ã), and in words, express what each of the following regions represent.

(1) The shaded region of Figure 2.11.
(2) The unshaded region of Figure 2.11.
(3) The shaded region of Figure 2.12.
(4) The unshaded region of Figure 2.12.
(5) The shaded region of Figure 2.13.
(6) The unshaded region of Figure 2.13.
(7) The shaded region of Figure 2.14.
(8) The unshaded region of Figure 2.14.

2.7   Algebra of Sets

So far we have concentrated our attention on unions and intersections of any two sets. In this section, we devote our attention to unions and intersections of more than two sets. Since $\cup$ and $\cap$ are binary operators and thus connect *two* sets only, we have to agree on the order in which the union or intersection of more than two sets is formed. For example, if $A = \{1, 2, 4\}$, $B = \{2, 3, 8\}$, and $C = \{1, 3, 8, 9\}$, then $A \cap B \cup C$ is ambiguous. However, $A \cap (B \cup C) = \{1, 2, 4\} \cap [\{2, 3, 8\} \cup \{1, 3, 8, 9\}] = \{1, 2, 4\} \cap \{1, 2, 3, 8, 9\} = \{1, 2\}$. Moreover, $(A \cap B) \cup C = [\{1, 2, 4\} \cap \{2, 3, 8\}] \cup \{1, 3, 8, 9\} = \{2\} \cup \{1, 3, 8, 9\} = \{1, 2, 3, 8, 9\}$. Hence $A \cap (B \cup C) \neq (A \cap B) \cup C$.

This example illustrates the necessity for punctuation. The parentheses are punctuation marks which indicate that the first operation ($\cup$ or $\cap$) to be performed is within the parentheses.

We learned from Definition 10 that the union of two sets A and B is itself a set, denoted by $A \cup B$. Thus the union of *two* sets is a *single* set. This property is called the *closure property for union*.

CLOSURE PROPERTY FOR UNION
If A and B are any sets, then $A \cup B$ is a unique set.

Recall that $A \cup B = \{x\colon (x \in A) \vee (x \in B)\}$ and that $B \cup A = \{x\colon (x \in B) \vee (x \in A)\}$. Since these two sets are identical from the fact that $p \vee q \rightleftarrows q \vee p$ is logically true, we see that $A \cup B = B \cup A$. This property is called the *commutative property for union*.

COMMUTATIVE PROPERTY FOR UNION
If A and B are any sets, then $A \cup B = B \cup A$.

For example, if $A = \{1, 5, 9, 13\}$ and $B = \{5, 13, 21\}$, then $A \cup B = \{1, 5, 9, 13, 21\}$ and $B \cup A = \{1, 5, 9, 13, 21\}$.

Next we consider $A \cup B \cup C$. We have already seen that, because $\cup$ is a binary operator, punctuation is necessary to indicate which operation is to be performed first. Thus we should compare $(A \cup B) \cup C$ and $A \cup (B \cup C)$. If $A = \{1, 3, 5, 7, 9\}$, $B = \{2, 5, 8, 11\}$, and $C = \{2, 4, 6, 8, 10\}$, then $(A \cup B) \cup C = \{1, 2, 3, 5, 7, 8, 9, 11\} \cup \{2, 4, 6, 8, 10\} = \{1, 2, 3, 4, 5, 6, 7, 8, 9, 10, 11\}$, and $A \cup (B \cup C) = \{1, 3, 5, 7, 9\} \cup \{2, 4, 5, 6, 8, 10, 11\} = \{1, 2, 3, 4, 5, 6, 7, 8, 9, 10, 11\}$.

In this example $(A \cup B) \cup C = A \cup (B \cup C)$. It is natural to wonder whether this relationship is true for *all* sets A, B, and C. The following argument is a proof that $(A \cup B) \cup C = A \cup (B \cup C)$ for any sets $A, B,$ and C.

By Definition 10, $(A \cup B) \cup C = \{x: (x \in A \cup B) \vee (x \in C)\}$ $= \{x: (x \in A \vee x \in B) \vee (x \in C)\}$ and $A \cup (B \cup C) = \{x: (x \in A)$ $\vee (x \in B \cup C)\} = \{x: (x \in A) \vee (x \in B \vee x \in C)\}$. Since $[(p \vee q)$ $\vee r] \rightleftarrows [p \vee (q \vee r)]$ is logically true, we see that $(A \cup B) \cup C$ $= A \cup (B \cup C)$. This property is called the *associative property for union*.

ASSOCIATIVE PROPERTY FOR UNION
If A, B, and C are any sets, then $(A \cup B) \cup C = A \cup (B \cup C)$.

Although it is frequently necessary to punctuate if we are to avoid ambiguity, the associative property makes it unnecessary to punctuate whenever the only operation is union. Thus, although $A \cap B \cup C$ is ambiguous, $A \cup B \cup C$ is *not* ambiguous. It may be proved from the associative property for union that $A_1 \cup A_2 \cup A_3 \cup \ldots \cup A_k$ is not ambiguous.

We have already seen that $A \cup \phi = A$ for any set A. For example, $\{1, 2, 3, 7, 11\} \cup \phi = \{1, 2, 3, 7, 11\}$. This property is called the *identity property for union*.

IDENTITY PROPERTY FOR UNION
If A is any set, then $A \cup \phi = A$.

It follows readily from the commutative property for union that $\phi \cup A = A$. The null set ϕ plays a role in the algebra of sets with respect to union similar to that of the number 0 in the algebra of numbers with respect to addition. In any algebra, the element with such a property with respect to a binary operation is called the *identity* element with respect to that binary operation. Thus 0 is the identity element with respect to addition of numbers, and ϕ is the identity element with respect to union of sets.

Recall that $\tilde{A}$ is the complement of A; that is, $\tilde{A} = \{x: x \in U \wedge x \notin A\}$. Thus if $U = \{1, 2, 3, 4, 5, 6, 7\}$ and $A = \{1, 3, 5, 7\}$, then $\tilde{A} = \{2, 4, 6\}$. Moreover, you will notice that $A \cup \tilde{A} = U$. This property, which is an immediate consequence of Definition 8 and Definition 10, is called the *complement property for union*.

COMPLEMENT PROPERTY FOR UNION
If A is any set, then $A \cup \tilde{A} = U$.

This property is illustrated in Figure 2.15, in which $\tilde{A}$ is indicated by the shaded region.

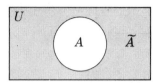

FIGURE 2.15

It follows readily from Definition 10 that $A \cup A = A$ for any set A. This property is called the *idempotent property for union.*

IDEMPOTENT PROPERTY FOR UNION
If A is any set, then $A \cup A = A$.

We state without proof the following properties for intersection. As the proofs are similar to those for union of sets, they are assigned to you as exercises.

CLOSURE PROPERTY FOR INTERSECTION
If A and B are any sets, then $A \cap B$ is a unique set.

COMMUTATIVE PROPERTY FOR INTERSECTION
If A and B are any sets, then $A \cap B = B \cap A$.

ASSOCIATIVE PROPERTY FOR INTERSECTION
If A, B, and C are any sets, then $(A \cap B) \cap C = A \cap (B \cap C)$.

IDENTITY PROPERTY FOR INTERSECTION
If A is any set, then $A \cap U = A$.

COMPLEMENT PROPERTY FOR INTERSECTION
If A is any set, then $A \cap \tilde{A} = \phi$.

IDEMPOTENT PROPERTY FOR INTERSECTION
If A is any set, then $A \cap A = A$.

Next we investigate $A \cap (B \cup C)$ and $(A \cap B) \cup (A \cap C)$. For example, if $A = \{1, 2, 4\}$, $B = \{2, 3, 8\}$, and $C = \{1, 3, 8, 9\}$, then

$A \cap (B \cup C) = \{1, 2, 4\} \cap [\{2, 3, 8\} \cup \{1, 3, 8, 9\}] = \{1, 2, 4\}$ $\cap \{1, 2, 3, 8, 9\} = \{1, 2\}$. Moreover, $A \cap B = \{1, 2, 4\} \cap \{2, 3, 8\}$ $= \{2\}$, and $A \cap C = \{1, 2, 4\} \cap \{1, 3, 8, 9\} = \{1\}$. Thus $(A \cap B)$ $\cup (A \cap C) = \{2\} \cup \{1\} = \{1, 2\}$. Hence, in this example, $A \cap$ $(B \cup C) = (A \cap B) \cup (A \cap C)$. You may wonder whether this property is true for all sets A, B, and C. The following argument proves that it is true for all sets A, B, and C. Recall that $A \cap (B \cup C) = \{x:$ $x \in A \wedge (x \in B \cup C)\} = \{x: x \in A \wedge (x \in B \vee x \in C)\}$. Moreover, $(A \cap B) \cup (A \cap C) = \{x: (x \in A \cap B) \vee (x \in A \cap C)\} = \{x:$ $(x \in A \wedge x \in B) \vee (x \in A \wedge x \in C)\}$.

Hence $A \cap (B \cup C) = (A \cap B) \cup (A \cap C)$ if and only if $\{x: x \in A \wedge (x \in B \vee x \in C)\} = \{x: (x \in A \wedge x \in B) \vee (x \in A$ $\wedge x \in C)\}$. In Chapter 1 we proved that $p \wedge (q \vee r) \rightleftarrows (p \wedge q)$ $\vee (p \wedge r)$ is logically true; that is, it is true for all sentences p, q, and r. In particular, it is true when p is the sentence $x \in A$, q is the sentence $x \in B$, and r is the sentence $x \in C$. Hence $(x \in A) \wedge (x \in B \vee x \in C)$ $\rightleftarrows (x \in A \wedge x \in B) \vee (x \in A \wedge x \in C)$ is true. Thus $\{x: (x \in A)$ $\wedge (x \in B \vee x \in C)\} = \{x: (x \in A \wedge x \in B) \vee (x \in A \wedge x \in C)\}$. Therefore, $A \cap (B \cup C) = (A \cap B) \cup (A \cap C)$. This property is called the *distributive property for intersection over union*.

THE DISTRIBUTIVE PROPERTY FOR INTERSECTION OVER UNION
If A, B, and C are any sets, then $A \cap (B \cup C) = (A \cap B)$ $\cup (A \cap C)$.

This property is illustrated in the Venn diagram in Figure 2.16. The student should be cautioned, however, that there are many other possible arrangements of A, B, and C.

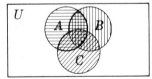

$A \cap (B \cup C)$

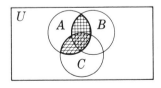

$(A \cap B) \cup (A \cap C)$

FIGURE 2.16

In a similar manner we may prove the *distributive property for union over intersection.*

THE DISTRIBUTIVE PROPERTY FOR UNION OVER INTERSECTION
If A, B, and C are any sets, then $A \cup (B \cap C) = (A \cup B) \cap (A \cup C)$.

For example, if $A = \{1, 2, 4\}$, $B = \{2, 3, 8\}$, and $C = \{1, 3, 8, 9\}$, then $A \cup (B \cap C) = \{1, 2, 4\} \cup (\{2, 3, 8\} \cap \{1, 3, 8, 9\}) = \{1, 2, 4\} \cup \{3, 8\} = \{1, 2, 3, 4, 8\}$. Moreover $(A \cup B) \cap (A \cup C) = (\{1, 2, 4\} \cup \{2, 3, 8\}) \cap (\{1, 2, 4\} \cup \{1, 3, 8, 9\}) = \{1, 2, 3, 4, 8\} \cap \{1, 2, 3, 4, 8, 9\} = \{1, 2, 3, 4, 8\}$. This property is illustrated in the Venn diagram in Figure 2.17. As previously stated, the student is cautioned that there are many other possible arrangements of A, B, and C.

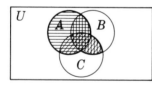

$A \cup (B \cap C)$ $(A \cup B) \cap (A \cup C)$

FIGURE 2.17

Now that we realize that there is a relationship between the algebra of sentences and the algebra of sets, we may wonder whether $\widehat{A \cup B} = \tilde{A} \cap \tilde{B}$ and $\widehat{A \cap B} = \tilde{A} \cup \tilde{B}$. For example, if $U = \{1, 2, 3, 4, 5, 6, 7, 8, 9, 10\}$, $A = \{1, 5, 9, 10\}$, and $B = \{1, 8, 9\}$, then $A \cup B = \{1, 5, 8, 9, 10\}$ and hence $\widehat{A \cup B} = \{2, 3, 4, 6, 7\}$. Moreover, $\tilde{A} = \{2, 3, 4, 6, 7, 8\}$ and $\tilde{B} = \{2, 3, 4, 5, 6, 7, 10\}$ and hence $\tilde{A} \cap \tilde{B} = \{2, 3, 4, 6, 7\}$. Although this example does not prove that $\widehat{A \cup B} = \tilde{A} \cap \tilde{B}$, it does encourage us to try to prove that $\widehat{A \cup B} = \tilde{A} \cap \tilde{B}$ for any sets A and B.

Recall that $\widehat{A \cup B} = \{x: x \notin A \cup B\}$. Then $\widehat{A \cup B} = \{x: \sim(x \in A \cup B)\} = \{x: \sim(x \in A \vee x \in B)\} = \{x: \sim(x \in A) \wedge \sim(x \in B)\} = \{x: x \in \tilde{A} \wedge x \in \tilde{B}\} = \tilde{A} \cap \tilde{B}$. The student should identify the step in which the logical truth $\sim(p \vee q) \rightleftarrows (\sim p \wedge \sim q)$ was used. The property $\widehat{A \cup B} = \tilde{A} \cap \tilde{B}$ is called the *DeMorgan property for union.*

THE DEMORGAN PROPERTY FOR UNION

If A and B are any sets, then $\widetilde{A \cup B} = \tilde{A} \cap \tilde{B}$.

The DeMorgan property for union is illustrated in the Venn diagram in Figure 2.18.

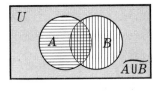

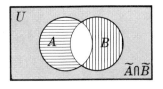

$\widehat{A \cup B}$

$\tilde{A} \cap \tilde{B}$

FIGURE 2.18

In a similar manner we can prove that $\widehat{A \cap B} = \tilde{A} \cup \tilde{B}$. This property is called the *DeMorgan property for intersection*.

THE DEMORGAN PROPERTY FOR INTERSECTION

If A and B are any sets, then $\widehat{A \cap B} = \tilde{A} \cup \tilde{B}$.

For example, if $U = \{1, 2, 3, 4, 5, 6, 7, 8, 9, 10\}$, $A = \{1, 5, 9, 10\}$, and $B = \{1, 8, 9\}$, then $A \cap B = \{1, 9\}$ and hence $\widehat{A \cap B} = \{2, 3, 4, 5, 6, 7, 8, 10\}$. Moreover, $\tilde{A} = \{2, 3, 4, 6, 7, 8\}$ and $\tilde{B} = \{2, 3, 4, 5, 6, 7, 10\}$ and hence $\tilde{A} \cup \tilde{B} = \{2, 3, 4, 5, 6, 7, 8, 10\}$. The DeMorgan property for intersection is illustrated in the Venn diagram in Figure 2.19.

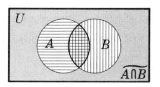

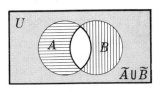

$\widehat{A \cap B}$

$\tilde{A} \cup \tilde{B}$

FIGURE 2.19

The *double complement property* follows readily from the definition of complement.

THE DOUBLE COMPLEMENT PROPERTY
If A is any set, then $\widetilde{\widetilde{A}} = A$.

At this point you should compare these properties with the analogous properties for sentences listed at the end of Section 1.9.

Exercise 2.7

I. If $U = \{0, 1, 2, 3, 4, 5, 6, 7, 8, 9\}$, $A = \{0, 2, 4, 6\}$, $B = \{1, 4, 6, 8\}$, $C = \{1, 3, 5, 9\}$, and $D = \phi$, compute each of the following.

(1) $A \cup B$

(2) $B \cup C$

(3) $A \cap B$

(4) $B \cap C$

(5) $C \cap B$

(6) $(B \cup A) \cup C$

(7) $(U \cap A) \cup B$

(8) $U \cap (A \cup B)$

(9) $C \cap (A \cup B)$

(10) $(C \cap A) \cup B$

(11) $(C \cup B) \cap (A \cup B)$

(12) $(C \cap A) \cup (C \cap B)$

(13) $A \cap (B \cup C)$

(14) $(A \cap B) \cup C$

(15) $(A \cup B) \cup C$

(16) $A \cup (B \cup C)$

(17) $D \cap A$

(18) $D \cap B$

(19) $U \cap D$

(20) $A \cup D$

(21) $A \cup \widetilde{B}$

(22) $A \cap \widetilde{B}$

(23) $\widetilde{A} \cup \widetilde{B}$

(24) $\widetilde{A \cap B}$

(25) $\widetilde{D}$

(26) $\widetilde{U}$

(27) $\widetilde{U} \cap D$

(28) $\widetilde{U} \cup D$

(29) $\widetilde{A \cup B \cup C}$

(30) $A \cup \widetilde{B \cup C}$

(31) $(A \cup B) \cup \widetilde{C}$

(32) $A \cup (B \cup \widetilde{C})$

(33) $\widetilde{A \cap B \cap C}$

(34) $A \cap \widetilde{B \cap C}$

(35) $(A \cap B) \cap \widetilde{C}$

(36) $A \cap (B \cap \widetilde{C})$

II. (1) List the twelve possible ways in which the union of three sets A, B, and C can be formed.

(2) Are the resulting 12 sets equal? Why?

III. (1) Illustrate the distributive property $A \cap (B \cup C) = (A \cap B) \cup (A \cap C)$ by Venn diagrams. Use *two* arrangements, each different from the arrangement in Figure 2.16.

(2) Illustrate the distributive property $A \cup (B \cap C) = (A \cup B) \cap (A \cup C)$ by Venn diagrams. Use *two* arrangements, each different from the arrangement in Figure 2.17.

IV. Use the distributive properties and the commutative properties as stated in this section to prove each of the following properties.

(1) $(A \cup B) \cap C = (A \cap C) \cup (B \cap C)$.
(2) $(A \cap B) \cup C = (A \cup C) \cap (B \cup C)$.

(*Note.* These are alternate forms of the distributive properties.)

V. Let $U = C_0 = \{x: x \text{ is a counting number}\}$, $A = \{x: x \text{ is less than } 100\}$, $B = \{x: x \text{ is even}\}$, $C = \{x: x \text{ is odd}\}$, and $D = \{0, 3, 6, 9, \ldots\}$.
Compute each of the following.

(1) $B \cap D$
(2) $C \cap D$
(3) $B \cap C$
(4) $B \cap A$
(5) $A \cap B$
(6) $A \cup C$
(7) $\tilde{C}$
(8) $\tilde{C} \cap A$
(9) $\tilde{B}$
(10) $A \cap (B \cup C)$
(11) $(B \cup C) \cap D$
(12) $(A \cup D) \cap C$
(13) $(A \cap C) \cup (D \cap C)$
(14) $\widetilde{A \cup B}$
(15) $\tilde{A} \cap \tilde{B}$
(16) $A \cap (\widetilde{B \cup C})$
(17) $A \cap (B \cup \tilde{C})$
(18) $\widetilde{A \cap (B \cup C)}$
(19) $(A \cap B) \cup \tilde{C}$
(20) $\widetilde{(A \cap B) \cup C}$

VI. (1) Prove that $[p \vee (q \wedge r)] \rightleftarrows [(p \vee q) \wedge (p \vee r)]$ is logically true.
(2) Use the logical truth in (1) to prove that $A \cup (B \cap C) = (A \cup B) \cap (A \cup C)$.
(3) Prove $A \cap \tilde{A} = \phi$, for any set A.
(4) Prove $A \cup \tilde{A} = U$, for any set A.

VII. Complete each of the following so that a true sentence results for all sets A, B, and C.

(1) $A \cup (B \cup C) = (A \cup B) \cup \underline{\quad}$.
(2) $A \cup (B \cup C) = A \cup (C \cup \underline{\quad})$.
(3) $A \cup (B \cap C) = (A \cup B) \cap (\underline{\quad} \cup C)$.
(4) $B \cap (C \cup A) = (\underline{\quad} \cap C) \cup (B \cap A)$.
(5) $C \cap (A \cup B) = (\underline{\quad} \cap A) \cup (\underline{\quad} \cap B)$.
(6) $A \cup (C \cap B) = (A \cup \underline{\quad}) \cap (\underline{\quad} \cup C)$.
(7) $(A \cap B) \cup C = (A \cup \underline{\quad}) \cap (\underline{\quad} \cup C)$.
(8) $(B \cup A) \cap C = (\underline{\quad} \cap C) \cup (A \cap \underline{\quad})$.
(9) $(A \cup B) \cap (A \cup C) = A \cup (\underline{\quad} \cap C)$.
(10) $(A \cap C) \cup (A \cap B) = A \cap (\underline{\quad} \cup B)$.
(11) $(A \cup C) \cup B = B \cup (A \cup \underline{\quad})$.
(12) $(B \cap A) \cap C = (A \cap \underline{\quad}) \cap C$.
(13) $\widetilde{A \cup B} \cup C = (\tilde{A} \cap \tilde{B}) \cup \underline{\quad}$.
(14) $A \cup (\widetilde{B \cup C}) = \underline{\quad} \cup (\tilde{B} \cap \tilde{C})$.
(15) $A \cap (\widetilde{B \cup C}) = A \cap \tilde{B} \cap \underline{\quad}$.
(16) $(\widetilde{B \cup C}) \cap A = \underline{\quad} \cap \tilde{C} \cap A$.

(17) $\widehat{A \cup B} \cap \tilde{C} = (\tilde{A} \cap \underline{\quad}) \cap \tilde{C}.$
(18) $\tilde{A} \cup \widehat{(B \cap C)} = (\tilde{A} \cup \underline{\quad}) \cup \tilde{C}.$
(19) $\widehat{A \cap (B \cup C)} = \tilde{A} \cup \tilde{B} \cup \underline{\quad}.$
(20) $\widehat{C \cup (B \cap A)} = \underline{\quad} \cap \widehat{B \cap A}.$

VIII. State the name of the property which guarantees that each of the following sentences is true for all sets A, B, *and* C.

    (1) $(A \cup B) \cup C = A \cup (B \cup C).$
    (2) $A \cup (C \cup B) = (A \cup C) \cup B.$
    (3) $A \cup (B \cup C) = A \cup (C \cup B).$
    (4) $A \cup (B \cup C) = (B \cup C) \cup A.$
    (5) $A \cap (B \cup C) = (A \cap B) \cup (A \cap C).$
    (6) $A \cup (B \cap C) = (A \cup B) \cap (A \cup C).$
    (7) $A \cup (B \cap C) = (C \cap B) \cup A.$
    (8) $A \cap (B \cup C) = (C \cup B) \cap A.$
    (9) $A \cup \widehat{B \cap C} = A \cup (\tilde{B} \cup \tilde{C}).$
    (10) $\widehat{A \cup B} \cap C = (\tilde{A} \cap \tilde{B}) \cap C.$

IX. State the truth value of each of the following sentences. The universal quantifier is understood; that is, the phrase "for all sets A, B, and C" is understood to be a part of each sentence.

    (1) $(A \cap B) \cup C = A \cap (B \cup C).$
    (2) $A \cup (B \cap C) = (A \cup B) \cap C.$
    (3) $A \cup (B \cap C) = (B \cap C) \cup A.$
    (4) $B \cap (A \cup C) = (A \cup C) \cap B.$
    (5) $B \cap (A \cup C) = (C \cup A) \cap B.$
    (6) $A \cup (B \cap C) = (C \cap B) \cup A.$
    (7) $\widehat{A \cup B} \cup C = (\tilde{A} \cup \tilde{B}) \cup C.$
    (8) $A \cap \widehat{(B \cap C)} = A \cap (\tilde{B} \cap \tilde{C}).$
    (9) $\widehat{A \cup B \cup C} = \tilde{A} \cap \tilde{B} \cap \tilde{C}.$
    (10) $\widehat{A \cap \tilde{B} \cap C} = \tilde{A} \cup \tilde{B} \cup \tilde{C}.$

X. Write the first 15 basic properties of sentences listed in Section 1.9. To the right of each of these properties write the corresponding property of sets. For example, corresponding to the associative property $(p \wedge q) \wedge r \rightleftarrows p \wedge (q \wedge r)$ is the associative property $(A \cap B) \cap C = A \cap (B \cap C)$. If t is a true sentence, observe that $p \wedge t \rightleftarrows p$ corresponds to $A \cap U = A$. What set property corresponds to $p \vee f \rightleftarrows p$?

2.8 Cartesian Product

We have already studied the binary operators $\cup$ and $\cap$ between any two sets A and B. You will recall that $A \cup B = \{x: x \in A \vee x \in B\}$

and $A \cap B = \{x \colon x \in A \wedge x \in B\}$. Now we shall study another binary operator between two sets A and B. The set $A \times B$ (read A *cross* B) is called the *Cartesian product of A and B*.

DEFINITION 13.   The *Cartesian product* of two sets A and B (written $A \times B$) is the set of all pairs (a, b) such that $a \in A$ and $b \in B$.

In set notation $A \times B = \{(a, b) \colon a \in A \wedge b \in B\}$. *Equality* of pairs is identity; that is, $(a, b) = (c, d)$ if and only if $a = c$ and $b = d$. The elements (a, b) of $A \times B$ are called *ordered pairs*. The reason for the word *ordered* is that, in general, $(a, b) \neq (b, a)$; that is, the *order* in which the elements a and b are written is important. For example, if $A = \{1, 2\}$ and $B = \{0, 2, 4\}$, then $A \times B = \{1, 0), (1, 2), (1, 4), (2, 0), (2, 2), (2, 4)\}$ and $B \times A = \{(0, 1), (0, 2), (2, 1), (2, 2), (4, 1), (4, 2)\}$. Thus $A \times B \neq B \times A$; that is, the operation is *not* commutative. The fact that this operation is *not* commutative should not surprise you. In mathematics and nature there are many noncommutative operations. For example, the operations of subtraction and division are noncommutative; that is, in general, $a - b \neq b - a$ and $a \div b \neq b \div a$. Henceforth, when we speak of the Cartesian product of A and B, without further qualification, we shall mean $A \times B$.

It is important to emphasize the distinction between the set $A \cap B$ and the set $A \times B$. Although the elements of $A \cap B$ are elements of A and also of B, the elements of $A \times B$ are *not* elements of A and are *not* elements of B. On the contrary, the elements of $A \times B$ are *ordered pairs* of elements—the first member of the pair being an element of A, and the second member of the pair being an element of B.

The concept of Cartesian product is extremely important in mathematics and applications. It is especially important in each of the following:

(1) developing the properties of the counting numbers with respect to multiplication,
(2) developing the properties of functions and their graphs,
(3) expressing the sample space of an experiment such as the roll of a pair of dice.

Example 1. $A = \{1, 3\}$ and $B = \{x, y\}$.
$A \times B = \{(1, x), (1, y), (3, x), (3, y)\}$.
$B \times A = \{(x, 1), (x, 3), (y, 1), (y, 3)\}$.
$A \cap B = \phi$.
$B \cap A = \phi$.

Example 2. $A = \{1, 2, 4, 8\}$ and $B = \{8, 9\}$.
$A \times B = \{(1, 8), (1, 9), (2, 8), (2, 9), (4, 8), (4, 9),$
$(8, 8), (8, 9)\}$.
$B \times A = \{(8, 1), (8, 2), (8, 4), (8, 8), (9, 1), (9, 2),$
$(9, 4), (9, 8)\}$.
$A \cap B = \{8\}$.
$B \cap A = \{8\}$.

Example 3. $C_0 = \{0, 1, 2, 3, 4, \ldots\}$ and $B = \{0, 1, 2, 3, 4\}$.
$C_0 \times B = \{(0, 0), (0, 1), (0, 2), (0, 3), (0, 4)$
$(1, 0), (1, 1), (1, 2), (1, 3), (1, 4)$
$\cdots$
$(k, 0), (k, 1), (k, 2), (k, 3), (k, 4),$
$\cdots$ $\}$.
$C_0 \cap B = \{0, 1, 2, 3, 4\} = B$, and $B \cap C_0 = B$.

Example 4. $C_0 = \{0, 1, 2, 3, 4, \ldots\}$
$C_0 \times C_0 = \{(0, 0), (0, 1), (0, 2), (0, 3), (0, 4), \ldots$
$(1, 0), (1, 1), (1, 2), (1, 3), (1, 4), \ldots$
$\cdots$
$(k, 0), (k, 1), (k, 2), (k, 3), (k, 4), \ldots$
$\cdots$ $\}$

In Examples 3 and 4 it is not possible to list all elements of the Cartesian products. However, we have listed enough elements of $C_0 \times B$ so that the patterns are established. As before, the three dots indicate the omission of elements from the listing. One can *visualize* the forms of $C_0 \times B$ and $C_0 \times C_0$ even though he cannot actually *list* all of the elements.

We have already seen that the null set has special properties which make it particularly useful and interesting in the study of mathematics. In particular, $A \cup \phi = A$. This is analogous to $a + 0 = a$ in arithmetic. To complete the analogy, we shall conclude this section with a discussion of the Cartesian product of two sets, one of which is the null set. For example, if $A = \{2, 4, 6, 8\}$, then $A \times \phi = \phi$. By definition of $A \times B$, the second member b of the ordered pair (a, b) is an element of B. Since $B = \phi$, there are no elements b of B. Thus there is *no* second member b in B to pair with a in A to form an ordered pair (a, b); that is, there is *no* ordered pair (a, b) of $A \times B$. Hence $A \times B = \phi$. It is easy to see that $A \times \phi = \phi$ for *any* set A. In fact $A \times B = \phi$ if and only if $A = \phi$ or $B = \phi$. Now the analogy is complete: in arithmetic $a \cdot 0 = 0$ for any number a; in set theory $A \times \phi = \phi$ for any set A.

Exercise 2.8

I. Compute $A \times B$ for each of the following pairs of sets.

(1) $A = \{2\}, B = \{0\}$
(2) $A = \{2\}, B = \{\ \}$
(3) $A = \{2\}, B = \{1, 2\}$
(4) $A = \phi, B = \{1, 3\}$
(5) $A = \{0, 1\}, B = \{1, 2, 3\}$
(6) $A = \{0, 1, 2, 3\}, B = \{1, 2, 3\}$
(7) $A = \{0\}, B = \{0, 1, 2, 3\}$
(8) $A = \{0\}, B = \{0, 1, 2, 3, \ldots\}$
(9) $A = \{10, 11, 12\}, B = \{1, 2, 3, 4, \ldots\}$
(10) $A = \{1, 2, 3, \ldots\}, B = C_0$

II. Compute $B \times A$ for each pair of sets in Exercise I.

III. (1) Give an example in which $(a, b) = (b, a)$.
(2) Under what condition is $(a, b) = (b, a)$?

IV. (1) Give an example in which $A \times B = B \times A$.
(2) Under what condition is $A \times B = B \times A$?

V. The Cartesian product $A \times B$ is given in each of the following. Compute A and B.

(1) $\{(1, 1), (1, 2), (1, 3), (5, 1), (5, 2), (5, 3)\}$
(2) $\{(1, 1), (1, 5), (2, 1), (2, 5), (3, 1), (3, 5)\}$
(3) $\{(0, 0), (0, 1), (0, 2)\}$

VI. (1) Count the elements in each finite set $A \times B$ in Exercise I.
(2) If A contains m elements and B contains k elements, intuitively, how many elements does $A \times B$ contain?

2.9 Equivalence Relation

Basic to the study of mathematics is the concept of *equivalence relation*. While Euclid used the equivalence relation in the writing of his *Elements of Geometry* and the student of geometry uses it today, the use is frequently tacit rather than explicit. Even the student of algebra frequently uses this concept without realizing it. For example, when we write $5 = 5$, we are using one of the properties of an equivalence relation.

The word *relation* has many common uses. We usually speak of the relation between objects or persons. One cubic foot of mercury weighs more than one cubic foot of lead. This is a relation between the densities of mercury and lead. Two persons may be related by blood; for example, one is the father of the other. Or they may be related by domicile; for example, each is the neighbor of the other. In mathematics the word *relation* has special significance.

In Definition 2, we noted that $A = B$ if and only if $A \subset B$ and $B \subset A$. We note that $A = B$ expresses a relation between two sets A and B. Similarly $A \subset B$ expresses a relation between A and B. Consider the relation "is equal to." First, notice that any set A is equal to itself; that is, $A = A$. Second, if $A = B$, then A and B are different names for the same set; that is, if $A = B$, then $B = A$. Third, if $A = B$ and $B = C$, then A, B, and C are different names for the same set; that is, if $A = B$ and $B = C$, then $A = C$. Because of the elegance and utility of this type of relation in mathematics, we give it the special name *equivalence relation*. The symbol **R** will be used to indicate a relation; that is, a **R** b means a is related to b. In this text we do not define the word *relation*. The examples will give you an intuitive idea of its meaning. In Definition 14 we define *equivalence relation* in terms of the undefined term *relation*.

DEFINITION 14. A relation **R** on a set S is an *equivalence relation* if and only if the following three properties are satisfied:

  (a) Reflexive Property (if $a \in S$, then a **R** a);
  (b) Symmetric Property (if $a, b \in S$ and a **R** b, then b **R** a);
  (c) Transitive Property (if $a, b, c \in S$ and a **R** b and b **R** c, then a **R** c).

You should recall that a, b, and c need not be different elements. It is possible that any two are equal or all three are equal.

Example 1.   Let S be a set of colored blocks. Let **R** be the relation "is of the same color as." If a, b, and c are any blocks of the set, then

  (a) a **R** a (any block a is of the same color as itself);
  (b) if a **R** b, then b **R** a (if a is of the same color as b, then b is of the same color as a);
  (c) if a **R** b and b **R** c, then a **R** c (if a is of the same color as b and b is of the same color as c, then a is of the same color as c).

Since the reflexive, symmetric, and transitive properties are satisfied, **R** is an equivalence relation.

Example 2.   Let $U = \{0, 1, 2, 3, 4\}$. Let S be the collection of all
                subsets of U. Let the relation **R** be $\subset$.

    (a) Since any set is a subset of itself, the reflexive prop-
                erty is obviously satisfied.

    (b) If $A = \{1, 3\}$ and $B = \{1, 2, 3\}$, then $A \subset B$ but
                $B \not\subset A$. Hence the symmetric property is *not*
                satisfied.

    (c) If $A \subset B$ and $B \subset C$, then $A \subset C$. Hence the
                transitive property is satisfied.

However, **R** is *not* an equivalence relation because only two of the
three properties are satisfied.

Example 3.   Let S be a collection of finite subsets of the counting
                numbers. Let **R** be the relation "contains the same number
                of elements as." Then for any A, B, C in S:

    (a) A contains the same number of elements as A;

    (b) If A contains the same number of elements as B,
                then B contains the same number of elements as A;

    (c) If A contains the same number of elements as B and
                B contains the same number of elements as C, then
                A contains the same number of elements as C.

Thus **R** is an equivalence relation; that is, the relation "contains the
same number of elements as" is an equivalence relation.

Example 4.   Let S be a collection of subsets of the counting numbers.
                Let **R** be the relation "is in one-to-one correspondence
                with." Then for any subsets A, B, C of S:

    (a) A **R** A (A is in one-to-one correspondence with A);

    (b) If A **R** B, then B **R** A (If A is in one-to-one corre-
                spondence with B, then B is in one-to-one corre-
                spondence with A);

    (c) If A **R** B and B **R** C, then A **R** C (If A is in one-to-
                one correspondence with B and B is in one-to-one
                correspondence with C, then A is in one-to-one cor-
                respondence with C).

Thus **R** is an equivalence relation; that is, the relation "is in one-to-one
correspondence with" is an equivalence relation.

Example 5.   Let S be a set of persons. Let **R** be the relation "is the mother of." For any a in S, it is false that a is the mother of a. Since the reflexive property fails, **R** is *not* an equivalence relation. It is *not* necessary to check the symmetric and transitive properties.

Example 6.   Let $S = \{1, 2, 3, 4, 5, 6, 7\}$, $A = \{1, 2, 3, 4\}$, $B = \{5, 6, 7\}$. For any $a, b \in S$, let a **R** b mean that a and b are both in the same set A or both in B. For example, 1 **R** 2 and 5 **R** 7, but 3 **R̸** 7. Thus

    (a) a **R** a (a is in the same subset as a);
    (b) If a **R** b, then b **R** a (if a is in the same subset as b, then b is in the same subset as a);
    (c) If a **R** b and b **R** c, then a **R** c (if a is in the same subset as b and b is in the same subset as c, then a is in the same subset as c).

Thus the relation **R** is an equivalence relation.
Note that the transitive property follows from the fact that $A \cap B = \phi$.
    The above discussion and examples illustrate that an equivalence relation on a set S separates the elements of S into mutually exclusive subsets; that is, into subsets such that $A = B$ or $A \cap B = \phi$ for all sets A and B. Thus in Example 1 the blocks in S are separated into mutually exclusive subsets such that all blocks of one color are in the same subset and no blocks of different colors are in the same subset. For a specified S the separation is shown in Figure 2.20.

$S = \{ \boxed{R^1}, \boxed{B^2}, \boxed{G^3}, \boxed{R^4}, \boxed{G^5}, \boxed{G^6}, \boxed{R^7}, \boxed{B^8}, \boxed{G^9},$
       $\boxed{G^{10}}, \boxed{R^{11}}, \boxed{B^{12}} \}$.
$A = \{ \boxed{R^1}, \boxed{R^4}, \boxed{R^7}, \boxed{R^{11}} \}$,
$B = \{ \boxed{B^2}, \boxed{B^8}, \boxed{B^{12}} \}$,
$C = \{ \boxed{G^3}, \boxed{G^5}, \boxed{G^6}, \boxed{G^9}, \boxed{G^{10}} \}$.
$S = A \cup B \cup C, A \cap B = \phi, B \cap C = \phi, A \cap C = \phi$.

FIGURE 2.20

Exercise 2.9

I. In each of the following, a set S and a relation **R** are specified. Determine whether each relation is an equivalence relation. If **R** is not an equivalence relation, tell which property of Definition 14 fails.

(1) Let $S = \{0, 1, 2, 3, \ldots, 999\}$. Let **R** be the relation "has the same number of digits as." Thus 57 **R** 91 and 301 **R** 817 but 3 $\not{R}$ 16.

(2) Two numbers are said to have the *same parity* if and only if they are both even or both odd. Let $S = \{0, 1, 2, 3, \ldots\}$ and **R** be the relation "has the same parity as."

(3) Let S be the set of persons and let **R** be the relation "is of the same weight as."

(4) Let S be the set of persons and let **R** be the relation "weighs within two pounds of."

(5) Let S be the set of persons and let **R** be the relation "was born in the same month as."

(6) Let S be the set of persons and let **R** be the relation "is the brother of."

(7) Let S be the set of persons and let **R** be the relation "has the same parents as."

(8) Let $S = \{1/2, 2/3, 4/5, 2/4, 3/6, 8/10\}$ and let **R** be the relation defined as follows: a/b **R** c/d if and only if $ad = bc$.

(9) Let $S = \{0, 1, 2, 3, \ldots, 100\}$ and let **R** be the relation "ends in the same digit as." For example, 17 **R** 67 but 17 $\not{R}$ 63.

(10) Let $S = \{0, 1, 2, 3, 4, \ldots, 23\}$ and **R** be the relation "leaves the same remainder when divided by 5." Thus 3 **R** 8 and 3 **R** 23 but 3 $\not{R}$ 9.

II. Separate the sets in Exercise I–(1), (2), (5), (8), (9), (10) into mutually exclusive subsets such that any two elements of one subset are related but no two elements of different subsets are related. (*Hint.* Read the discussion concerning Example 1 and exhibit the mutually exclusive subsets as in Figure 2.20.)

III. (1) Let S be a set of sentences $p, q, r, \ldots$ and let **R** be the relation "if ... then ... ." Prove that **R** is not an equivalence relation. Which property fails?

(2) Let S be a set of sentences $p, q, r, \ldots$ and let **R** be the relation "is equivalent to." Prove that **R** is an equivalence relation.

(3) Let S be a set of triangles and let **R** be the relation "is congruent to" (has the same size and shape as). Prove that **R** is an equivalence relation.

(4) Let S be a set of triangles and let **R** be the relation "is similar to" (has the same shape as). Prove that **R** is an equivalence relation.

(5) Let S be a set of arrows and let **R** be the relation "has the same length as." Prove that **R** is an equivalence relation.

Chapter 3

THE SET OF COUNTING NUMBERS

3.1 Counting

Even a two-year-old child knows something about numbers. He can usually count a few objects. While his knowledge of numbers is limited, it grows as he grows. Some ancient tribes could count "one, two." If the number of objects to be counted was more than two, they counted "one, two, many." Our knowledge of numbers has grown immensely over the last 2,000 years. In fact, in the last 200 years our knowledge has increased more than in all of the preceding years. Recall that the set of counting numbers is the set $C_0 = \{0, 1, 2, \ldots\}$; that is, the numbers used in counting. You are already familiar with some properties of the counting numbers. In this chapter we make a systematic study of the set of counting numbers and their properties. You have already encountered such numbers as 5, 10, 1, 15/2, 7½, 1/3, π, 2, ⁻3, 22/7, 3.142, and 0.98. In the following chapters we make a systematic study of the real number system, which includes all of the foregoing numbers. We show that the properties of the counting numbers can be extended to the real numbers. Actually "5," "π," "⁻3," "3.14," et cetera, are not numbers but symbols for numbers. The number whose symbol is "5" is a concept or idea, whereas "5" is a mark on the paper, a symbol for the concept. The symbol for a number is called a *numeral*. Thus 5, π, ⁻3, 3.14, et cetera, are really *numerals* rather than *numbers*. This is analogous to the use of a person's name to symbolize the person. For example, the name "Mary" is frequently used to represent the person Mary. Whenever the probability of ambiguity is small, we shall refer to the numerals as numbers. Thus, we shall usually use phrases such as *the number 5* to mean *the number whose numeral is "5."*

72

In Chapter 1 we studied the algebra of sentences. In Chapter 2 we developed the algebra of sets from the algebra of sentences. In this chapter we use the algebra of sets and the fact that we know how to count (in order) to obtain the basic properties of the set of counting numbers with respect to the operations of addition and multiplication. Our main objective is to study the *concepts* rather than to learn how to count, add, and multiply. The concepts of *set* and *counting* are closely related. In fact, whenever we count objects, we are actually counting the members of a set. As mentioned above, even the preschool child learns to count the elements of a sufficiently small set. When he does this, he is answering the question "*how many* elements does the set contain?" For example, he learns that the set of fingers on one hand contains *five* elements. Before long he learns that the set of toes on one foot contains *five* elements. If there are *five* members of his family, he soon learns that the number of elements in this set is equal to the number of elements in the set of fingers on one hand. In fact, he discovers that the number of elements in each of the three sets is *five*. At the same time he realizes that the physical properties of the three sets are different. In a similar manner, he discovers that he has *two* ears, *two* eyes, *two* arms, *two* legs, et cetera. While the sets of objects are not the same, they do have a common property; each has *two* elements. As a matter of fact, when a child thinks of *two,* he visualizes many sets, each consisting of two elements. Thus the number of elements in a given set does not depend on the physical properties of the set. It is a characteristic of the set itself.

You will notice that any set consisting of five elements is in one-to-one correspondence with any other set consisting of five elements. In particular, the set $\{\Box, 0, \triangle, +, ?\}$ is in one-to-one correspondence with the set $\{1, 2, 3, 4, 5\}$. Two one-to-one correspondences are shown in Figure 3.1.

$$
\begin{array}{ccccc}
\Box & 0 & \triangle & + & ? \\
\updownarrow & \updownarrow & \updownarrow & \updownarrow & \updownarrow \\
1 & 2 & 3 & 4 & 5
\end{array}
\qquad
\begin{array}{ccccc}
? & \triangle & \Box & 0 & + \\
\updownarrow & \updownarrow & \updownarrow & \updownarrow & \updownarrow \\
1 & 2 & 3 & 4 & 5
\end{array}
$$

$$(a) \qquad\qquad (b)$$

FIGURE 3.1

This is precisely the method we employ in counting the number of elements in any finite set. We establish a one-to-one correspondence between the elements of the given set and a subset of the set of counting numbers. For example, if the chairs in a classroom are numbered 1, 2, 3, . . . , 30, each student occupies exactly one chair, each chair is occupied by exactly one student, all chairs are occupied, and no students are standing, then one concludes that there are 30 students in the class. The one-to-one correspondence is obvious. As a further example, consider a double decker bus whose lower seats are numbered 1, 2, ..., 30 and whose upper seats are numbered 31, 32, ..., 60. All upper seats are occupied, but no seats on the lower deck are occupied, and no one is standing. How many passengers are in the bus? To answer the question we establish a one-to-one correspondence between the set of passengers and the set {31, 32, ..., 60} and then establish a one-to-one correspondence between the set {31, 32 ..., 60} and the set {1, 2, ..., 30} as shown in Figure 3.2.

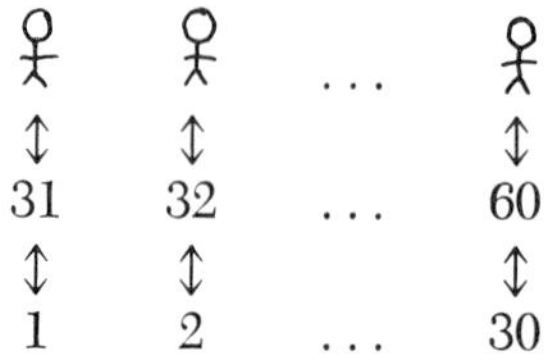

$$
\begin{array}{ccccc}
\text{☂} & \text{☂} & \cdots & & \text{☂} \\
\updownarrow & \updownarrow & & & \updownarrow \\
31 & 32 & \cdots & & 60 \\
\updownarrow & \updownarrow & & & \updownarrow \\
1 & 2 & \cdots & & 30
\end{array}
$$

FIGURE 3.2

Thus there are 30 passengers in the bus.

In general, to count the number of elements in some nonempty finite set of k elements, we establish a one-to-one correspondence between this set and the proper subset {1, 2, ..., k} of the set of all counting numbers. You should note that the elements of the set {1, 2, ..., k} must be *in order*. For example, if a child counts 1, 2, 3, 4, 6, we tell him that he is counting incorrectly. When a child counts his marbles, he puts them down one by one and counts 1, 2, 3, ..., 25. He is really establishing a one-to-one correspondence between his set of marbles and the set {1, 2, 3, ..., 25}.

$$
\begin{array}{ccccc}
\bigcirc & \bigcirc & \cdots & \bigcirc & \text{(marbles)} \\
\updownarrow & \updownarrow & & \updownarrow & \\
1 & 2 & \cdots & 25 & \text{(numbers)}
\end{array}
$$

Although he may not be aware of the one-to-one correspondence, this correspondence does exist. Eventually when he thinks of the number *five*, for example, he associates this number with various sets, each of which contains *five* elements. Thus we see that *counting is a process which assigns a counting number to each finite set*. Consequently, a counting number is an abstract concept which is associated with a given class of finite equivalent sets. For example, the counting number 2 is an abstract concept associated with every set which is equivalent to the set

{1, 2}. In particular the counting number 0 is associated with the empty set.

We now give a formal definition of the number of elements in a finite set.

DEFINITION 1. For any finite nonempty set A, *the number of elements in A is equal to the nonzero counting number k* if and only if there is a one-to-one correspondence between A and $\{1, 2, 3, \ldots, k\}$.

To simplify our language, we denote the number of elements in a finite set A by $n(A)$. For example, if $A = \{1, a, b, 9\}$, then A is in one-to-one correspondence with the set $\{1, 2, 3, 4\}$. Hence $n(A) = 4$. Since the empty set contains no elements, we say that $n(\phi) = 0$.

Now consider the sets $A = \{a, b, 1, 2, 0\}$ and $B = \{5, 10, 15, 20, 25\}$. Since there is a one-to-one correspondence between A and $\{1, 2, \ldots, 5\}$, we see that $n(A) = 5$. Since there is a one-to-one correspondence between $\{1, 2, \ldots, 5\}$ and B, we see that $n(B) = 5$.

Recall that two sets are equivalent if and only if there is a one-to-one correspondence between them. As we learned in Chapter 2, equivalence between sets is actually an equivalence relation. Thus the transitive property is satisfied; that is, since A is equivalent to $\{1, 2, 3, 4, 5\}$ and $\{1, 2, 3, 4, 5\}$ is equivalent to B, it follows that A is equivalent to B. Thus there is a one-to-one correspondence between A and B. This example illustrates that if $n(A) = n(B)$, then A is equivalent to B. The following theorem states that this is true in general and also that the converse is true.

THEOREM 1. Any two finite sets A and B are equivalent if and only if $n(A) = n(B)$.

Theorem 1 is of the form $p \rightleftarrows q$. Recall that $p \rightleftarrows q$ is equivalent to $(p \rightarrow q) \wedge (q \rightarrow p)$. Thus there are really *two* theorems which must be proved: (1) $p \rightarrow q$ and (2) $q \rightarrow p$; that is (under the assumption that A and B are finite sets), we must prove the following theorems:

(1) If A is equivalent to B, then $n(A) = n(B)$;
(2) If $n(A) = n(B)$, then A is equivalent to B.

In the proof of Theorem 1, we indicate the proof of (1) by ($\rightarrow$) and the proof of (2) by ($\leftarrow$). To prove (1) we let $A \approx B$ and prove that $n(A) = n(B)$; to prove (2) we let $n(A) = n(B)$ and prove that $A \approx B$. Now we proceed with the proof of the theorem.

Proof.	*If A* and *B* are empty, the theorem is obvious.	
(→)	Let $B \approx A$,	s
	and let A be a nonempty finite set.	p
	If A is a nonempty finite set, then there exists a nonzero counting number k such that $n(A) = k$.	$p \to q$
	If $n(A) = k$, then $A \approx \{1, 2, \ldots, k\}$.	$q \to r$
	If $B \approx A$ and $A \approx \{1, 2, \ldots, k\}$, then $B \approx \{1, 2, \ldots, k\}$.	$(s \wedge r) \to w$
	If $B \approx \{1, 2, \ldots, k\}$, then $n(B) = k$.	$w \to t$
	If $n(B) = k$ and $k = n(A)$, then $n(B) = n(A)$.	$(t \wedge q) \to u$
	Therefore $n(B) = n(A)$.	$C: u$
(←)	Conversely,	
	let $n(A) = n(B)$,	v
	and let A be a nonempty finite set.	p
	If A is a nonempty finite set, then there exists a nonzero counting number k such that $n(A) = k$.	$p \to q$
	If $n(A) = k$, then $A \approx \{1, 2, \ldots, k\}$.	$q \to r$
	If $n(A) = k$ and $n(A) = n(B)$, then $k = n(B)$.	$(q \wedge v) \to j$
	If $k = n(B)$, then $\{1, 2, \ldots, k\} \approx B$.	$j \to h$
	If $A \approx \{1, 2, \ldots, k\}$ and $\{1, 2, \ldots, k\} \approx B$, then $A \approx B$.	$(r \wedge h) \to e$
	Therefore A is equivalent to B.//	$C: e$

In Chapter 2 when you established one-to-one correspondences between two finite sets, you probably realized that two finite sets A and B may be put into one-to-one correspondence if and only if the number of elements in A is equal to the number of elements in B. This is precisely the point we wish to emphasize—any two finite sets A and B are equivalent if and only if $n(A) = n(B)$. This explains why we may count the elements in any set B which is equivalent to A when we really wish to know how many elements A contains. For example, if a restaurateur knows that he has 100 seats available for a banquet sponsored by a certain club and sees that all seats except 3 are occupied, he knows that 97 seats are occupied. Without actually counting the number of club members present, he knows that there are 97 members present. As another example, if one wishes to know how many paid spectators attended a local basketball game, he does not have to count the people present. In fact, if he did, he would probably get an erroneous result. He can merely count the tickets collected at the door. This is a much easier counting process.

Exercise 3.1

I. Exhibit a one-to-one correspondence between each of the following sets and one of the sets $\{1\}$, $\{1, 2\}$, $\{1, 2, 3\}$, $\{1, 2, 3, 4\}$, $\{1, 2, 3, 4, 5\}$, $\{1, 2, 3, 4, 5, 6\}$, $\{1, 2, 3, 4, 5, 6, 7\}$.

  (1) $\{2, 5, 8\}$
  (2) $\{2, 4, 6, 8, 10\}$
  (3) $\{a, b, 6, 8, 10\}$
  (4) $\{2\}$
  (5) $\{3, 6, 9\}$
  (6) $\{3, 6, 9, 12\}$
  (7) $\{0, 3, 6, 9, 12, 15\}$
  (8) $\{10, 20, 30, 40, 50\}$
  (9) $\{21, 22, 23, 24, 25\}$
 (10) $\{50, 52, 54, 56, 58, 60, 62\}$

II. Use the results of Exercise I to compute the number of elements in each set in Exercise I.

III. Compute $n(A \times B)$ for each of the following pairs of sets.

  (1) $A = \{0\}, B = \{1, 2\}$
  (2) $A = \{1, 2\}, B = \{7, 8\}$
  (3) $A = \{1, 2\}, B = \{7, 8, 9\}$
  (4) $A = \{2, 4\}, B = \{1, 2, 4, 7\}$
  (5) $A = \{0, 1, 2\}, B = \{0, 1, 2, 3, 4\}$
  (6) $A = \{ \ \}, B = \{0, 1, 2, 8\}$

IV. Compute $n(B \times A)$ for each pair of sets in Exercise III.

V. Use Theorem 1 to decide whether $n(A) = n(B)$ for each of the following pairs of sets.

  (1) $A = \{1, 11, 21\}, B = \{0, 1, 2\}$
  (2) $A = \phi, B = \{ \ \}$
  (3) $A = \phi, B = \{0\}$
  (4) $A = \{1\}, B = \{0\}$
  (5) $A = \{1, 3, 5, 7, 9\}, B = \{2, 4, 6, 8, 10\}$
  (6) $A = \{0, 1, 2, \ldots, 30\}, B = \{61, 62, \ldots, 90\}$

VI. Compute $n(A \cup B)$ for each of the following pairs of sets.

  (1) $A = \{\text{Ralph, Marcia, Leslie}\}, B = \{\text{Mother, Father}\}$, $(A \cap B = \phi)$

(2) $A = \{\boxed{1}, \boxed{2}, \boxed{3}\}$, $B = \{\boxed{5}, \boxed{7}, \boxed{8}, \boxed{9}\}$
(3) $A = \{$Carol, Merlin, Susan$\}$, $B = \{$Tracy, Marion$\}$
(4) $A = \{0, 5, 7\}$, $B = \{0, 2, 7\}$
(5) $A = \{$marble, frog, turtle, string$\}$, $B = \{$penny, nickel, dime$\}$

VII. Discuss briefly the meaning of *counting number.*

3.2 Addition of Counting Numbers

In the preceding section we studied the procedure for counting the number of elements in any finite set. This led us to a better understanding of the concept of counting number. In this section we shall study the procedure for computing the sum of any two counting numbers. That is, we wish to consider the problem of counting the elements in two disjoint sets. For example, consider a small boy whose pants pockets contain the things one might expect to find in a small boy's pockets. Suppose that his left pocket contains a dime, a stick of gum, a knife, and a marble and that his right pocket contains a rock, a pencil, and a bug. Letting A denote the set of articles in his left pocket, letting B denote the set of articles in his right pocket, and letting the initials of the articles denote the articles, we may write $A = \{d, g, k, m\}$ and $B = \{r, p, b\}$. Clearly $n(A) = 4$ and $n(B) = 3$. Moreover $A \cap B = \phi$ and $A \cup B = \{d, g, k, m, r, p, b\}$. Thus $n(A \cup B) = 7$. How does he count the objects in his pockets? One way he could count them is to empty his pockets, put all objects together onto his mother's dining room table, and point at each of them in turn and count 1, 2, 3, 4, 5, 6, 7, thus establishing a one-to-one correspondence between the new set $A \cup B$ and the set $\{1, 2, 3, 4, 5, 6, 7\}$. For some reason the boy may not wish to mix the objects. Thus he may empty his pockets onto the table in *two* separate sets and count 1, 2, 3, 4 for the first set and then count 1, 2, 3 for the second set. In this way he discovers that the number of elements in the left pocket was 4 and the number of elements in the right pocket was 3. The boy realizes now that the 4 objects and the 3 objects combined are 7 objects. It does not take him long to realize that any time he has 4 objects and 3 more objects he has a total of 7 objects. This leads him to say "4 and 3 is 7" when he really means that 4 objects and 3 more objects are 7 objects. When he says "4 and 3 is 7" he has devised a mathematical model of the physical problem of combining 4 objects and 3 more objects. Thus, if he has 4 apples and 3 more apples, he still says "4 and 3 is 7."

Since he has combined the two counting numbers 4 and 3 to obtain a new counting number 7, he has used *and* in the sense of a binary operator. The mathematician uses the symbol $+$ for this binary operator, writes $4 + 3 = 7$, and says "four plus three equals seven." Recalling that $n(A) = 4$, $n(B) = 3$, $A \cap B = \phi$, and $n(A \cup B) = 7$, we see that $n(A \cup B) = n(A) + n(B)$. So far we have defined the binary operator $+$ only to combine the counting numbers 4 and 3. For obvious reasons we wish to define the operator $+$ to combine any two counting numbers a and b to form their sum $a + b$.

If a and b are any two counting numbers, there exist finite sets A and B such that $n(A) = a$, $n(B) = b$, and $A \cap B = \phi$. This enables us to make the following definition.

DEFINITION 2. The *sum* $a + b$ of the counting numbers a and b is the counting number $n(A \cup B)$, in which $n(A) = a$, $n(B) = b$, and $A \cap B = \phi$.

It can be proved that any disjoint sets C and D such that $n(C) = a$ and $n(D) = b$ may be used in place of A and B in the above definition. Hence the sum in Definition 2 is well-defined. If A and B are two disjoint finite sets, then $n(A \cup B) = n(A) + n(B)$. Although one does not call this fact to mind when he adds two counting numbers, this fact is fundamental in any addition process.

Example 1.   If $A = \{3, 6, 9, 12, 15\}$ and $B = \{5, 11, 17\}$, then $n(A) = 5$ and $n(B) = 3$. Moreover, $A \cup B = \{3, 5, 6, 9, 11, 12, 15, 17\}$, $A \cap B = \phi$, and hence $n(A \cup B) = 8$. Now $n(A \cup B) = n(A) + n(B)$. Hence $8 = 5 + 3$.

Example 2.   If $A = \{a, b, 3, 5\}$ and $B = \{a, 3, 4\}$, then $A \cup B = \{a, b, 3, 4, 5\}$. Thus $n(A \cup B) = 5$, but $n(A) = 4$ and $n(B) = 3$. Hence $n(A \cup B) \neq n(A) + n(B)$. The reason that $n(A \cup B) \neq n(A) + n(B)$ is that $A \cap B \neq \phi$; that is, A and B have the elements a and 3 in common.

Example 3.   If $A = \{1, 2, \ldots, a\}$, then $n(A) = a$. Moreover, $n(\phi) = 0$, $A \cup \phi = A$, and $A \cap \phi = \phi$. Thus $n(A \cup \phi) = n(A) + n(\phi) = a + 0$. But $n(A \cup \phi) = n(A) = a$. Hence $a + 0 = a$.

Definition 2 tells us that the sum of any two counting numbers is a unique counting number. Thus when we add two counting numbers we obtain a unique counting number. As we do not obtain a different kind of number, we say that the set of counting numbers is *closed* under the operation of addition. This property of the counting numbers is called the *closure property for addition* of counting numbers.

CLOSURE PROPERTY FOR ADDITION

If a and b are any two counting numbers, then $a + b$ is a unique counting number. That is, for all a and b, if $a \in C_0$ and $b \in C_0$, then $(a + b) \in C_0$.

Now recall the commutative property for the union of two sets A and B. In Chapter 2 we learned that $A \cup B = B \cup A$ for any two sets A and B. In particular, if A and B are disjoint finite sets, then $A \cup B = B \cup A$. Hence $n(A \cup B) = n(B \cup A)$. Since $n(A \cup B) = n(A) + n(B)$ and $n(B \cup A) = n(B) + n(A)$, it follows that $n(A) + n(B) = n(B) + n(A)$. For any counting numbers a and b there exist finite disjoint sets A and B such that $n(A) = a$ and $n(B) = b$. Therefore $a + b = b + a$. This important property of the counting numbers is called the *commutative property for addition* of counting numbers.

COMMUTATIVE PROPERTY FOR ADDITION

For all a and b, if $a \in C_0$ and $b \in C_0$, then $a + b = b + a$.

The commutative property for addition tells us that the order in which we add two counting numbers is immaterial; that is, it does not matter whether we add b to a or a to b. Although the two addition problems are different, the two results are equal. For example, if a small boy has three marbles in his left pocket and five marbles in his right pocket, he could compute the total number of marbles in both pockets by saying $3 + 5 = 8$ or $5 + 3 = 8$. Similarly, if he has three pennies and you give him five more pennies, then he has a total of eight pennies; three pennies plus five pennies equal eight pennies. On the other hand, if he has five pennies and you give him three more pennies, then he has a total of eight pennies; he says $5 + 3 = 8$. Actually the small boy eventually discovers the commutative property for himself, without paying much attention to it or worrying about a name for it. It seems natural to him that the commutative property should be a property of the counting numbers. You should realize, however, that the commutative property for addition of counting numbers is a fortunate consequence of the commutative property for the union of sets. You may wonder why we are so concerned over such an *obvious* property. There are two important reasons for this. First, although it seems obvious that $3 + 4 = 4 + 3$, it is far from obvious to many students that $3 + x = x + 3$ for any counting number x. A conscious study of the commutative property for the addition of any two counting numbers enables the student to work more confidently later in algebra. Second, although most binary operations in mathematics are commutative, there are several binary operations which are not. If we do not investigate the commutative property for addition of counting numbers, the student may tacitly assume that all binary operations in mathematics are commutative.

Since addition is a binary operation, it is strictly defined for exactly *two* numbers. If three or more numbers are to be added, we must agree on the order in which the numbers will be added. For example, if the numbers 5, 2, and 8 are to be added, one person may say $5 + 2 = 7$ and $7 + 8 = 15$. Another person may say $2 + 8 = 10$ and $5 + 10 = 15$. Notice that each person added the numbers *in pairs*. No matter how fast you may add the three numbers, you must first add two of the numbers and then add that sum to the third number. The first person solved the problem $(5 + 2) + 8$, while the second person solved the different problem $5 + (2 + 8)$. Although the two problems are different, the two answers are equal. The parentheses are punctuation marks which indicate that the first addition to be performed is within the parentheses.

The above discussion leads us to *conjecture that* $(a + b) + c$ $= a + (b + c)$ *for any three counting numbers a, b, and c.* The close analogy between the closure and commutative properties for the union of sets and the corresponding properties of the addition of counting numbers gives us a hint at the method of proof of this conjecture. If a, b, and c are any nonzero counting numbers, then there exist *disjoint* sets A, B, and C *equivalent* to the sets $\{1, 2, \ldots, a\}$, $\{1, 2, \ldots, b\}$, and $\{1, 2, \ldots, c\}$, respectively; that is, there exist disjoint sets A, B, and C such that $n(A) = a$, $n(B) = b$, and $n(C) = c$.

Now $(A \cup B) \cup C = A \cup (B \cup C)$.
Thus $n[(A \cup B) \cup C] = n[A \cup (B \cup C)]$,
$\qquad n(A \cup B) + n(C) = n(A) + n(B \cup C)$,
$\qquad [n(A) + n(B)] + n(C) = n(A) + [n(B) + n(C)]$,
$\qquad [a + b] + c = a + [b + c]$.

The above sequence of steps is a proof of the *associative property for addition* of counting numbers.

ASSOCIATIVE PROPERTY FOR ADDITION
For all a, b, and c, if $a \in C_0$, $b \in C_0$, and $c \in C_0$; then $(a + b) + c = a + (b + c)$.

If you wonder why we are concerned over the associative property, you should re-read the comments following the commutative property. When one computes the sum $(40 + 2) + 98$, he unconsciously applies the associative property and *thinks* $40 + (2 + 98) = 40 + 100 = 140$. He may compute the sum $(197 + 89) + 3$ as follows: $(197 + 3) + 89 = 200 + 89 = 289$. He has actually applied the associative and commutative properties as follows:

$(197 + 89) + 3 = 197 + (89 + 3) = 197 + (3 + 89) = (197 + 3) + 89.$

All of us realize that $5 + 0 = 5$ and $2 + 0 = 2$. Our experience leads us to *conjecture that* $a + 0 = a$ *for any counting number a*. Obviously, if $a = 0$, then $a + 0 = a$, because $0 + 0 = 0$. Let us prove that $a + 0 = a$ for any nonzero counting number a. If a is a nonzero counting number, then there exists a finite set A such that $n(A) = a$.

Moreover, $A \cup \phi = A$ and $A \cap \phi = \phi$.
Now $a + 0 = n(A) + n(\phi)$
$= n(A \cup \phi)$
$= n(A)$
$= a.$

We have proved that $a + 0 = a$ for any counting number a. How do we know that there is not another counting number z, different from zero, such that $a + z = a$ for some counting number a? The following valid argument is a proof that 0 is the only counting number with this property.

If $a \neq 0$ and $z \neq 0$, then there exist finite sets A and Z such that $A = \{1, 2, \ldots, a\}$ and $Z = \{a + 1, a + 2, \ldots, a + z\}$.
Clearly $A \cap Z = \phi$.
Moreover, $A \cup Z = \{1, 2, \ldots, a, a + 1, a + 2, \ldots, a + z\}$ and $A = \{1, 2, \ldots, a\}$.
Thus $A \cup Z \neq A$,
$n(A \cup Z) \neq n(A)$,
$n(A) + n(Z) \neq n(A)$,
$a + z \neq a.$
Hence if $a \neq 0$ and $z \neq 0$, then $a + z \neq a$.
If $a = 0$ and $z \neq 0$, then $a + z = 0 + z = z \neq 0$.
Thus $a + z \neq a$.
Hence if $a = 0$ and $z \neq 0$, then $a + z \neq a$.
Consequently, if $z \neq 0$, then $a + z \neq a$.
By the contrapositive, if $a + z = a$, then $z = 0$.

The counting number 0 is called the *additive identity*. The important property of the additive identity is called the *identity property for addition* of counting numbers.

IDENTITY PROPERTY FOR ADDITION

The counting number 0 has the property that $a + 0 = a$ for any counting number a. Moreover, if $a + z = a$, for some counting number a, then $z = 0$.

An alternative statement of the identity property for addition of counting numbers is the following: for all counting numbers a, $a + z = a$ if and only if $z = 0$.

From the commutative property for addition, it follows directly that $0 + a = a$ for any counting number a.

The following example illustrates all of the above properties.

Example 4.   When we write $[(a + 3) + (b + 0)] + 5 = (a + b) + 8$ we are reasoning as follows:

$$[(a + 3) + (b + 0)] + 5 = [(a + 3) + b] + 5 \text{ (by identity property)}$$

$$[(a + 3) + b] + 5 = [a + (3 + b)] + 5 \text{ (by associative property)}$$

$$[a + (3 + b)] + 5 = [a + (b + 3)] + 5 \text{ (by commutative property)}$$

$$[a + (b + 3)] + 5 = [(a + b) + 3] + 5 \text{ (by associative property)}$$

$$[(a + b) + 3] + 5 = (a + b) + [3 + 5] \text{ (by associative property)}$$

$$(a + b) + [3 + 5] = (a + b) + 8 \text{ (by addition fact)}$$

Therefore $[(a + 3) + (b + 0)] + 5 = (a + b) + 8$ (by transitive property).

You should realize that the closure property is actually used in each of the above steps in the proof. You will note that brackets [ ] are used as punctuation symbols in the same manner as parentheses ( ). If more punctuation is needed, braces { } may be used. The reason for using brackets and braces rather than more parentheses is that their use makes it easier to locate the right-hand mate of the left-hand symbol.

Exercise 3.2

I. (1) Complete enough entries of the following addition table so that the remaining entries may be computed by means of the commutative property for addition.

+	0	1	2	3	4	5	6	7	8	9
0										
1										
2										
3										
4										
5										
6										
7										
8										
9										

(2) How many addition facts are required if only the commutative property for addition is known?

(3) How many addition facts are required if only the commutative and identity properties enumerated in this section are known?

(4) How many addition facts would be needed if we did not have any of the above properties?

II. In the order used, from left to right, identify the property or definition which makes each of the following sentences true.

(1) $5 + 7 = 12$.

(2) $7 + 5 = 12$.

(3) $5 + 7 = 7 + 5$.

(4) $(5 + 7) + 3 = 5 + (7 + 3)$.

(5) $(5 + 7) + 3 = 12 + 3$.

(6) $(5 + 7) + 3 = 3 + (5 + 7)$.

(7) $(5 + 7) + 3 = 3 + 12$.

(8) $(5 + 7) + 3 = 5 + (3 + 7)$.

(9) $5 + 0 = 0 + 5$.

(10) $5 + 0 = 5$.

(11) $5 + (0 + 3) = 5 + 3$.

(12) $(5 + 0) + 3 = 5 + 3$.

(13) $5 + (3 + 0) = 8$.

(14) $(7 + 2) + 3 = 3 + 9$.

(15) $7 + (2 + 3) = 3 + 9$.

(16) $(3 + 7) + (5 + 4) = 10 + 9$.

(17) $3 + (7 + 9) = (3 + 7) + (5 + 4)$.

(18) $(3 + 7) + (5 + 0) = 12 + 3$.

(19) $(3 + 0) + (5 + 7) = 12 + 3$.

(20) $[(2 + 5) + (7 + 3)] + (6 + 0) = 7 + (10 + 6)$.

III. Prove that each of the following open sentences can be converted to a true sentence by a prefix of the type "for all counting numbers a and b."

  (1) $(a + b) + 0 = b + a$.
  (2) $a + (t + 2) = 2 + (a + t)$.
  (3) $3 + (4 + x) = x + 7$.
  (4) $4 + (a + b) = (a + 4) + b$.
  (5) $15 + (t + 2) = 12 + (t + 5)$.
  (6) $(a + 3) + (t + 6) = (a + t) + 9$.
  (7) $11 + (a + b) = (7 + a) + (4 + b)$.
  (8) $[(s + t) + (6 + a)] + (0 + b) = [(b + a) + (t + s)] + 6$.
  (9) $[(5 + 4)t + (3 + 2)t] + (7 + 0)t = 9t + (5 + 7)t$.
  (10) $[(5 + 4)t + 3t] + (2 + 1)t + 0 = 15t$.

IV. Explain the details involved when a child adds 5 apples to 4 apples. (*Note.* He has 4 apples and adds 5 apples to these.)

V. Employ Definition 2 to prove each of the following.

  (1) $2 + 3 = 5$.   (6) $2 + 2 = 4$.
  (2) $1 + 1 = 2$.   (7) $3 + 0 = 3$.
  (3) $5 + 1 = 6$.   (8) $(4 + 4) + 4 = 12$.
  (4) $1 + 5 = 6$.   (9) $2 + (2 + 2) = 6$.
  (5) $0 + 7 = 7$.   (10) $(2 + 3) + (1 + 4) = 10$.

VI. In a local basketball game Ronnie scored 5 points the first quarter, 6 points the second quarter, 0 points the third quarter, and 8 points the fourth quarter. Set up a mathematical model of this physical problem necessary to compute the total number of points scored by Ronnie. (Be sure to punctuate properly by means of braces, brackets, and parentheses.)

VII. Compute each of the following by means of the commutative property, the associative property, and the definition of addition. In each case identify the properties.

  (1) $897 + (3 + 85)$.
  (2) $897 + (85 + 3)$.
  (3) $(401 + 82) + 99$.
  (4) $5575 + (88 + 25)$.
  (5) $(15 + 2) + 85$.

VIII. By inspection determine whether there exists a counting number such that each of the following open sentences can be converted to a true sentence by replacement of the variable by that counting number.

(1) $x + 5 = 6$. (6) $7 + t = 4$.
(2) $a + 3 = 10$. (7) $0 + t = 7$.
(3) $a + 7 = 7$. (8) $z + 8 = 0$.
(4) $7 + 2a = 13$. (9) $a + 0 = 0$.
(5) $7 + b = b + 7$. (10) $a + 5a = 2a$.

IX. Prove that the following are equal for any counting numbers a, b, and c.

(1) $a + (b + c)$. (7) $(a + b) + c$.
(2) $a + (c + b)$. (8) $(a + c) + b$.
(3) $(b + c) + a$. (9) $b + (a + c)$.
(4) $b + (c + a)$. (10) $(b + a) + c$.
(5) $c + (a + b)$. (11) $(c + a) + b$.
(6) $c + (b + a)$. (12) $(c + b) + a$.

X. Prove that $(a + b) + (a + b) + (a + b) = (a + a + a) + (b + b + b)$ for any counting numbers a and b.

3.3 Multiplication of Counting Numbers

In the last section we investigated the properties of addition. In this section we investigate the concept and the properties of multiplication. As the following simple example illustrates, many problems in daily life involve multiplication. Four boys decide to go on an overnight camping trip, and each boy agrees to take 3 potatoes. How many potatoes do they take altogether?

Since each boy takes 1 set of 3 potatoes, the 4 boys take 4 disjoint sets of 3 potatoes each. Letting B_1, B_2, B_3, B_4 be the 4 disjoint sets of potatoes, we compute the set of all potatoes by computing their union, $B_1 \cup B_2 \cup B_3 \cup B_4$. The total number of potatoes is $n(B_1 \cup B_2 \cup B_3 \cup B_4)$.

Since $B_1 \cup B_2 \cup B_3 \cup B_4 = \{[(B_1 \cup B_2) \cup B_3] \cup B_4\}$ it follows that

$$
\begin{aligned}
n(B_1 \cup B_2 \cup B_3 \cup B_4) &= n\{[(B_1 \cup B_2) \cup B_3] \cup B_4\} \\
&= n[(B_1 \cup B_2) \cup B_3] + n(B_4) \\
&= [n(B_1 \cup B_2) + n(B_3)] + n(B_4) \\
&= [\{n(B_1) + n(B_2)\} + n(B_3)] + n(B_4) \\
&= [\{3 + 3\} + 3] + 3 \\
&= 12.
\end{aligned}
$$

We introduce the notation $4 \cdot 3$ for the number of elements in the union of the four disjoint sets B_1, B_2, B_3, B_4 (each consisting of 3 elements). In general, if a and b are any counting numbers, the *product* $a \cdot b$ is as defined in Definition 3.

DEFINITION 3. The *product* of the counting numbers a and b is the counting number $a \cdot b$ defined as follows:

(a) If $a \neq 0$, then $a \cdot b = n(B_1 \cup B_2 \cup \ldots \cup B_a)$ in which $n(B_1) = n(B_2) = \ldots = n(B_a) = b$ and $B_i \cap B_j = \phi$ if $i \neq j$.

(b) If $a = 0$, then $a \cdot b = 0$.

The combination of any two counting numbers a and b by means of the binary operator $\cdot$ to form a third counting number $a \cdot b$ (read *a times b*), called the *product* of a and b, is the binary operation called *multiplication*. Alternate notations for $a \cdot b$ are ab, $a \times b$, $a(b)$, and $(a)(b)$.

For example, $3 \cdot 5 = n(B_1 \cup B_2 \cup B_3) = [n(B_1) + n(B_2)] + n(B_3)$, in which $n(B_1) = n(B_2) = n(B_3) = 5$, $B_1 \cap B_2 = \phi$, $B_1 \cap B_3 = \phi$, and $B_2 \cap B_3 = \phi$. Thus $3 \cdot 5 = (5 + 5) + 5 = 10 + 5 = 15$.

By the associative property for addition, the sum $(5 + 5) + 5$ is equal to the sum $5 + (5 + 5)$, and there is no ambiguity if the parentheses are omitted. Henceforth, we may omit the parentheses and write $3 \cdot 5 = 5 + 5 + 5$. More generally, by the associative property for addition we prove that all punctuations of $3 + 3 + 3 + 3$ yield the same counting number. Thus there is no ambiguity if we omit the punctuation in $[(3 + 3) + 3] + 3$. The following property, which may be proved from the associative property for addition and the commutative property for addition, states that the sum of any number of counting numbers may be written in any order without punctuation. In Exercise 3.2–IX you were asked to prove this property for $k = 3$.

GENERALIZED COMMUTATIVE AND ASSOCIATIVE PROPERTY FOR ADDITION (GCAAPFA)

If $a_1, a_2, a_3, \ldots, a_k$ are any counting numbers, then all arrangements and punctuations of $a_1 + a_2 + a_3 + \ldots + a_k$ yield the same counting number.

Since all punctuations and arrangements of $a_1 + a_2 + \ldots + a_k$ yield the same counting number, there is no ambiguity if the punctuation is omitted. Thus the sum $a_1 + a_2 + \ldots + a_k$ may be written in any order without punctuation.

For example, $\{[(3 + 1) + 2] + 9\} + 8 = (3 + 1) + [2 + (9 + 8)]$ $= (2 + 8) + (9 + 1) + 3 = 2 + 8 + 9 + 1 + 3$, etc.

The following theorem states that multiplication of two counting numbers may be treated as repeated addition, provided one of them is not 0.

THEOREM 2. If a and b are counting numbers and $a \neq 0$,
then $ab = \underbrace{b + b + \ldots + b}_{a \text{ summands}}$.

Proof.   By Definition 3, $ab = n(B_1 \cup B_2 \cup \ldots \cup B_a)$, in which $n(B_1) = n(B_2) = \ldots = n(B_a) = b$ and $B_i \cap B_j = \phi$ if $i \neq j$.

Thus $ab = n(B_1 \cup B_2 \cup \ldots \cup B_{a-1} \cup B_a)$
$= n(B_1 \cup B_2 \cup \ldots \cup B_{a-1}) + n(B_a)$ (by Definition 2)
$= n(B_1 \cup B_2 \cup \ldots \cup B_{a-2}) + n(B_{a-1}) + n(B_a)$
(by Definition 2 and GCAAPFA)
$= n(B_1 \cup B_2 \cup \ldots \cup B_{a-3}) + n(B_{a-2}) + n(B_{a-1}) + n(B_a)$ (by Definition 2 and GCAAPFA)

$=$.   .   .
.   .   .
.   .   .

$= n(B_1) + n(B_2) + \ldots + n(B_a)$
$= \underbrace{b + b + \ldots + b}_{a \text{ summands}}$. $(n(B_i) = b)$ //

The following examples illustrate Theorem 2.

Example 1. $7 \cdot 4 = 4 + 4 + 4 + 4 + 4 + 4 + 4 = 28$.

Example 2. $4 \cdot 7 = 7 + 7 + 7 + 7 = 28$.

Example 3. $4 \cdot 0 = 0 + 0 + 0 + 0 = 0$.

Example 4. $4 \cdot 3 = 3 + 3 + 3 + 3 = 12$.

We now investigate whether there is a relationship between the product of two counting numbers and the Cartesian product of two sets. Consider the following sets:

$$A = \{1, 2, 3, 4\}, B = \{b, c, d\}$$

$A \times B = \{(1, b), (1, c), (1, d), (2, b), (2, c), (2, d), (3, b), (3, c), (3, d), (4, b), (4, c), (4, d)\}$

$$= \{(1, b), (1, c), (1, d)\} \cup \{(2, b), (2, c), (2, d)\} \cup \{(3, b),$$
$$(3, c), (3, d)\} \cup \{(4, b), (4, c), (4, d)\}$$
$$= (\{1\} \times B) \cup (\{2\} \times B) \cup (\{3\} \times B) \cup (\{4\} \times B)$$
$$= B_1 \cup B_2 \cup B_3 \cup B_4, \text{ where } B_i = \{(i, b), (i, c), (i, d)\}.$$

Then $n(A \times B) = n(B_1 \cup B_2 \cup B_3 \cup B_4)$.
However, the B_i are mutually disjoint and $n(B_i) = 3$.
Hence $n(B_1 \cup B_2 \cup B_3 \cup B_4) = 4 \cdot 3$ (by Definition 3).
Thus $n(A \times B) = 4 \cdot 3$.
However, $n(A) = 4$ and $n(B) = 3$.
Consequently $n(A \times B) = n(A) \cdot n(B)$.

This example illustrates a close relationship between the product of two counting numbers and the Cartesian product of two sets. The following theorem, which states this relation in general, will be useful in the development of the multiplicative properties of the counting numbers.

THEOREM 3.   If a and b are any counting numbers and A and B are any finite sets such that $n(A) = a$ and $n(B) = b$, then $ab = n(A \times B)$.

Proof.

Case 1. $a = 0$.
Then $A = \phi$ and $A \times B = \phi \times B = \phi$.
Thus $ab = 0b = 0$ by Definition 3, and $n(A \times B) = n(\phi) = 0$.
Hence $ab = n(A \times B)$ (if $a = 0$).

Case 2. $a \neq 0$
Let A and B be any finite sets such that $n(A) = a$ and $n(B) = b$.
Then $A \approx \{1, 2, \ldots, a\}$, and $A \times B \approx (\{1\} \times B) \cup (\{2\} \times B) \cup \ldots \cup (\{a\} \times B) = B_1 \cup B_2 \cup \ldots \cup B_a$, where $B_i = (\{i\} \times B) = \{(i, b): b \in B\}$.
Thus $n(A \times B) = n(B_1 \cup B_2 \cup \ldots \cup B_a)$.
However, the B_i are mutually disjoint and $n(B_i) = b$.
Hence $n(B_1 \cup B_2 \cup \ldots \cup B_a) = a \cdot b$ (by Definition 3).
Thus $n(A \times B) = ab$ (if $a \neq 0$).
Hence $ab = n(A \times B)$ for any counting numbers a and b and any finite sets A and B such that $n(A) = a$ and $n(B) = b$. //

The following examples illustrate Theorem 3.

Example 5. $3 \cdot 2 = n(\{1, 2, 3\} \times \{1, 2\}) = n(\{(1, 1), (1, 2), (2, 1),$
$(2, 2), (3, 1), (3, 2)\}) = 6.$

Example 6. $4 \cdot 0 = n(\{1, 2, 3, 4\} \times \{ \ \}) = n(\{ \ \}) = 0.$

Example 7. $2 \cdot 4 = n(\{a, b\} \times \{c, d, x, y\}) = n(\{(a, c), (a, d),$
$(a, x), (a, y), (b, c), (b, d), (b, x), (b, y)\}) = 8.$

Example 8. $1 \cdot 3 = n(\{1\} \times \{a, b, c\}) = n(\{(1, a), (1, b), (1, c)\})$
$= 3.$

The *closure property for multiplication* of counting numbers follows readily from Definition 3.

CLOSURE PROPERTY FOR MULTIPLICATION
If a and b are any counting numbers, then $a \cdot b$ is a unique counting number. That is, for all a and b, if $a \in C_0$ and $b \in C_0$, then $ab \in C_0$.

You know from experience that $3 \cdot 5 = 5 \cdot 3$. We wish to prove that $ab = ba$ for *any* counting numbers a and b. We shall base our proof on Theorem 3. Let A and B be finite sets such that $n(A) = a$ and $n(B) = b$. Since $ab = n(A) \, n(B) = n(A \times B)$ and $ba = n(B) \, n(A) = n(B \times A)$ it is sufficient to prove that $n(A \times B) = n(B \times A)$. By Theorem 1, $A \times B \approx B \times A$ if and only if $n(A \times B) = n(B \times A)$. Hence we shall prove that $A \times B \approx B \times A$. First we illustrate with an example.

To prove that $2 \cdot 3 = 3 \cdot 2$, we let $A = \{1, 2\}$ and $B = \{a, b, c\}$. Then $A \times B = \{(1, a), (1, b), (1, c), (2, a), (2, b), (2, c)\}$ and $B \times A = \{(a, 1), (a, 2), (b, 1), (b, 2), (c, 1), (c, 2)\}$. Although $A \times B \neq B \times A$, it is clear that $A \times B$ is equivalent to $B \times A$, as shown in the following one-to-one correspondence.

$A \times B = \{(1, a), (1, b), (1, c), (2, a), (2, b), (2, c)\}.$
$\qquad\quad \updownarrow \quad\ \updownarrow \quad\ \updownarrow \quad\ \updownarrow \quad\ \updownarrow \quad\ \updownarrow$
$B \times A = \{(a, 1), (b, 1), (c, 1), (a, 2), (b, 2), (c, 2)\}.$
Hence $n(A \times B) = n(B \times A)$.
Thus $n(A)n(B) = n(B)n(A)$.
But $n(A) = 2$ and $n(B) = 3$.
Therefore $2 \cdot 3 = 3 \cdot 2$.

Now we shall prove that $A \times B$ is equivalent to $B \times A$ for any finite sets A and B; that is, that $A \times B$ is in one-to-one correspondence with $B \times A$. Let $A = \{c_1, c_2, \ldots, c_a\}$ and $B = \{d_1, d_2, \ldots, d_b\}$. The following scheme establishes a one-to-one correspondence between $A \times B$ and $B \times A$.

$A \times B = \{(c_1, d_1), (c_1, d_2), \ldots, (c_1, d_b), \ldots, (c_a, d_1), \ldots, (c_a, d_b)\}$.
$B \times A = \{(d_1, c_1), (d_2, c_1), \ldots, (d_b, c_1), \ldots, (d_1, c_a), \ldots, (d_b, c_a)\}$.
Thus $A \times B$ is equivalent to $B \times A$ (if $A \neq \phi$ and $B \neq \phi$).

If $A = \phi$ or $B = \phi$, then $A \times B = \phi$ and $B \times A = \phi$. Thus $A \times B$ is equivalent to $B \times A$ (if $A = \phi$ or $B = \phi$). Hence $A \times B$ is equivalent to $B \times A$ for any finite sets A and B.

Thus $A \times B \approx B \times A$
$n(A \times B) = n(B \times A)$ (by Theorem 1)
        $ab = ba$ (by Theorem 3)

We have proved that $ab = ba$ for any counting numbers a and b. This property is called the *commutative property for multiplication* of counting numbers.

COMMUTATIVE PROPERTY FOR MULTIPLICATION
For all a and b, if $a \in C_0$ and $b \in C_0$, then $ab = ba$.

The commutative property for multiplication reduces the number of multiplication facts which an elementary school child must memorize. For example, after a child has learned that $2 \cdot 5 = 10$, he need not memorize the multiplication fact $5 \cdot 2 = 10$. This follows immediately from the commutative property for multiplication. Thus the number of multiplication facts to be memorized is reduced to approximately one-half of the total number which would have to be memorized if it were not for the commutative property.

In the proof of the commutative property we have incidentally proved an important property of 0; namely, if $a = 0$ or $b = 0$, then $ab = 0$. This leads us to investigate the truth of the following sentence: *If a and b are counting numbers, then $ab = 0$ if and only if $a = 0$ or $b = 0$.*

To prove that this is true, let A and B be sets such that $n(A) = a$ and $n(B) = b$.

Then $ab = 0$ if and only if $n(A \times B) = 0$.
$n(A \times B) = 0 \rightleftarrows A \times B = \phi$,
$A \times B = \phi \rightleftarrows (A = \phi \lor B = \phi)$,

$(A = \phi \ \lor \ B = \phi) \rightleftarrows (n(A) = 0 \ \lor \ n(B) = 0),$
$(n(A) = 0 \ \lor \ n(B) = 0) \rightleftarrows (a = 0 \ \lor \ b = 0).$
Thus $ab = 0 \rightleftarrows (a = 0 \ \lor \ b = 0).$

We call this important property the *multiplication property of zero.*

MULTIPLICATION PROPERTY OF ZERO
For all a and b, if $a \in C_0$ and $b \in C_0$, then $ab = 0$ if and only if $a = 0$ or $b = 0$.

It should be clear from the properties of the biconditional (or the contrapositive) that $ab \neq 0$ if and only if $a \neq 0$ and $b \neq 0$. You will make frequent use of this later. Some students who do not understand this property commit the error of assuming that if $ab = 4$, for example, then $a = 4$ or $b = 4$. The following examples illustrate the application of the multiplication property of zero.

Example 9.   If $5a = 0$, compute a.
$5a = 0 \rightleftarrows (5 = 0 \ \lor \ a = 0).$
But $5 \neq 0$.
Therefore $5a = 0 \rightleftarrows a = 0.$

Example 10.   If $ab = 0$ and $b \neq 0$, compute a.
$ab = 0 \rightleftarrows (a = 0 \ \lor \ b = 0).$
But $b \neq 0$.
Therefore $a = 0$.

Example 11.   If $r \neq 0$, prove that $3r \neq 0$.
$(3 \neq 0 \ \land \ r \neq 0) \rightleftarrows 3r \neq 0.$
$3 \neq 0 \ \land \ r \neq 0.$
Therefore $3r \neq 0$.

Another property of the counting numbers, called the *cancellation property for multiplication,* is very similar to the multiplication property of zero, even though it does not appear similar. Before stating it, we shall illustrate it by means of examples. If $3b = 3c$, your intuition tells you that $b = c$. However, if $0b = 0c$, you may be tempted to conclude that $b = c$. Since $0 \cdot 3 = 0 \cdot 5$ and $3 \neq 5$, you see immediately that you cannot conclude from $0b = 0c$, that $b = c$. This probably leads you to conjecture that $(ab = ac \ \land \ a \neq 0) \rightarrow (b = c)$. Whenever we make a conjecture, we should feel some obligation to attempt to prove that it is true or that it is false. Since the above example leads us to suspect that it is true, we shall attempt to prove the cancellation property for multiplication: *for all a, b, and c, if a,b,c $\in C_0$, a $\neq$ 0, and ab = ac, then b = c.* If $b = 0$, then $ab = 0$ and thus $ac = 0$. Since $a \neq 0$ and $ac = 0$, if follows that $c = 0$. Similarly the conjecture is true for $c = 0$. Thus it is sufficient to prove the conjecture for $b \neq 0$ and $c \neq 0$. Let $A = \{r_1,$ $r_2, \ldots, r_a\}$, $B = \{s_1, s_2, \ldots, s_b\}$, $C = \{t_1, t_2, \ldots, t_c\}$. Since $ab = ac$, $n(A \times B) = n(A \times C)$.

Thus $A \times B$ is equivalent to $A \times C$; that is, $n(A \times B) = n(A \times C)$. $A \times B = (A \times \{s_1\}) \cup (A \times \{s_2\}) \cup \ldots \cup (A \times \{s_b\})$, and $A \times C = (A \times \{t_1\}) \cup (A \times \{t_2\}) \cup \ldots \cup (A \times \{t_c\})$. Consequently $b = c$.

We restate the cancellation property for multiplication of counting numbers.

CANCELLATION PROPERTY FOR MULTIPLICATION
For all a, b, and c if $a,b,c \in C_0$, $a \neq 0$, and $ab = ac$, then $b = c$.

Now that we have studied the properties of 0, we wish to investigate the properties of the counting number 1. By Theorem 2, $1 \cdot 7 = 7$ and $7 \cdot 1 = \underbrace{1 + 1 + 1 + 1 + 1 + 1 + 1}$. Thus it is easy

1 summand   7 summands

to see that $1 \cdot 7 = 7$ and $7 \cdot 1 = 7$. In general, if a is any counting number then $a \cdot 1 = a$ and $1 \cdot a = a$. This is an immediate consequence of Theorem 2.

If $au = a$ for some nonzero counting number a, then $au = a$ and $a \cdot 1 = a$ and hence $au = a1$. It follows from the cancellation property that $u = 1$. Hence the counting number 1 is the only counting number with the property that $a \cdot 1 = a$. This property is called the *identity property for multiplication* of counting numbers.

IDENTITY PROPERTY FOR MULTIPLICATION
The counting number 1 has the property that $a \cdot 1 = a$ for any counting number a. Moreover, if $au = a$ for some counting number $a \neq 0$, then $u = 1$.

An alternative statement of the identity property for multiplication of counting numbers is the following: *for all nonzero counting numbers a, au = a if and only if u = 1.*

From the commutative property for multiplication, it follows easily that $1 \cdot a = a$ for any counting number a.

Since multiplication is a binary operation, it is strictly defined for exactly two numbers. If three or more numbers are to be multiplied, we must agree on the order in which the numbers will be multiplied. For example, if the numbers 5, 2, and 8 are to be multiplied, one person may say $5 \cdot 2 = 10$ and $10 \cdot 8 = 80$. Another person may say $2 \cdot 8 = 16$ and $5 \cdot 16 = 80$. Notice that each person multiplied the numbers in pairs. No matter how fast you multiply the three numbers, you must first multiply two of the numbers and then multiply that product by the third number. The first person solved the problem $(5 \cdot 2) \cdot 8$, while the second person solved the different problem $5 \cdot (2 \cdot 8)$. Although the two problems are different, the two answers are equal. As with addition, the parentheses are punctuation marks which indicate that the first multiplication to be performed is within the parentheses.

The above discussion leads us to conjecture that $(a \cdot b) \cdot c = a \cdot (b \cdot c)$ for any three counting numbers a, b, and c.

We could prove the truth of this conjecture by means of the Cartesian product. To do so, we would have to prove that $(A \times B) \times C$ is equivalent to $A \times (B \times C)$ and then apply Theorem 3 and Theorem 1. In the exercises you will be asked to supply the details of the proof. We shall prove that $a(bc) = (ab)c$ for any counting numbers a, b, and c. This proof will be based on Definition 3 and Theorem 2. First we shall prove that $4 \cdot (3 \cdot 5) = (4 \cdot 3) \cdot 5$.

$$4(3 \cdot 5) = \underbrace{(3 \cdot 5) + (3 \cdot 5) + (3 \cdot 5) + (3 \cdot 5)}_{4 \text{ summands}}$$

$$= \underbrace{\overbrace{(5+5+5)}^{3 \text{ summands}} + \overbrace{(5+5+5)}^{3 \text{ summands}} + \overbrace{(5+5+5)}^{3 \text{ summands}} + \overbrace{(5+5+5)}^{3 \text{ summands}}}_{4 \text{ sets of summands}}$$

$$= \underbrace{5 + 5 + 5 + 5 + 5 + 5 + 5 + 5 + 5 + 5 + 5 + 5}_{(4 \cdot 3) \text{ summands}}$$

$$= (4 \cdot 3) \cdot 5.$$

If $a = 0$, or $b = 0$, or $c = 0$, then $a(bc) = 0$ and $(ab)c = 0$, and hence $a(bc) = (ab)c$.

Let $a \neq 0$, $b \neq 0$, and $c \neq 0$.

Then $a(bc) = \underbrace{bc + bc + \ldots + bc}_{a \text{ summands}}$

But $\underbrace{bc + bc + \ldots + bc}_{a \text{ summands}}$

$$= \underbrace{\overbrace{c + c + \ldots + c}^{b \text{ summands}} + \overbrace{(c + c + \ldots + c)}^{b \text{ summands}} + \ldots + \overbrace{(c + c + \ldots + c)}^{b \text{ summands}}}_{a \text{ sets of summands}}$$

$$\text{Now } \underbrace{(c + c + \ldots + c)}_{b \text{ summands}} + \underbrace{(c + c + \ldots + c)}_{b \text{ summands}} + \ldots + \underbrace{(c + c + \ldots + c)}_{b \text{ summands}}$$

$$\underbrace{}_{a \text{ sets of summands}}$$

$$= \underbrace{c + c + \ldots + c.}_{ab \text{ summands}}$$

Also $\underbrace{c + c + \ldots + c}_{ab \text{ summands}} = (ab)c.$

The above is a proof of the *associative property for multiplication* of counting numbers.

ASSOCIATIVE PROPERTY FOR MULTIPLICATION
For all a, b, and c, if $a,b,c \in C_0$, then $(ab)c = a(bc)$.

The following examples illustrate the application of the associative property for multiplication.

Example 12.   Compute $(37 \cdot 5) \cdot 20$.
$$(37 \cdot 5) \cdot 20 = 37 \cdot (5 \cdot 20) = 37 \,(100) = 3700.$$

Example 13.   Compute $(5 \cdot 27) \cdot 20$
$$(5 \cdot 27) \cdot 20 = (27 \cdot 5) \cdot 20 = 27 \cdot (5 \cdot 20) = 27 \,(100)$$
$$= 2700.$$

Example 14.   Prove that $a \cdot (s \cdot 5) = 5(as)$
$$a \cdot (s \cdot 5) = a \cdot (5 \cdot s) = (a \cdot 5)s = (5 \cdot a)s = 5 \cdot (as)$$
$$= 5(as).$$

Because of the associative property for multiplication, $(ab)c$ and $a(bc)$ are equal. Since there are no other ways in which we could punctuate abc, written in this order, we see that it is possible to omit the parentheses without ambiguity. We should always remember, however, that multiplication is a binary operation and hence parentheses would be necessary if we did not agree that abc may be interpreted as either $(ab)c$ or $a(bc)$. By the associative property both interpretations are equivalent. In general, we agree to write $a_1 a_2 \ldots a_k$ without punctuation since all punctuations yield the same result. This fact, called the *generalized associative property for multiplication* can be proved from the associative property of multiplication. In fact, we could prove the *generalized commutative and associative property for multiplication* of counting numbers, which states that $a_1 a_2 \ldots a_k$ may be written in any order and without parentheses. In the exercises of this section you should not apply the generalized commutative and associative property for multiplication.

GENERALIZED COMMUTATIVE AND ASSOCIATIVE PROPERTY
FOR MULTIPLICATION (GCAAPFM)

If a_1, a_2, ..., a_k are any counting numbers, then all arrangements and punctuations of $a_1 \cdot a_2 \cdot \ldots \cdot a_k$ yield the same counting number.

Exercise 3.3

I. In the order used, from left to right, identify the property or definition which makes each of the following sentences true.

(1) $5 \cdot 7 = 35$
(2) $7 \cdot 5 = 35$
(3) $5 \cdot 7 = 7 \cdot 5$
(4) $(5 \cdot 7) \cdot 3 = 5 \cdot (7 \cdot 3)$
(5) $(5 \cdot 7) \cdot 3 = 35 \cdot 3$
(6) $(5 \cdot 7) \cdot 3 = 3 \cdot (5 \cdot 7)$
(7) $(5 \cdot 7) \cdot 3 = 5 \cdot (3 \cdot 7)$
(8) $(5 \cdot 7) \cdot 3 = (3 \cdot 7) \cdot 5$
(9) $5 \cdot 1 = 1 \cdot 5$
(10) $5 \cdot 1 = 5$
(11) $5 \cdot (1 \cdot 3) = 5 \cdot 3$
(12) $(5 \cdot 1) \cdot 3 = 5 \cdot 3$
(13) $5 \cdot (3 \cdot 1) = 3 \cdot 5$
(14) $(7 \cdot 2) \cdot 3 = 3 \cdot 14$
(15) $7 \cdot (2 \cdot 3) = 3 \cdot 14$
(16) $(3 \cdot 7)(5 \cdot 4) = 21 \cdot 20$
(17) $3 \cdot (7 \cdot 9) = (3 \cdot 7)(3 \cdot 3)$
(18) $(3 \cdot 7) \cdot (5 \cdot 4) = 3 \cdot (7 \cdot 20)$
(19) $(3 \cdot 1)(5 \cdot 7) = 35 \cdot 3$
(20) $[(2 \cdot 5)(7 \cdot 3)](6 \cdot 1) = 10 \cdot (21 \cdot 6)$

II. Prove that each of the following open sentences can be converted to a true sentence by a prefix of the type "for all a, b, and c."

(1) $(ab) \cdot 1 = ba$
(2) $a(t \cdot 2) = 2(a \cdot t)$
(3) $3 \cdot (4m) = m \cdot 12$
(4) $4 \cdot (ab) = (a \cdot 4) \cdot b$
(5) $15(t \cdot 2) = t \cdot 30$
(6) $(a \cdot 3)(t \cdot 6) = (at) \cdot 18$
(7) $11 \cdot (ab) = (11\,b) \cdot a$
(8) $7 \cdot (a \cdot 2) = 14a$
(9) $9(4a \cdot 3) = 108a$
(10) $[(at)\,r] \cdot 3 = 3a\,(tr)$

III. Give a physical example to illustrate the concept of multiplication.

IV. Employ Definition 3 to prove that each of the following sentences is true.

(1) $1 \cdot 3 = 3$ (6) $4 \cdot 0 = 0$

(2) $3 \cdot 1 = 3$ (7) $4 \cdot 3 = 12$

(3) $3 \cdot 2 = 6$ (8) $4 \cdot 2 = 8$

(4) $2 \cdot 3 = 6$ (9) $3 \cdot 5 = 15$

(5) $0 \cdot 4 = 0$ (10) $3 \cdot 4 = 12$

V. Employ Theorem 2 to prove that each sentence in Exercise IV is true.

VI. Employ Theorem 3 to prove that each sentence in Exercise IV is true.

VII. Compute each of the following by means of the commutative property, the associative property, and the definition of multiplication. In each case identify the properties.

(1) $50 \, (2 \cdot 7)$ (6) $[(4 \cdot 4) \cdot 3] \cdot 5$

(2) $(90 \cdot 4) \, 25$ (7) $3 \cdot [5 \cdot (2 \cdot 8)]$

(3) $4 \, (3 \cdot 25)$ (8) $[2 \cdot (7 \cdot 3)] \cdot 5$

(4) $(15 \cdot 2) \, 50$ (9) $[(20 \cdot 2) \cdot 5] \cdot 4$

(5) $[(5 \cdot 3) \, 2] \, 6$ (10) $50 \cdot [(4 \cdot 2) \cdot 25]$

VIII. By inspection, determine whether there exists a counting number such that each of the following open sentences can be converted to a true sentence by replacement of the variable by that counting number.

(1) $3a = 0$ (6) $1a = 0$

(2) $7x = 0$ (7) $1a + 0 = 0$

(3) $3x = 12$ (8) $4a = 0$

(4) $3x = 3 \cdot 4$ (9) $0a = 5$

(5) $5a = 0$ (10) $1a = a$

IX. Prove that for all counting numbers a, b, and c all of the following are equal.

(1) $a(bc)$ (7) $(ab)c$

(2) $a(cb)$ (8) $(ac)b$

(3) $(bc)a$ (9) $b(ac)$

(4) $b(ca)$ (10) $(ba)c$

(5) $c(ab)$ (11) $(ca)b$

(6) $c(ba)$ (12) $(cb)a$

X. (1) Complete enough entries of the following multiplication table so that the remaining entries may be computed by means of the commutative property for multiplication.

·	0	1	2	3	4	5	6	7	8	9
0										
1										
2										
3										
4										
5										
6										
7										
8										
9										

(2) How many multiplication facts are required if only the commutative property for multiplication is known?

(3) How many multiplication facts are required if only the commutative and identity properties enumerated in this section are known?

(4) How many multiplication facts would be needed if we did not know any of the above properties?

3.4 The Distributive Property

Each of the properties studied so far has been concerned with exactly one binary operation—either addition or multiplication. In this section we shall study a property which involves *two* binary operations—addition and multiplication. Since $2 \cdot 3 + 7$ is ambiguous unless we agree on its meaning, we must punctuate it properly to indicate whether we wish to multiply first or add first. If we wish to multiply first, we write $(2 \cdot 3) + 7$; the answer is 13. If we wish to add first, we write $2(3 + 7)$; the answer is 20. In order to avoid writing parentheses in the former case, we shall *agree* that multiplication takes precedence over addition; that is, we shall *agree* that $2 \cdot 3 + 7$ shall mean $(2 \cdot 3) + 7$. In general, we agree that $ab + c$ shall mean $(ab) + c$. Although the parentheses in $2 \cdot (3 + 7)$, or $2(3 + 7)$, are necessary to indicate that the *addition* is to be performed first, our agreement makes it unnecessary to write the parentheses whenever it is understood that the *multiplication* is to be performed first. This convention eliminates excessive punctuation in complicated expressions. To summarize, we agree that $a(b + c)$ shall mean the product of a and $(b + c)$, while $ab + c$ shall mean the sum of ab and c. Actually, we *could* have agreed that addition takes precedence over multiplication. It must be emphasized, however, that mathematicians have agreed that multiplication takes precedence over addition unless punctuated otherwise.

Now that we have agreed on the order of multiplication and addition, we are prepared to give two examples of a fundamental property of the counting numbers.

Example 1. $2(7 + 3) = 2(10) = 20.$
Moreover, $(2 \cdot 7) + (2 \cdot 3) = 2 \cdot 7 + 2 \cdot 3 = 14 + 6 = 20.$
Thus $2(7 + 3) = 2 \cdot 7 + 2 \cdot 3.$

Example 2. $5(10 + 3) = 5(13) = 65.$
Moreover, $5 \cdot 10 + 5 \cdot 3 = 50 + 15 = 65.$
Thus $5(10 + 3) = 5 \cdot 10 + 5 \cdot 3.$

The above examples illustrate an important property of the counting numbers; *if a, b, and c are any counting numbers, then* $a(b + c) = ab + ac$. Before we prove this property, we state and prove the following theorem.

THEOREM 4.   If A, B, and C are any sets, then $A \times (B \cup C)$
$= (A \times B) \cup (A \times C).$

Proof. $A \times (B \cup C) = \{(a,x): a \in A \wedge x \in B \cup C\}$
$= \{(a,x): a \in A \wedge (x \in B \vee x \in C)\}$
$= \{(a,x): (a \in A \wedge x \in B) \vee$
$(a \in A \wedge x \in C)\}$
$(p \wedge (q \vee s) \rightleftarrows (p \wedge q) \vee (p \wedge s)$ is logically true)
$= (A \times B) \cup (A \times C).$
Hence $A \times (B \cup C) = (A \times B) \cup (A \times C).\mathbin{/\!/}$

Theorem 4 will enable us to prove the *distributive property for multiplication over addition*.

DISTRIBUTIVE PROPERTY FOR MULTIPLICATION OVER ADDITION
For all a, b, and c if a, b, $c \in C_0$, then $a(b + c) = ab + ac$.

To prove this property, let A, B, C be sets such that $n(A) = a$, $n(B) = b$, $n(C) = c$, and $B \cap C = \phi$.

$A \times (B \cup C) = (A \times B) \cup (A \times C)$ (by Theorem 4),
$n[A \times (B \cup C)] = n[(A \times B) \cup (A \times C)],$
$n[A \times (B \cup C)] = n(A \times B) + n(A \times C),$ (since
$(A \times B) \cap (A \times C) = \phi),$
$n(A)[n(B \cup C)] = n(A)n(B) + n(A)n(C)$ (by Theorem 3),
$n(A)[n(B) + n(C)] = n(A)n(B) + n(A)n(C)$ (by Definition 2).
Hence $a[b + c] = ab + ac.$

Notice that $(A \times B) \cap (A \times C) = \phi$ because the second members of the ordered pairs of $A \times B$ are all different from the second members of the ordered pairs of $A \times C$. The reason for this is that the elements of B are all different from the elements of C.

The above proof of the distributive property for multiplication over addition is based on Theorem 3. We now give a proof based on Theorem 2. If $a = 0$, then it is obvious that $a(b + c) = ab + ac$. The following proof is for the case in which $a \neq 0$.

$$a(b + c) = \underbrace{(b + c) + (b + c) + \ldots + (b + c)}_{a \text{ summands}} \quad \text{(by Theorem 2)}$$

$$= \underbrace{(b + b + \ldots + b)}_{a \text{ summands}} + \underbrace{(c + c + \ldots + c)}_{a \text{ summands}} \quad \text{(by GCAAPA)}$$

$$= ab + ac. \qquad\qquad\qquad\qquad\qquad \text{(by Theorem 2)}$$

We have proved that $a(b + c) = ab + ac$ for all counting numbers a, b, and c.

The distributive property for multiplication over addition is extremely useful in the justification of the computational devices employed in multiplication and division. In Chapters 4, 5, and 6, when we justify those devices, we shall use two forms of the distributive property. The second form, $(b + c)a = ba + ca$, follows readily from the commutative property for multiplication and the distributive property above.

Since there are two distributive properties in the algebra of sentences and two in the algebra of sets, you may wonder whether there are two distributive properties in the algebra of the counting numbers. The following example proves that there cannot be a distributive property for addition over multiplication.

Example 3. $4 + (7 \cdot 3) = 4 + 21 = 25.$
$(4 + 7) \cdot (4 + 3) = (11)(7) = 77.$
Hence $4 + (7 \cdot 3) \neq (4 + 7) \cdot (4 + 3).$

Whenever we prove that a sentence involving the quantifier *all* is false by exhibiting one example, that example is known as a *counterexample*. For example, to prove that the sentence "all birds fly" is false, all we need to do is exhibit *one* bird that does not fly; that bird is a counterexample.

Thus there is no distributive property for addition over multiplication of counting numbers; that is, if a, b, and c are any counting numbers, we cannot assert that $a + (bc) = (a + b)(a + c)$. Henceforth we refer, without ambiguity, to the distributive property for multiplication over addition as simply the *distributive property.*

The following examples illustrate some applications of the distributive property.

Example 4. $5 \cdot 14 = 5(10 + 4) = 5 \cdot 10 + 5 \cdot 4 = 50 + 20 = 70.$

Example 5. $103 \cdot 7 = 7 \cdot 103 = 7(100 + 3) = 7 \cdot 100 + 7 \cdot 3 = 700 + 21 = 721.$

Example 6. $103 \cdot 7 = (100 + 3) \cdot 7 = 100(7) + 3(7) = 700 + 21 = 721.$

Example 7. In a local basketball game, Paul scored 7 points the first half and 8 points the second half. Ronnie scored twice as many points each half as Paul scored. How many points did Ronnie score the first half, the second half, and the entire game? Ronnie scored $2(7)$ points the first half and $2(8)$ points the second half. Thus Ronnie scored a total of $2(7) + 2(8)$ points the entire game. Alternatively, Ronnie scored a total of $2(7 + 8)$ points the entire game. Hence $2(7 + 8) = 2(7) + 2(8)$.

Example 8. $3a + 7a = (3 + 7)a = 10a.$ [*Note.* We have used the distributive property in the form $ba + ca = (b + c)a.$]

Example 9. $a(b + c + d) = a[(b + c) + d] = a(b + c) + ad = (ab + ac) + ad = ab + ac + ad.$

In Example 9 we proved that $a(b + c + d) = ab + ac + ad$ for any counting numbers a, b, c, and d. In general, $a(b_1 + b_2 + \ldots + b_k) = ab_1 + ab_2 + \ldots + ab_k$ for any counting numbers $a, b_1, b_2, \ldots, b_k$. This property, called the *generalized distributive property*, may be proved from the distributive property in Example 9.

GENERALIZED DISTRIBUTIVE PROPERTY (GDP)

If $a, b_1, b_2, \ldots, b_k$ are any counting numbers, then $a(b_1 + b_2 + \ldots + b_k) = ab_1 + ab_2 + \ldots + ab_k$, and $(b_1 + b_2 + \ldots + b_k)a = b_1a + b_2a + \ldots + b_ka$.

Exercise 3.4

I. Use the distributive property to prove each of the following.

(1) $2(3 + 5) = 16$
(2) $5(11 + 9) = 100$

(3) $99(10 + 1) = 1089$
(4) $85(7 + 3) = 850$
(5) $9a = 7a + 2a$, for all counting numbers a
(6) $11x = 3x + 8x$, for all counting numbers x
(7) $12t = 5t + 7t$
(8) $13y = 9y + 4y$
(9) $19k = 10k + 9k$
(10) $2b = b + b$

II. Use the distributive property to prove each of the following.

(1) $5(7) + 5(3) = 50$
(2) $7(5) + 7(15) = 140$
(3) $8(91) + 8(9) = 800$
(4) $3(690) + 3(310) = 3000$
(5) $3a + 4a = 7a$, for all counting numbers a
(6) $8x + 7x = 15x$, for all counting numbers x
(7) $3y + 6y = 9y$
(8) $2b + b = 3b$
(9) $a \cdot a + 5a = (a + 5)a$
(10) $7t + tt = (7 + t)t$

III. Prove each of the following in two ways.

(1) $(3 + 7)5 = 50$
(2) $(5 + 3)2 = 16$
(3) $2 \cdot 9 + 2 \cdot 1 = 20$
(4) $30 = 3 \cdot 7 + 3 \cdot 3$
(5) $30a = 3 \cdot 7a + 3 \cdot 3a$, for all counting numbers a
(6) $10 = 2 \cdot 4 + 2 \cdot 1$
(7) $10 \cdot 5 + 20 \cdot 5 = 150$
(8) $4 \cdot 7 + 6 \cdot 7 = 70$
(9) $5(6b) + 4(6b) = 54b$
(10) $3(2at) + 5(2at) = 16at$

IV. Employ the distributive property $a(b + c) = ab + ac$ and the commutative property for multiplication to prove $(b + c)a = ba + ca$ for all counting numbers a, b, and c.

V. Apply the generalized distributive property to each of the following.

(1) $3(a + b + x)$
(2) $5(a + 2b + 3c)$
(3) $a(2 + b + c + x)$

(4) $(a + x + y + v)b$

(5) $ax + ay + az$

(6) $3ab(2a + 3c + w + x + 2y + 5z)$

(7) $6a + 2b + 4c + 8d$

(8) $15w + 25x + 35y + 10z$

(9) $8ab + 12ac + 16ad + 28ax$

(10) $6at + 9as + 15ax + 27ay$

3.5   Order Properties of the Set of Counting Numbers

Recall that when we count the number of objects in a finite set A we establish a one-to-one correspondence between A and one of the sets $\{1\}, \{1, 2\}, \{1, 2, 3\}, \ldots, \{1, 2, \ldots, k\}$. Although we may not realize it, we have established an *order* relation between every two counting numbers. For example, we associate the number *three* with some set of three elements, usually the set $\{1, 2, 3\}$. Similarly we associate the number *four* with the set $\{1, 2, 3, 4\}$. Since $\{1, 2, 3\}$ is a *proper* subset of $\{1, 2, 3, 4\}$, we immediately conclude that the number *three* is less than the number *four*. In general, if $\{1, 2, \ldots, a\}$ is a proper subset of $\{1, 2, \ldots, b\}$, we conclude that a is less than b. We make the following definition of the order relation *is less than*.

DEFINITION 4.   The counting number a *is less than* the counting number b if and only if there exist finite sets A and B such that $n(A) = a$, $n(B) = b$, and A is a proper subset of B.

It follows from Definition 4 that a is less than b if and only if $\{1, 2, \ldots, a\}$ is a proper subset of $\{1, 2, \ldots, b\}$.

You should observe that Definition 4 does not apply to *all* sets A and B such that $n(A) = a$ and $n(B) = b$. It does assert that there must *exist* two sets A and B such that $n(A) = a$, $n(B) = b$, and A is a proper subset of B before we can conclude that a is less than b. For example, the counting number 4 is less than the counting number 6. This is true because $A = \{1, 2, 3, 4\}$ is a proper subset of $B = \{1, 2, 3, 4, 5, 6\}$. Notice that the choices of A and B are not unique. For example, we could have chosen $A = \{5, 9, 7, a\}$ and $B = \{5, 9, 7, a, 3, b\}$.

Recall that the empty set is a proper subset of any nonempty set. Because of this fact, we are able to prove the following theorem.

THEOREM 5.   The counting number 0 is less than every nonzero counting number c.

Proof.   Since $c \neq 0$, there exists a nonempty finite set C such
                  that $n(C) = c$.
                  Hence ϕ is a proper subset of C.
                  By Definition 4, $n(\phi)$ is less than $n(C)$.
                  But $n(\phi) = 0$ and $n(C) = c$.
                  Thus 0 is less than c. //

We introduce the notation $<$ to indicate *is less than*. Thus we
write $0 < 5$ and read *0 is less than 5*. Any open sentence or sentence of
the form $a < b$ is called an *inequality*.

If a and b are two different counting numbers, can we assert that
$a < b$ or $b < a$? The following theorem answers this question.

THEOREM 6.   For all a and b, if $a, b \in C_0$ and $a \neq b$, then $a < b$ or
              $b < a$ (but not both).

Proof.

Case 1. $a = 0$.
                 Then $b \neq 0$ (since $a \neq b$).
                 Thus $a < b$ (by Theorem 5).

Case 2. $b = 0$.
                 Then $a \neq 0$ (since $a \neq b$).
                 Thus $b < a$ (by Theorem 5).

Case 3. $a \neq 0$ and $b \neq 0$.
                 Then $\{1, 2, \ldots, a\} \neq \{1, 2, \ldots, b\}$ (since $a \neq b$).
                 Thus $\{1, 2, \ldots, a\}$ is a proper subset of $\{1, 2, \ldots, b\}$
                 or $\{1, 2, \ldots, b\}$ is a proper subset of $\{1, 2, \ldots, a\}$
                 (but not both).

Hence, by Definition 4, $a < b$ or $b < a$ (but not both). //

Theorem 6 enables us to state the following important property of
the counting numbers, called the *trichotomy property* of the counting
numbers.

TRICHOTOMY PROPERTY
If a and b are any counting numbers, then one and only one of the
following is true:
(1) $a = b$,
(2) $a < b$,
(3) $b < a$.

Example 1.   If $a = 5$ and $b = 5$, then $a = b$.

Example 2.   If $a = 5$ and $b = 8$, then $a < b$.

Example 3.   If $a = 7$ and $b = 6$, then $b < a$.

Notice that the sentence "$5 < 8$" may be associated with the sentence "$5 + 3 = 8$." Similarly, the sentence "$4 < 6$" may be associated with the sentence "$4 + 2 = 6$." Conversely, the sentence "$4 + 2 = 6$" may be associated with the sentence "$4 < 6$" or with the sentence "$2 < 6$." You may wonder whether the sentence "$a < b$" may be associated with the sentence "$a + k = b$" for any a, $b \in C_0$ and some nonzero counting number k. The following theorem answers this question.

THEOREM 7.   The counting number a is less than the counting number b if and only if there exists a nonzero counting number k such that $a + k = b$.

Proof.

$(\rightarrow)$ Let $a < b$.

Then there exist finite sets A and B such that $n(A) = a$, $n(B) = b$, and A is a proper subset of B (by Definition 4),

Let $K = \{x: x \in B \land x \notin A\}$.

$K \neq \phi$ (since A is a proper subset of B).

Hence $n(K) = k \neq 0$.

Now $A \cup K = B$ and $A \cap K = \phi$.

Thus $n(A \cup K) = n(B)$.

Hence $a + k = b$ (by Definition 2).

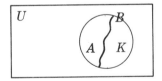

$(\leftarrow)$ Conversely, let $a + k = b$ for some counting number $k \neq 0$.

Then there exist finite sets A, B, and K such that $n(A) = a$, $n(B) = b$, $n(K) = k$, $n(A) + n(K) = n(B)$, $A \cup K = B$, and $A \cap K = \phi$.

Hence $a < b$ (by Definition 4). //

The following examples do not illustrate Theorem 7, but should help you to understand the *proof* of the theorem.

Example 4. $3 < 5$.

Choose $A = \{1, 2, 3\}$ and $B = \{1, 2, 3, 4, 5\}$.

Then A is a proper subset of B.

Since we desire a nonempty set K such that $A \cup K = B$ and $A \cap K = \phi$, we must choose $K = \{4, 5\}$.

Then $n(A) = 3$, $n(K) = 2$, and $n(B) = 5$.

Hence $3 + 2 = 5$.

Example 5. $2 + 4 = 6$.

We desire A, K, and B such that $n(A) = 2$, $n(K) = 4$, and $n(B) = 6$.

We may choose $A = \{1, 2\}$ and $B = \{1, 2, 3, 4, 5, 6\}$.

Since $A \cap K = \phi$ and $A \cup K = B$, we must choose $K = \{3, 4, 5, 6\}$

Now $n(A) = 2$, $n(B) = 6$, and A is a proper subset of B. Thus $2 < 6$.

You know that $3 < 7$ and $2 + 3 < 2 + 7$. Hence we conclude that $(3 < 7) \rightarrow (2 + 3 < 2 + 7)$. Since $0 + 3 < 0 + 7$, we conclude that $(3 < 7) \rightarrow (0 + 3 < 0 + 7)$.

These examples are particular cases of the following theorem.

THEOREM 8.   For all a, b, and c, if $a,b,c \in C_0$ and $a < b$, then $c + a < c + b$.

Proof.   Let $a < b$.

Then $a + k = b$ for some $k \in \{1, 2, 3, \ldots\}$,

$c + (a + k) = c + b$,

$(c + a) + k = c + b$.

Hence $(c + a) < (c + b)$ (by Theorem 7).//

Similarly, $3 < 7$ and $2(3) < 2(7)$. Thus we conclude that $[3 < 7] \rightarrow [2(3) < 2(7)]$. However, since $0(3) = 0(7)$, the trichotomy property tells us that $0(3)$ cannot be less than $0(7)$. The following theorem is a generalization of this fact.

THEOREM 9.   For all a, b, and c if $a,b,c \in C_0$, $c \neq 0$, and $a < b$, then $ca < cb$.

Proof.   Let $a < b$ and $c \neq 0$.

Then $a + k = b$, for some $k \in \{1, 2, 3, \ldots\}$,

$c(a + k) = cb$,

$ca + ck = cb, ck \neq 0$ (by the multiplication property of 0).

Hence $ca < cb$ (by Theorem 7)./⁄

As above, we see that $[(2 < 5) \wedge (5 < 8)] \rightarrow [2 < 8]$. Similarly, $[(4 < 7) \wedge (7 < 9)] \rightarrow [4 < 9]$. These examples motivate us to state and prove the following theorem.

THEOREM 10.   For all counting numbers a, b, and c if $(a < b) \wedge (b < c)$, then $a < c$.   (transitive property for $<$)

Proof.   Let $a < b$ and $b < c$.

Then $a + k_1 = b$, for some $k_1 \neq 0$, and $b + k_2 = c$, for some $k_2 \neq 0$.

Thus $(a + k_1) + k_2 = c$,

$a + (k_1 + k_2) = c$,

$a + k = c$ and $k = k_1 + k_2 \neq 0$.

Hence $a < c$ (by Theorem 7)./⁄

Theorem 10 is a statement of the transitive property for the relation $<$.

To determine whether $<$ is an equivalence relation, we must decide whether the relation is reflexive and symmetric, as well as transitive. Since $a + 0 = a$ but $a + k \neq a$ if $k \neq 0$, we see that a cannot be less than a. Hence the reflexive property is not satisfied for the relation $<$. Thus the relation $<$ is *not* an equivalence relation. By the trichotomy property, if $a < b$, then $b \not< a$. Hence the symmetric property fails also.

We conclude this section with a discussion of two fundamental order properties of the counting numbers.

WELL ORDERING PROPERTY

If A is any nonempty subset of C_0, then there is one and only one element a_0 of A which is less than any other element of A.

The element a_0 in the well ordering property is called the *least element* of A. Thus, the well ordering property guarantees that every nonempty set of counting numbers has exactly one least element. For example, if $A = \{9, 4, 5, 7, 11\}$, then $a_0 = 4$. If $A = \{3, 6, 9, \ldots\}$, then $a_0 = 3$. In particular, if $A = C_0$, the least element is zero.

ARCHIMEDEAN PROPERTY

If a is any nonzero counting number and b is any counting number such that $a < b$, then there exists a nonzero counting number k such that $b < ak$.

For example, if $a = 5$ and $b = 103$, then $k = 21$. Obviously, the choice of k is not unique. For example, one could choose $k = 25$.

Exercise 3.5

I. By means of Definition 4, determine whether each of the following inequalities is a true sentence.

(1) $5 < 8$ (6) $0 < 0$
(2) $3 < 5$ (7) $4 < 0$
(3) $1 < 1$ (8) $4 < 8$
(4) $4 < 4$ (9) $1 < 4$
(5) $6 < 5$ (10) $9 < 10$

II. By means of Theorem 7, determine whether each of the inequalities in Exercise I is a true sentence.

III. Illustrate the transitive property for order in each of the following.

(1) $a = 3, b = 4, c = 6$ (6) $a = 4, b = 7, c = 5$
(2) $a = 7, b = 11, c = 18$ (7) $a = 0, b = 2, c = 1$
(3) $a = 2, b = 3, c = 4$ (8) $a = 5, b = 0, c = 3$
(4) $a = 1, b = 3, c = 5$ (9) $a = 7, b = 5, c = 2$
(5) $a = 9, b = 7, c = 8$ (10) $a = 4, b = 2, c = 0$

IV. Illustrate the Archimedean property in each of the following.

(1) $a = 2, b = 19$ (4) $a = 5, b = 600$
(2) $a = 3, b = 19$ (5) $a = 8, b = 81$
(3) $a = 3, b = 18$ (6) $a = 8, b = 79$

3.6   The Number Line

In this section we give a geometric representation of the set of counting numbers. This representation on the *number line* should help you to fix in mind the concept of counting number and the properties of the counting numbers. We are already familiar with rulers, yardsticks, meter sticks, and tape measures. As we know, the numerals on such a measuring device indicate the *positions* of points or the *measures* of the distances of these points from the left end of the device. For example, the numeral 5 on a yardstick indicates the position of a point which is 5 inches from the left end of the yardstick. Similarly the numeral "8" on the yardstick indicates the position of a point which is 8 inches from the left end of the yardstick. Since the point labeled 5 is to the *left* of the point labeled 8 on the yardstick, it seems natural to write 5 to the *left* of 8 when we write an order relationship between 5 and 8. Thus when we write 5 < 8 we are being consistent with our geometric concept of points on a yardstick.

Geometrically we can represent C_0 on the *number line* as illustrated in Figure 3.3. We *label* any point with the symbol 0 and choose *any* point to the right of the 0-point and label it with the symbol 1.

$$0 \quad 1 \quad 2 \quad 3 \quad \ldots$$

FIGURE 3.3

Then we choose the distance from the point labeled 0 to the point labeled 1 as the unit of measurement. Using this unit of measurement, we mark a point one unit to the right of the point labeled 1 and label this point with the symbol 2. Proceeding in this manner, we label a point on the number line corresponding to each counting number. Thus we establish a one-to-one correspondence between the set of counting numbers and the set of labeled points on the number line. The points are labeled by the numerals 0, 1, 2, 3, . . . and indicated by heavy dots as in Figure 3.3. As usual, the three dots indicate that the labeling process continues indefinitely. Moreover, the number line extends indefinitely to the right and to the left.

Notice that there are many other points of the number line which are not labeled. In fact, between any two labeled points, there are infinitely many unlabeled points. You may believe that there are only a finite number of points between the two points labeled 0 and 1. If so, you probably base your belief on the fact that it is possible to fill in the space between 0 and 1 by marking a finite number of dots between these two points. The fallacy in this argument is that any figure you can draw, such as Figure 3.3, is a *physical* model of the *mathematical* concept of *number line*. While the physical *dot* has dimensions, the mathematical *point* is dimensionless.

There is another fact which we should mention. When we represent the counting numbers geometrically on the number line, we are really assuming the order relation and the order properties studied in the preceding section. If we did not have the concept of order, we would not know how to label the points on the number line.

Now we are ready to illustrate the addition of two counting numbers on the number line. Visualize the number line as a long straight street whose main intersection is labeled 0. The successive intersections to the east are labeled 1, 2, 3, ... If we walk 3 blocks east of the main intersection and then walk 5 blocks east from there, our final position is 8 blocks east of the main intersection. This illustrates the fact that $3 + 5 = 8$. The arrows above the model of the number line in Figure 3.4 indicate the distance and direction of each walk.

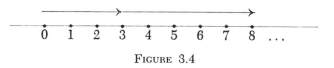

FIGURE 3.4

Figure 3.5 illustrates the fact that $5 + 3 = 8$.

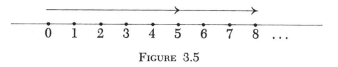

FIGURE 3.5

Next we illustrate the multiplication of two counting numbers on the number line. Recalling that Theorem 2 tells us that $3 \cdot 4 = 4 + 4 + 4$, we see that the problem of multiplication of the counting numbers 3 and 4 reduces to the addition problem of $(4 + 4) + 4$, which is illustrated in Figure 3.6.

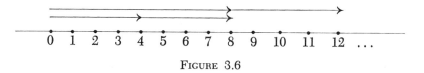

FIGURE 3.6

The transitive property of order is illustrated in Figure 3.7 for the counting numbers 2, 5, and 8. Notice that 2 is to the left of 5 and 5 is to the left of 8 and hence 2 is to the left of 8. Thus $[(2 < 5) \wedge (5 < 8)] \to [2 < 8]$.

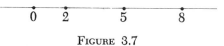

FIGURE 3.7

The Archimedean property of order is illustrated in Figure 3.8 for the counting numbers $a = 2$ and $b = 9$. Since we need five arrows, each of length 2 units, we may choose $k = 5$. Thus $9 < 5 \cdot 2$.

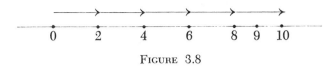

FIGURE 3.8

Later we shall study other sets of numbers such as the negative integers, the rational numbers, and the irrational numbers. The number line will be a useful aid in our study of their properties.

Exercise 3.6

I. (1) Sketch a model of the number line and label the points 0, 1, 2, ..., 20.
   (2) Use the model to illustrate that $0 < 1$, $1 < 2$, $5 < 7$, and $7 < 10$.
   (3) Illustrate the transitive property of order for $a = 3$, $b = 7$ and $c = 8$.
   (4) Illustrate the addition $5 + 8 = 13$.
   (5) Illustrate the addition $(5 + 2) + 9 = 16$.
   (6) Illustrate the addition $5 + (2 + 9) = 16$.
   (7) Illustrate the multiplication $4 \cdot 3 = 12$.
   (8) Illustrate the multiplication $2 \cdot 7 = 14$.
   (9) Illustrate the Archimedean property for $a = 3$ and $b = 15$.
  (10) Illustrate the Archimedean property for $a = 2$ and $b = 18$.

II. (1) Illustrate the multiplication $2 \cdot 3 = 6$.
   (2) Illustrate the multiplication $2 \cdot 4 = 8$.
   (3) Illustrate the addition $6 + 8 = 14$.
   (4) Illustrate the multiplication $2(3 + 4) = 14$.
   (5) Illustrate the distributive property $2(3 + 4) = 2 \cdot 3 + 2 \cdot 4$.
   (6) Illustrate that $2 + 3 = 3 + 2$.
   (7) Illustrate that $2(4) = 4(2)$.
   (8) Illustrate that $(2 \cdot 3) \cdot 2 = 2 \cdot (3 \cdot 2)$.

Chapter 4

NUMERATION SYSTEMS

4.1 Egyptian Numeration System

The ancient shepherd used the idea of one-to-one correspondence in accounting for his sheep. If his flock was small enough, he had no need for an elaborate accounting system. However, if his flock was large, he kept a bag of pebbles—one pebble for each member of the flock. If some of the pebbles were left over after he had herded in the flock for the night, he knew that some of his sheep were missing. Later he needed to communicate the actual number of sheep in his flock. In oral communication he used *names* for the numbers, and in written communication he used *symbols* for the numbers. The names of the numbers depended on the particular language spoken in his region, whereas the symbols for the numbers did not.

The Egyptians denoted the number *one* by the symbol | (a vertical stroke), the number *two* by the symbol | |, the number *three* by the symbol | | |, ..., and the number *nine* by the symbol | | | | | | | | |. As this symbolism is a natural abstraction of the one-to-one correspondence by means of pebbles, we may assume that the Egyptians originally represented larger numbers also by vertical strokes. However, as they soon realized the need for more efficient communication, they invented special symbols for some of the larger numbers. Possibly they had been counting by use of their toes. Since each person had ten toes, it seemed natural to introduce a special symbol for the number *ten*. They used the *heelbone* symbol ∩ to represent the number ten. Since counting *thirteen* objects, for example, required counting all *ten* toes and then *three* toes again, they symbolized the number thirteen by ∩ | | |. Since

112

counting *fifty-seven* objects required the use of all toes *five* times and then *seven* toes again, the number *fifty-seven* was represented by the symbol ∩ ∩ ∩ ∩ ∩ | | | | | | | . It is easy to see that this numeration system becomes awkward when the number to be represented is large. For this reason the Egyptians invented special symbols for larger numbers. All of these symbols and the numbers which they represent are listed in Figure 4.1.

Egyptian Symbol	Number
| (Vertical stroke)	one
∩ (Heelbone)	ten
⑨ (Coil of rope or scroll)	hundred
⚘ (Lotus flower)	thousand
⌐ (Bent line or finger)	ten thousand
⤳ (Burbot)	hundred thousand
⚎ (Astonished man)	million

FIGURE 4.1

It is interesting to note that the Egyptian symbol for one million is that of an astonished man. Even today there appears to be something magical and astonishing about one million—especially to a child. Notice that each symbol in Figure 4.1 represents ten of the symbol above it. For example, the symbol ⑨ represents ∩ ∩ ∩ ∩ ∩ ∩ ∩ ∩ ∩ ∩ . Addition in this numeration system is particularly simple. For example, to add ∩ ∩ ∩ ∩ | | | | | | and ∩ ∩ ∩ ∩ ∩ ∩ ∩ | | | | | we write ∩ ∩ ∩ ∩ ∩ ∩ ∩ ∩ ∩ ∩ ∩ | | | | | | | | | | | and notice that this reduces to ∩ ∩ ∩ ∩ ∩ ∩ ∩ ∩ ∩ ∩ ∩ | . The latter symbol may be rewritten ⑨ ∩ ∩ | and is read *one hundred twenty-one*. Although a child could probably learn to add in the Egyptian system quicker than in the Hindu-Arabic numeration system which we use today, it is easy to see that the notation for certain numbers, for example nine thousand nine hundred ninety-nine, may become awkward and large. Another weakness of the Egyptian system is that new symbols will have to be invented to represent larger numbers or the numeral will be unmanageably long.

If it were not for the repetition of the symbols in the Egyptian system, it would be necessary to have as many different individual symbols as there are counting numbers. Notice that there is no symbol to represent the counting number zero.

Exercise 4.1

I. Write the Egyptian numeral for each of the following counting numbers.

(1) 7
(2) 22
(3) 99
(4) 44
(5) 109
(6) 1,250
(7) 11,101
(8) 119,497
(9) 500,003
(10) 6,120,909

II. Compute the sum $a + b$ in the Egyptian numeration system.

(1) $a = 13, b = 29$
(2) $a = 100, b = 650$
(3) $a = 78, b = 23$
(4) $a = 99, b = 9$
(5) $a = 1, b = 39$
(6) $a = 11, b = 29$

III. List some of the disadvantages of the Egyptian numeration system.

4.2 Roman Numeration System

Another numeration system, which is very similar to the Egyptian system, is the well-known Roman numeration system. The numerals of this system are capital letters which are used in repetitive sequence when necessary. The first ten counting numbers are represented in the Roman system by I, II, III, IV, V, VI, VII, VIII, IX, X. You will notice that only three different individual symbols are needed to represent the first ten counting numbers; namely, I, V, and X. One advantage of the Roman system over the Egyptian system is that many numerals are more easily recognized in the Roman system. For example, since V represents *five* and I represents *one*, we easily recognize that VII represents *seven*. The corresponding symbol | | | | | | | of the Egyptian system is not as readily recognized as the numeral for the number seven.

We are already familiar with the fact that the Romans symbolized the number *nine* by IX and the number *eleven* by XI. Thus we see that the *order* in which the symbols are written is important. However, in the Egyptian system, the number *eleven* may be symbolized by either ∩ | or | ∩; that is, the order in which the individual symbols are written is immaterial. Consequently, addition in the Roman system is more complicated than in the Egyptian system. Extreme care must be exercised if one is to avoid errors in calculation.

In Figure 4.2 the first fifty counting numbers are symbolized in the Roman numeration system.

I	II	III	IV	V	VI	VII	VIII	IX	X
XI	XII	XIII	XIV	XV	XVI	XVII	XVIII	XIX	XX
XXI	XXII	XXIII	XXIV	XXV	XXVI	XXVII	XXVIII	XXIX	XXX
XXXI	XXXII	XXXIII	XXXIV	XXXV	XXXVI	XXXVII	XXXVIII	XXXIX	XL
XLI	XLII	XLIII	XLIV	XLV	XLVI	XLVII	XLVIII	XLIX	L

FIGURE 4.2

Figure 4.3 (a) is a list of the Roman numerals corresponding to the counting numbers 1, 5, 10, 50, 100, 500, and 1000. Notice that there is no symbol for the counting number zero.

Roman Numeral	Counting Number
I	one
V	five
X	ten
L	fifty
C	one hundred
D	five hundred
M	one thousand

(a)

Roman Numeral	Counting Number
I	1
IV	4
IX	9
XL	40
XC	90
CD	400
CM	900

(b)

FIGURE 4.3

Actually, in the original Roman system *four* was symbolized by IIII and *nine* was symbolized by VIIII. Later, according to some historians, in order to save space, clock manufacturers replaced the symbol IIII by the symbol IV, and the symbol VIIII by the symbol IX. This principle of subtraction was extended to all numerals involving four, nine, forty, ninety, four hundred, nine hundred, et cetera. Figure 4.3(b) is a list of the Roman numerals corresponding to the counting numbers 1, 4, 9, 40, 90, 400, and 900.

It is not our purpose to make a detailed study of the Roman numeration system. However, for the purpose of contrast of this system with the Egyptian system of the preceding section and with the Hindu-Arabic system of the following section, we shall conclude this section with some examples of addition in the Roman system. Notice that some of the symbols in the intermediate steps of the calculation are not bona fide Roman numerals but are symbols to facilitate our calculation.

Example 1.   Compute the sum $63 + 13$ in the Roman system.
$63 + 13 = LXIII + XIII = LXXIIIIII = LXXVI = 76.$

Example 2.   Compute the sum $64 + 16$ in the Roman system.
$64 + 16 = LXIV + XVI = LXIIII + XVI = LXXVIIIII$
$= LXXVV = LXXX = 80.$

Exercise 4.2

I. Write the Roman numeral for each of the following counting numbers.

(1) 44
(2) 56
(3) 90
(4) 490
(5) 497
(6) 999
(7) 1999
(8) 49
(9) 51
(10) 1,051

II. Compute the sum $a + b$ in the Roman numeration system.

(1) $a = 13, b = 29.$
(2) $a = 99, b = 9.$
(3) $a = 1, b = 39.$
(4) $a = 78, b = 33.$
(5) $a = 1006, b = 209.$
(6) $a = 940, b = 94.$

III. List some of the disadvantages of the Roman numeration system.

4.3   Hindu-Arabic Numeration System

In the two preceding sections we discussed briefly the Egyptian numeration system and the Roman numeration system. In the history of mathematics there have been many such systems, most of which are now obsolete. While we shall not discuss all of them in detail, we can name a few of them: the Babylonian, the Greek, the Mayan, and the Hindu-Arabic numeration systems. Since the latter system has many outstanding features, it is the most widely used system in the world today. Although you have been using the Hindu-Arabic numeration system ever since you learned how to count, we shall make a comprehensive study of this system. The two preceding sections should help you to appreciate and understand the Hindu-Arabic numeration system.

In its earliest use (circa 500 B.C.) the Hindu-Arabic system consisted of nine different individual symbols, which have evolved through the centuries to the familiar symbols 1, 2, 3, 4, 5, 6, 7, 8, 9. An essential difference between this system and the two previous ones is that the symbols here are nonrepetitive; for example, in the Egyptian system *three* is symbolized by | | |, in the Roman system by III, whereas in the Hindu-Arabic system *three* is symbolized by the individual symbol 3. Although it seems logical to use the three strokes | | | to represent the number *three*, we shall see the superiority of the Hindu-Arabic system. However, prior to the invention of the symbol 0 in the ninth century, the Hindu-Arabic system had no distinct advantages over the previously discussed ones. Although it was known in Europe in the thirteenth century, this superior numeration system did not replace the Roman numeration system until the sixteenth century.

In its present form the Hindu-Arabic system consists of the symbols 0, 1, 2, 3, 4, 5, 6, 7, 8, 9 called *digits*. We write the two-digit symbol 11 to indicate the number *eleven*. The reason for this choice of digits is that in counting eleven objects on one's toes, one counts all of his toes *once* and then *one* toe again. Similarly we write 23 to indicate the number *twenty-three*, because in counting twenty-three objects on one's toes, one counts all of his toes *twice* and then *three* toes again. In any two-digit number, the left digit indicates the number of times one would count all of his toes, and the right digit indicates the number of toes he would count once more. According to this convention, if one counts *ten* objects on his toes, he counts all toes *once* and *none* again. For this reason, the number *ten* is denoted by 10. Thus we see that the *number* zero and the *numeral* 0 play important roles in the Hindu-Arabic system.

In counting a set of objects on one's toes, one really establishes a one-to-one correspondence between his set of toes and each pile of ten objects. For example, the number thirty-four, symbolized by the numeral 34, tells us how many elements there are in three piles of ten elements each and one pile of four elements. The number ninety tells us how many elements there are in *nine* piles of *ten* elements each. Similarly the numeral 99 tells us how many elements there are in nine piles of ten elements each and one pile of nine elements. To write a numeral which tells us how many elements there are in ten piles of ten elements each, we must use three digits. Since there are ten piles of ten, it seems natural to write the numeral 100. The number symbolized by 100 is called *one hundred*. Thus the ten piles of ten elements each may be combined into a single pile of one hundred elements. The numeral 357 tells us how many elements there are in *three* piles of one hundred elements each, *five* piles of ten elements each, and *seven* piles of one element each (or one pile of *seven* elements). Thus in the Hindu-Arabic numeration system, the number represented by a numeral depends not only on the digits of the numeral but also on the *positions* of these digits in the numeral. For example, the numeral 123 represents *one* hundred, *two* tens, and *three* ones. On the other hand, the numeral 312 represents *three* hundreds, *one* ten, and *two* ones. The idea of *place value* as determined by the *position* of a digit in a numeral is one of the most important concepts in mathematics. The two numeration systems studied previously lacked this outstanding feature.

The following examples illustrate the important concept of *place value* as well as the concept of *face value*.

Example 1.   Each digit of the three-digit numeral 573 has two values —a face value and a place value. The face value of 3 is 3, and the place value of 3 is 1. The face value of 7 is 7, and the place value of 7 is 10. The face value of 5 is 5, and the place value of 5 is 100.

Example 2.   The digits of the numeral 67,275 have the following values:

digit	face value	place value
5	5	1
7	7	10
2	2	100
7	7	1,000
6	6	10,000

The right digit of a numeral is called the *units* digit, the second digit from the right is called the *tens* digit, the third digit from the right is called the *hundreds* digit, the fourth digit from the right is called the *thousands* digit, et cetera. Since the *place value* of any digit (except the units digit) is equal to *ten* times the place value of the digit immediately to the right, one thousand is equal to ten times one hundred, ten thousand is equal to ten times one thousand, one hundred thousand is equal to ten times ten thousand, and one million is equal to ten times one hundred thousand. Thus $100 = (10)(10)$, $1,000 = (10)(10)(10)$, $10,000 = (10)(10)(10)(10)$, $100,000 = (10)(10)(10)(10)(10)$, and $1,000,000 = (10)(10)(10)(10)(10)(10)$. In the next section we shall study a simpler method of writing products such as $(10)(10)(10)(10)$.

Since each digit of a numeral in the Hindu-Arabic system has two values—a *face value* and a *place value*, it is clear that any counting number may be symbolized by a numeral consisting of no more than ten different digits and that no counting number may be symbolized by two different numerals. Thus this numeration system has the following advantages.

(1) The invention of new symbols to represent larger numbers is not required.

(2) Each counting number is symbolized by one and only one numeral.

(3) Each digit has a place value and a face value.

(4) The place value of each digit (except the units digit) is ten times the place value of the digit immediately to the right.

Because the place value of each digit is ten times the place value of the digit immediately to the right, we say that the *base* of the Hindu-Arabic numeration system is *ten*.

Exercise 4.3

I. Express each of the following numerals in terms of units, tens, hundreds, et cetera.

(1) 27   (6) 1,123,567
(2) 305   (7) 1020
(3) 40   (8) 30,765
(4) 401   (9) 11,826,891
(5) 10,103   (10) 10,009,010

II. Name the place value and the face value of each digit in each numeral in Exercise I.

III. Write the Hindu-Arabic numeral for each of the following numbers.

(1) Seven
(2) Twenty-four
(3) Two hundred twenty-seven
(4) One thousand nine hundred sixty-four
(5) One million four hundred seven
(6) One million four hundred seven thousand

IV. Write each of the following as a product of tens.

(1) 10 million
(2) 100 million
(3) one billion (1000 million)
(4) ten
(5) one hundred
(6) ten thousand

V. (1) Write the largest five digit numeral possible.
(2) Write the smallest five digit numeral possible.
(3) Write the largest seven digit numeral possible.
(4) Write the smallest seven digit numeral possible.
(5) Write the largest one digit numeral possible.
(6) Write the smallest one digit numeral possible.

4.4 Exponents

In the preceding section we learned that the place value of any digit is ten times the place value of the digit immediately to the right. For example, the place value of the millions digit (the seventh digit from the right) is $(10)(10)(10)(10)(10)(10)$ times the place value of the units digit. It would be convenient to have a simpler notation for such repeated products. Recalling Theorem 2 of Chapter 3 of the product ab expressed as repeated addition $\underbrace{b + b + \ldots + b}_{a \text{ summands}}$, we make an analogous definition of repeated multiplication.

DEFINITION 1. For any counting number a and any nonzero counting number m, $a^m = \underbrace{a \cdot a \cdot \ldots \cdot a}_{m \text{ factors}}$.

The number a is called the *base*,
the number m is called the *exponent*,
and the number a^m is called an *exponential*.

For example, $10^6 = (10)(10)(10)(10)(10)(10)$, $5^3 = (5)(5)(5)$, and $2^1 = 2$. If it were not for the generalized associative property for multiplication, we could not define the exponential a^m as above. The exponential a^m is read *a to the m-power* or more simply *a to the m*. For example, 5^6 is read *5 to the sixth power* or simply *5 to the 6*. While a^2 may be read *a to the two*, we usually read it *a-squared*. Similarly a^3 is usually read *a-cubed*.

Recalling the original problem, we see that the place value of the tens digit is 10 times the place value of the units digit, the place value of the hundreds digit is 10^2 times the place value of the units digit, the place value of the thousands digit is 10^3 times the place value of the units digit, etc. Thus we see that the place value of the millions digit is 10^6 times the place value of the units digit and 10^4 times the place value of the hundreds digit. Figure 4.4 illustrates the concept of place value in terms of exponential notation.

Exponential	Units
10^{12}	trillions
10^{11}	hundred billions
10^{10}	ten billions
10^9	billions
10^8	hundred millions
10^7	ten millions
10^6	millions
10^5	hundred thousands
10^4	ten thousands
10^3	thousands
10^2	hundreds
10^1	tens

FIGURE 4.4

The exponential notation, which was introduced by the eminent sixteenth-century French mathematician René Descartes, helps us to better understand the Hindu-Arabic numeration system. In particular, the concept of place value becomes clearer, and the rules for addition and multiplication usually given in the elementary schools become meaningful and understandable. To illustrate the former, we analyze the numeral 375. The place value concept allows us to write 375 as 3 hundreds + 7 tens + 5 units. The exponential notation allows us to write $375 = 3(10^2) + 7(10) + 5(1)$. This form better conveys the exact meaning of 375. Similar analysis yields the following results:

$$1{,}253 = 1(10^3) + 2(10^2) + 5(10^1) + 3(1),$$
$$93{,}706 = 9(10^4) + 3(10^3) + 7(10^2) + 0(10^1) + 6(1),$$
$$800{,}380 = 8(10^5) + 0(10^4) + 0(10^3) + 3(10^2) + 8(10^1) + 0(1),$$
$$13 = 1(10^1) + 3(1),$$
$$10{,}700{,}000 = 1(10^7) + 0(10^6) + 7(10^5) + 0(10^4) + 0(10^3) + 0(10^2)$$
$$+ 0(10^1) + 0(1).$$

Since $a^3 = a \cdot a \cdot a$ and $a^5 = a \cdot a \cdot a \cdot a \cdot a$, we see that $a^3 \cdot a^5$
$= \underbrace{(a \cdot a \cdot a)}_{\text{3-factors}} \underbrace{(a \cdot a \cdot a \cdot a \cdot a)}_{\text{5-factors}} = \underbrace{a \cdot a \cdot a \cdot a \cdot a \cdot a \cdot a \cdot a}_{\text{8-factors}} = a^8$. The above
result follows immediately from the relationship between counting and
addition developed in Chapter 3. Similarly $a^2 \cdot a^5 = a^{2+5} = a^7$ and $a^1 \cdot a^4$
$= a^{1+4} = a^5$. The following theorem is a generalization of these results.

THEOREM 1.   If k and m are any nonzero counting numbers and a is
any counting number, then $a^k \cdot a^m = a^{k+m}$.

Proof. $a^k \cdot a^m = \underbrace{(a \cdot a \cdot \ldots \cdot a)}_{k \text{ factors}} \underbrace{(a \cdot a \cdot \ldots \cdot a)}_{m \text{ factors}} = \underbrace{a \cdot a \cdot \ldots \cdot a}_{(k+m) \text{ factors}}$

$= a^{k+m}. /\!/$

For example, $10^4 \cdot 10^7 = 10^{4+7} = 10^{11}$, $5 \cdot 5^6 = 5^{1+6} = 5^7$, $7^3 \cdot 7^2 = 7^{3+2}$
$= 7^5$, and $2^3 \cdot 2^4 \cdot 2^9 = 2^{3+4+9} = 2^{16}$. However, Theorem 1 does *not* say
that $a^k + a^m = a^{k+m}$. In fact, $2^3 + 2^4 \neq 2^{3+4}$. Theorem 1 applies only to the
product of two exponentials, not to their *sum*. However, in certain cases
the sum of two or more exponentials may be computed by the commutative, associative, and distributive properties. The following examples
illustrate the method.

Example 1. $5a + 3a + 4a = (5 + 3 + 4)a = 12a.$

Example 2. $5a^2 + 3a^2 + 4a^2 = (5 + 3 + 4)a^2 = 12a^2.$

Example 3. $4a^5 + 9a^5 = (4 + 9)a^5 = 13a^5.$

Example 4. $3a^2 + 4a^3 + 5a^2 + a^3 = 3a^2 + 5a^2 + 4a^3 + a^3$
$= (3 + 5)a^2 + (4 + 1)a^3 = 8a^2 + 5a^3.$

Example 5. $2a^3 + a^2 + 5a + 4 + a^4 + a^3 + 3a^2 + 5$
$= a^4 + 2a^3 + a^3 + a^2 + 3a^2 + 5a + 4 + 5$
$= a^4 + (2 + 1)a^3 + (1 + 3)a^2 + 5a + (4 + 5)$
$= a^4 + 3a^3 + 4a^2 + 5a + 9.$

Example 6. $3(10^3) + 7(10^2) + 5(10) + 8(1) + 4(10^3) +$
$3(10^2) + 6(10) + 7(1)$
$= 3(10^3) + 4(10^3) + 7(10^2) + 3(10^2) + 5(10) +$
$6(10) + 8(1) + 7(1)$
$= (3 + 4)(10^3) + (7 + 3)(10^2) + (5 + 6)(10) +$
$(8 + 7)(1)$
$= 7(10^3) + 10(10^2) + 11(10) + 15(1).$

Example 7.
$$a(10^4) + b(10^3) + 2(10^2) + 1(10) + c(10^3) +$$
$$3(10^2) + a(10) + b(1)$$
$$= a(10^4) + b(10^3) + c(10^3) + 2(10^2) + 3(10^2) +$$
$$1(10) + a(10) + b(1)$$
$$= a(10^4) + (b + c)(10^3) + (2 + 3)(10^2) +$$
$$(1 + a)(10) + b(1)$$
$$= a(10^4) + (b + c)(10^3) + 5(10^2) +$$
$$(1 + a)(10) + b(1).$$

Exercise 4.4

I. Write each of the following as an exponential whose base is indicated.

(1) 16 (base 2)
(2) 16 (base 4)
(3) 125 (base 5)
(4) 64 (base 2)
(5) 64 (base 8)
(6) 1000 (base 10)
(7) 10,000,000 (base 10)
(8) 10 (base 10)
(9) 343 (base 7)
(10) 243 (base 3)
(11) 64 (base 4)
(12) 5 (base 5)
(13) $a \cdot a$ (base a)
(14) a^2b^2 (base ab)
(15) 36 (base 6)

II. Compute each of the following exponentials.

(1) 3^3
(2) 2^5
(3) 5^2
(4) 1^{15}
(5) 10^2
(6) 10^6
(7) 12^2
(8) 4^4
(9) 7^3
(10) $(2 + 3)^3$
(11) $2^3 + 3^3$
(12) $2^3 \cdot 3^3$
(13) $2^3 \cdot 2^2$
(14) $2^2 \cdot 2^4$
(15) 2^6
(16) $(4 + 5)^3$
(17) $(1 + 2)^2$
(18) $(8 + 2)^6$
(19) $(5 + 5)^5$
(20) $(1 + 1)^3$

III. Express each of the following numerals in powers of ten.
For example, $375 = 3(10^2) + 7(10) + 5(1)$.

(1) 71
(2) 234
(3) 6,105
(4) 823
(5) 10,100
(6) 23,761
(7) 1,120,900
(8) 1,004,689
(9) 200,000,010
(10) 606,006,666

IV. Express each of the following in the form a^k.

(1) $a^3 \cdot a^5$ (6) $2^3 \cdot 2^2 \cdot 2^1 \cdot 2^5 \cdot 2^4$

(2) $2^3 \cdot 2^7$ (7) $10^4 \cdot 10^1 \cdot 10^3$

(3) $10^2 \cdot 10^3$ (8) $(17)^{12} \cdot (17)^5$

(4) $5^2 \cdot 5^3 \cdot 5^4$ (9) $7^b \cdot 7^c \ (b \neq 0, c \neq 0)$

(5) $b^7 \cdot b^3 \cdot b^{10}$ (10) $a^b \cdot a^c \cdot a^d \ (b \neq 0, c \neq 0, d \neq 0)$

V. Compute each of the following sums as in the above examples.

(1) $3b^2 + 4b^2$

(2) $2(10^5) + 3(10^5) + 5(10^5)$

(3) $3c^7 + 6c^7 + c^7$

(4) $3(2^5) + 2(2^5) + 4(2^5) + 2^5$

(5) $3b^2 + 4b + 1 + 2b^2 + b + 3$

(6) $6c^3 + 4c + 2 + c^3 + 2c^2 + c$

(7) $2(10^4) + 3(10^3) + 7(10^2) + 1(10^1) + 7 + 4(10^3) +$
$$2(10^2) + 5$$

(8) $4(10^2) + 5(10^1) + 2(10^2) + 3(10^2) + 5$

(9) $7a^3 + 2a + 5 + a^2 + 3a + 1 + 8a^3 + 4$

(10) $5c^3 + c + 1 + 6c^4 + 2c^2 + 3$

4.5 Addition of Counting Numbers Expressed in the Hindu-Arabic Numeration System

In Section 3.2 we studied the addition of counting numbers and derived the elementary properties for the addition of counting numbers. All counting numbers were represented by numerals in the Hindu-Arabic numeration system. Henceforth in this text, unless otherwise specified, all numbers will be represented by Hindu-Arabic numerals. If there is no danger of confusion, the *numeral* representing a *number* will frequently be referred to as a *number*. For example, the phrase "the number 67" will mean "the number sixty-seven symbolized in the Hindu-Arabic numeration system by the numeral 67." The advantages of the shorter phrase should be apparent.

We are familiar with the well-known computational devices for the addition of counting numbers. In this section we shall justify the procedures employed in these devices. For example, the sum $36 + 42$ is commonly computed as follows:

$$\begin{array}{r} 36 \\ + 42 \\ \hline 78 \end{array}$$

Let us analyze and justify this device. Recall that $36 = 3(10) + 6(1)$ and $42 = 4(10) + 2(1)$.

Thus $36 + 42 = [3(10) + 6(1)] + [4(10) + 2(1)]$ (equivalence relation)

$$= 3(10) + 4(10) + 6(1) + 2(1)$$ (generalized commutative and associative property for addition)

$$= (3 + 4)(10) + (6 + 2)(1)$$ (distributive property)

$$= 7(10) + 8(1)$$ (definition of addition)

$$= 78.$$ (Hindu-Arabic numeration system)

Notice that the above procedure justifies our adding the two units digits (6 and 2) to obtain the units digit (8) of the sum, and adding the two tens digits (3 and 4) to obtain the tens digit (7) of the sum 78. The only addition facts needed are those shown in the addition table of Exercise 3.2–I.

The next example involves a sum in which one must "carry." The sum $207 + 68$ is usually computed in the following manner:

$$\begin{array}{r} 207 \\ + 68 \\ \hline 275 \end{array}$$

Now we analyze and justify this device.

$$207 + 68 = [2(10^2) + 0(10^1) + 7(1)] + [6(10^1) + 8(1)]$$
$$= 2(10^2) + 0(10) + 7(1) + 6(10) + 8(1)$$
$$= 2(10^2) + [0(10) + 6(10)] + [7(1) + 8(1)]$$
$$= 2(10^2) + [0(10) + 6(10)] + 15(1)$$
$$= 2(10^2) + [0(10) + 6(10) + 1(10)] + 5(1)$$
$$= 2(10^2) + (0 + 6 + 1)(10) + 5(1)$$
$$= 2(10^2) + 7(10) + 5(1)$$
$$= 275.$$

Notice that the 15 units are equivalent to 10 units + 5 units (by Exercise 3.2–I) and that the 10 units + 5 units are equivalent to one ten + 5 units. The one *ten* is "carried" and added to the zero tens and six tens. This justifies the "carry" procedure in this example. Moreover, this example illustrates that one adds the two units digits to obtain the units digit of the sum, and similarly for the remaining digits, provided that one "carries" whenever necessary.

The following example involves more than one "carry." One usually computes the sum $795 + 845$ as follows:

$$\begin{array}{r} 795 \\ + 845 \\ \hline 1640 \end{array}$$

The justification of this device is shown below.

$$
\begin{aligned}
795 + 845 &= [7(10^2) + 9(10^1) + 5(1)] + [8(10^2) + 4(10^1) + 5(1)] \\
&= [7(10^2) + 8(10^2)] + [9(10^1) + 4(10^1)] + [5(1) + 5(1)] \\
&= (7 + 8)(10^2) + (9 + 4)(10^1) + (5 + 5)(1) \\
&= (7 + 8)(10^2) + (9 + 4)(10^1) + 10(1) \\
&= (7 + 8)(10^2) + (9 + 4)(10^1) + 1(10) + 0(1) \\
&= (7 + 8)(10^2) + (9 + 4 + 1)(10^1) + 0(1) \\
&= (7 + 8)(10^2) + 14(10^1) + 0(1) \\
&= (7 + 8)(10^2) + (10 + 4)(10^1) + 0(1) \\
&= (7 + 8)(10^2) + 1(10^2) + 4(10^1) + 0(1) \\
&= (7 + 8 + 1)(10^2) + 4(10^1) + 0(1) \\
&= (10 + 6)(10^2) + 4(10^1) + 0(1) \\
&= 1(10^3) + 6(10^2) + 4(10^1) + 0(1) \\
&= 1640.
\end{aligned}
$$

While the above examples do not prove the validity of the usual devices for adding counting numbers, they do justify the validity of these devices and also suggest the general method of proof. Because the notation is tedious and little is to be gained from its inclusion, we do not include the general proof. We wish to emphasize that one can compute the sum of any two counting numbers by the use of the addition table in Exercise 3.2–I and the computational devices studied here. Hereafter, the usual term *algorithm* will be used to refer to any computational device. This method is easily generalized to the computation of the sum of more than two counting numbers.

Exercise 4.5

I. Justify each of the following additions.

	(1)	(2)	(3)	(4)	(5)
	23	23	56	243	89
	74	77	75	665	97
	97	100	131	908	76
					262

	(6)	(7)	(8)	(9)	(10)
	73	731	999	778	9879
	85	28	875	876	268
	68	95	287	583	389
	226	854	2161	2237	10,536

4.6 Multiplication of Counting Numbers Expressed in the Hindu-Arabic Numeration System

In the preceding section we justified the algorithm concerning the addition of two counting numbers. In this section we justify the algorithm for the multiplication of two counting numbers. The principal property of the counting numbers which we shall employ is the distributive property. Since it may not be immediately apparent to you how the distributive property is to be employed in a particular problem, we first consider the following examples.

Example 1. $(a + b)k = ak + bk.$

Example 2. $(a + b)(c + d) = [a + b](c + d) = [a + b](c)$
$$+ [a + b](d)$$
$$= ac + bc + ad + bd.$$

(*Note.* There are two applications of the distributive property. We wrote $(a + b)$ as $[a + b]$ to emphasize that we wished to consider $a + b$ as a single counting number in the first application of the distributive property.)

Example 3. $(a + b + c)(d + e) = (a + b + c)d + (a + b + c)e$
$$= ad + bd + cd + ae + be + ce.$$

Example 4. $(a + b + c)(a + c + f) = (a + b + c)a + (a + b + c)c$
$$+ (a + b + c)f$$
$$= a^2 + ab + ac + ac + bc + c^2$$
$$+ af + bf + cf$$
$$= a^2 + ab + 2ac + bc + c^2 + af$$
$$+ bf + cf.$$

·Now we are ready to justify the multiplication algorithm. The product of 32 and 4 is usually computed by the algorithm as follows:

$$
\begin{array}{r}
32 \\
\times \quad 4 \\
\hline
128
\end{array}
$$

According to the algorithm, we say "$4 \cdot 2 = 8$, write 8 in the units position; $4 \cdot 3 = 12$, write 2 in the tens position, carry 1 to the hundreds position." Let us analyze and justify this algorithm. Recalling that $32 = 3(10) + 2(1)$, we see that

$4 \cdot 32 = 4[3(10) + 2(1)] = 4[3(10)] + 4[2(1)] = 12(10) + 8(1)$
$\quad = (10 + 2)(10) + 8(1) = (10)(10) + 2(10) + 8(1)$
$\quad = 1(10^2) + 2(10) + 8(1)$
$\quad = 128.$

The product of 57 and 62 is usually computed as follows:

$$
\begin{array}{r}
57 \\
\times\ 62 \\
\hline
114 \\
3420 \\
\hline
3534
\end{array}
$$

The following sequence of steps is a justification of the algorithm. Since $57 = 5(10) + 7(1)$ and $62 = 6(10) + 2(1)$, we see that

$$
\begin{aligned}
(57)(62) &= [5(10) + 7][6(10) + 2] \\
&= \{[5(10) + 7][6(10)]\} + \{[5(10) + 7][2]\} \\
&= \{5(10) \cdot 6(10) + 7 \cdot 6(10)\} + \{5(10) \cdot 2 + 7 \cdot 2\} \\
&= \{30(10^2) + 42(10)\} + \{10(10) + 14\} \\
&= \{3(10)(10^2) + [4(10) + 2](10)\} + \{10(10) + 10 + 4\} \\
&= \{3(10^3) + 4(10^2) + 2(10) + 0(1)\} + \{1(10^2) + 1(10) \\
&\qquad + 4(1)\} \\
&= 3420 + 114 \\
&= 3534.
\end{aligned}
$$

When we employ the algorithm to multiply 57 by 62, we are really performing the above computation in contracted form. However, you should realize the important role of the generalized commutative and associative, and the generalized distributive properties in the algorithm. Also, you will notice that the only addition and multiplication facts needed are those in the tables of Exercise 3.2–I and 3.3–X.

Another method for justifying the algorithm for multiplying any two counting numbers involves the use of the algorithm for multiplying any counting number by a one-digit counting number. Before we analyze this general procedure, let us give a closer analysis of the latter algorithm. The product $9{,}685 \cdot 8$ is usually computed as follows:

$$
\begin{array}{r}
9,685 \\
\times\qquad 8 \\
\hline
77,480
\end{array}
$$

Now

$$
\begin{aligned}
8(9685) &= 8[9(10^3) + 6(10^2) + 8(10) + 5(1)] \\
&= 8(9)(10^3) + 8(6)(10^2) + 8(8)(10) + 8(5)(1) \\
&= 8(9)(10^3) + 8(6)(10^2) + 8(8)(10) + 40 \\
&= 8(9)(10^3) + 8(6)(10^2) + 64(10) + 4(10) \\
&= 8(9)(10^3) + 8(6)(10^2) + 68(10) \\
&= 8(9)(10^3) + 8(6)(10^2) + [6(10) + 8](10) \\
&= 8(9)(10^3) + 48(10^2) + 6(10^2) + 8(10) \\
&= 8(9)(10^3) + 54(10^2) + 8(10)
\end{aligned}
$$

$$= 8(9)(10^3) + [5(10) + 4](10^2) + 8(10)$$
$$= 72(10^3) + 5(10^3) + 4(10^2) + 8(10)$$
$$= 77(10^3) + 4(10^2) + 8(10)$$
$$= [7(10) + 7](10^3) + 4(10^2) + 8(10)$$
$$= 7(10^4) + 7(10^3) + 4(10^2) + 8(10)$$
$$= 7(10^4) + 7(10^3) + 4(10^2) + 8(10) + 0(1)$$
$$= 77,480.$$

The above detailed justification of the algorithm for multiplying any counting number by a one-digit counting number illustrates clearly the "carry" procedure as well as the abbreviated rule for multiplying digit-by-digit.

We now give the alternate justification of the algorithm for multiplying any two counting numbers. The product $(943)(678)$, computed by the algorithm, is 639,354. The work is shown below.

$$
\begin{array}{r}
943 \\
\times\ 678 \\
\hline
7544 \\
6601 \\
5658 \\
\hline
639,354
\end{array}
$$

Since $678 = 6(10^2) + 7(10) + 8(1)$, we may write:

$$
\begin{aligned}
(943)(678) &= 943[6(10^2) + 7(10) + 8] \\
&= 943[6(10^2)] + 943[7(10)] + 943[8] \\
&= [943(6)](10^2) + [943(7)](10) + [943(8)] \\
&= 5658(10^2) + 6601(10) + 7544(1) \\
&= 565,800 + 66,010 + 7544 \\
&= 639,354.
\end{aligned}
$$

Notice the reason for "shifting" the second partial product one place to the left and the third partial product two places to the left in the algorithm. The second partial product is really not 6601, but 66,010, and the third partial product is really not 5658 but 565,800.

Exercise 4.6

I. As in the examples of this section, apply the distributive property to each of the following.

(1) $2(a + b)$
(2) $2(3a + 5)$
(3) $7(1 + 7a + 2b)$
(4) $10[3(10^2) + 4(10) + 7]$

(5) $(a + 2b)(c + 2)$
(6) $(2 + t)(a + u + 1)$
(7) $(a + b)(a + b)$
(8) $(a + b + c)^2$
(9) $(7 + a)[a(10^2) + b(10) + 4(1)]$
(10) $[a(10^4) + b(10^3) + c(10^2) + t][x(10^2) + y(10)]$

II. Compute each of the following products by first expressing the numerals in powers of 10 [for example, $276 = 2(10^2) + 7(10) + 6(1)$].

(1) $(26)(10)$
(2) $(26)(10^3)$
(3) $(276)(10^2)$
(4) $(5)(10^6)$
(5) $(1)(10^9)$
(6) $(13)(10^4)$
(7) $(139)(10^4)$
(8) $(15)(10^5)$
(9) $(150)(10^4)$
(10) $(1500)(10^3)$

III. Justify the algorithm for multiplying each of the following pairs of counting numbers. Do not use the alternate method of the text.

(1) 24 and 63
(2) 85 and 17
(3) 873 and 58
(4) 589 and 83
(5) 405 and 560
(6) 5063 and 67

IV. Justify the algorithm for multiplying each of the following pairs of counting numbers. Use the alternate method of the text.

(1) 64 and 23
(2) 87 and 15
(3) 583 and 65
(4) 784 and 29
(5) 917 and 276
(6) 419 and 783
(7) 7653 and 427
(8) 4356 and 783
(9) 5397 and 6802
(10) 3769 and 8083

V. (1) Why are partial products added in a multiplication problem?
(2) Why are successive partial products shifted to the left?

4.7 Base Five Numeration System

In preceding sections we studied the Hindu-Arabic numeration system, which contains the ten distinct symbols 0, 1, ..., 9. Any number may be symbolized in this system by means of these ten symbols in such a manner that the place value of any digit (except the units digit) is ten times the place value of the digit immediately to the right. For these reasons we say that the Hindu-Arabic numeration system is of *base ten*. The choice of ten as the base was probably more accidental than deliberate and probably was based on the fact that man was born with *ten* toes and *ten* fingers. Actually, by counting on fingers *and* toes, he could have developed a system of base *twenty*. Moreover, if he had counted on one hand only, he could have developed a system of base *five*.

Before we investigate other numeration systems, we shall give some of the reasons for such an investigation. First, when we study other numeration systems, we gain a new insight to and better understanding of our present numeration system. Second, the problems encountered by the teacher or the parent when he studies a numeration system of base other than ten are similar to the problems encountered by the child when he studies the Hindu-Arabic numeration system in arithmetic (which is as strange to him as these other systems may be to you). Third, the computations of many electronic digital computers are performed in base *two*. Fourth, such a study for its own sake is both interesting and beautiful.

Let us consider the number five. The Egyptian numeral ∣∣∣∣∣, the Roman numeral V, and the Hindu-Arabic numeral 5 are different *symbols* representing the single number *five*. Other numeration systems use different numerals to represent the number *five*. Now we shall make a systematic study of a numeration system similar to the Hindu-Arabic numeration system but with base *five* rather than base *ten*. We may employ the five fingers of one hand as a physical model for a base five numeration system. Thus we may count on our fingers one, two, three, four, five, six (all the fingers on the hand, and one again), seven (all the fingers on the hand, and two again), etc. As in the Hindu-Arabic numeration system we would like to have a numeral for the number *six* which indicates that we have counted all the fingers of the hand and then counted one finger again. If we use the numeral ⊡ to represent the number *one*, then we would represent the number *six* by the numeral ⊡ ⊡. In the numeral ⊡ ⊡ the left ⊡ indicates that all the fingers of the one hand have been counted once and the right ⊡ indicates that one finger has been counted again. As in the Hindu-Arabic numeration system, we shall call the individual symbols in a numeral the *digits* of the numeral. Thus the right digit of ⊡⊡ is ⊡, and the left digit is ⊡. Also, we would like to have a numeral for the number *five* which indicates that we have counted all the fingers of the one hand and none again. Since the left symbol ⊡ in the numeral ⊡⊡ for the number *six* indicates that we have counted all the fingers on one hand once and the right symbol ⊡ indicates that we have counted one finger again, the numeral for the number *five* should consist of the left symbol ⊡ and a right symbol to indicate no fingers again. Consequently we see the need for a symbol to represent the number of elements in the empty set. If we choose the symbol □ to indicate $n(\phi)$, we see that the numeral ⊡□ represents the number *five*. Although we have symbols to represent the numbers zero, one, five, and six, we still need symbols for the numbers two, three, and four. If we choose the symbols ⊡, ⊡, and ⊞ to represent the numbers two, three, and four, respectively, and if we retain the concept of place value in the Hindu-Arabic numeration system, we may represent any counting number by means of these five symbols. For example, to count thirteen objects on the fingers of one hand, one may divide the thirteen objects into two piles of five objects each and a third pile of three objects. In the process he counts all the fingers of the one hand *twice* and then *three* fingers again. Thus he would represent the number *thirteen* by the symbol ⊡⊡. Notice that the digit ⊡ has two values—a face value *two* and a place value *five*— and that the digit ⊡ has two values—a face value *three* and a place value *one*. For this reason ⊡ is called the *units* digit and ⊡ is called the *fives* digit. In general, the right digit is called the *units* digit, the second digit from the right is called the *fives* digit, the third digit from the right is called the *twenty-fives* digit, the fourth digit from the right is called the *one hundred twenty-fives* digit, et cetera. The place value of any digit (except the units digit) is *five* times the place value of the digit immediately to the right.

The first twenty-seven counting numbers may be symbolized as follows:

□, ⊡, ⊡, ⊡, ⊞, ⊡□, ⊡⊡, ⊡⊡, ⊡⊞, ⊡⊡, ⊡⊞, ⊡□, ⊡⊡, ⊡⊡, ⊡⊞, ⊞⊞, ⊞□, ⊞⊡, ⊞⊡, ⊞⊡, ⊞⊞, ⊞□, ⊞⊡, ⊞⊡, ⊞⊡, ⊞⊞, ⊡□□, ⊡□⊡

Since the symbol ⊡□⊡ informs us that there are *one twenty-five*, *zero fives*, and *one unit*, we see that □□⊡ is actually the numeral for the number twenty-six.

Notice the importance of the symbol □ . If we did not have a symbol for zero, we could not symbolize the number five without inventing a new symbol. This, in turn, would make it difficult to represent the numbers ten, fifteen, twenty, et cetera. Moreover, the symbol □ is required to symbolize numbers like twenty-six.

Now that we have learned to count in base five, we would like to learn to add. Thus we shall develop an addition table similar to that in Exercise 3.2–I. Since the present system contains five symbols, the entries in the table will consist of the five numerals representing the numbers zero, one, two, three, and four. The addition table is shown in Figure 4.5.

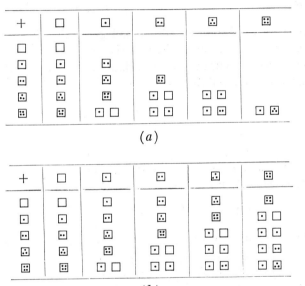

FIGURE 4.5

Figure 4.5(b) is obtained from Figure 4.5(a) by application of the commutative property for addition of counting numbers.

The exponential notation and the place value concept allow us to write ⊡⊡ = ⊡(⊡□) + ⊡(⊡). Similarly we may write ⊞⊡□⊞ = four (*one hundred twenty-fives*) + two (*twenty-fives*) + zero (*fives*) + three (*units*) = ⊞(⊡□)⁺ + ⊡(⊡□)⁺ + □(⊡□)⁺ + ⊞(⊡), and ⊡⊞⊡□□ = ⊡(⊡□)⁺ + ⊞(⊡□)⁺ + ⊡(⊡□)⁺ + □(⊡□)⁺ + □(⊡). Notice that the symbol ⊞(⊡) represents the number three, whereas the symbol ⊡⊡ represents the number sixteen; i.e., the parentheses here indicate multiplication.

Now let us compute the sum ⊡ ⊡ + ⊡ ⊡. Since ⊡ ⊡ = ⊡(⊡ □) + ⊡(⊡) and ⊡ ⊡ = ⊡(⊡ □) + ⊡(⊡) we see that

⊡ ⊡ + ⊡ ⊡ = [⊡(⊡ □) + ⊡(⊡)] + [⊡(⊡ □) + ⊡(⊡)]   (equivalence relation)

= [⊡(⊡ □) + ⊡(⊡ □)] + [⊡(⊡) + ⊡(⊡)]   (generalized commutative and associative property for addition)

= (⊡ + ⊡)(⊡ □) + (⊡ + ⊡)(⊡)   (distributive property)

= ⊡(⊡ □) + ⊡(⊡)   (definition of addition)

= ⊡ ⊡.   (base five numeration system)

Notice that we have actually added the units digits of the two numerals to compute the units digit of the sum, and the fives digits of the two numerals to compute the fives digit of the sum. Hence we could have arranged the computation as follows:

$$
\begin{array}{r}
⊡\ ⊡ \\
+\ ⊡\ ⊡ \\
\hline
⊡\ ⊡
\end{array}
$$

The next example involves a sum in which one must "carry." The sum ⊡ ⊡ ⊡ + ⊡ ⊡ ⊡ may be computed as follows:

⊡ ⊡ ⊡ + ⊡ ⊡ ⊡ = [⊡(⊡ □)^⊡ + ⊡(⊡ □) + ⊡] +
                                        [⊡(⊡ □)^⊡ + ⊡(⊡ □) + ⊡]

= [⊡(⊡ □)^⊡ + ⊡(⊡ □)^⊡] + [⊡(⊡ □) + ⊡(⊡ □)] + [⊡ + ⊡]

= (⊡ + ⊡)(⊡ □)^⊡ + (⊡ + ⊡)(⊡ □) + (⊡ + ⊡)

= ⊡(⊡ □)^⊡ + (⊡ □ + ⊡)(⊡ □) + ⊡

= ⊡(⊡ □)^⊡ + (⊡ □)(⊡ □) + ⊡(⊡ □) + ⊡

= [⊡(⊡ □)^⊡ + ⊡(⊡ □)^⊡] + ⊡(⊡ □) + ⊡

= (⊡ + ⊡)(⊡ □)^⊡ + ⊡(⊡ □) + ⊡

= ⊡(⊡ □)^⊡ + ⊡(⊡ □) + ⊡

= ⊡ ⊡ ⊡.

Notice that the seven fives are equivalent to five *fives* + two *fives* (that is, to one *twenty-five* + two *fives*). The □ (representing one *twenty-five*) is carried and added to the sum of the one *twenty-five* and the two *twenty-fives*. Hence we could have arranged the computation as follows.

$$
\begin{array}{r}
⊡\ \ \ \ \\
⊡\ ⊡\ ⊡ \\
+\ ⊡\ ⊡\ ⊡ \\
\hline
⊡\ ⊡\ ⊡
\end{array}
$$

This example illustrates that one adds the two units digits to obtain the units digit of the sum, and similarly for the remaining digits, provided that one "carries" whenever necessary. In addition to this algorithm, one needs only the addition facts from Figure 4.5 to add any two counting numbers in base five.

Exercise 4.7

I. Write each of the following sets of counting numbers as sets of numerals in base five.

(1) {twenty-seven, twenty-eight, . . . , thirty-five}
(2) {one hundred nineteen, one hundred twenty, . . . , one hundred thirty-one}
(3) {six hundred twenty-three, six hundred twenty-four, . . . , six hundred thirty-seven}

II. Write each of the following numerals in terms of units, fives, twenty-fives, et cetera.

(1) ⚀ ⚀ □   (6) ⚁ □ □ ⚀
(2) ⚁ □ ⚀   (7) ⚀ ⚁ □ ⚀
(3) ⚀ ⚀ ⚁   (8) ⚁ ⚀ □ ⚁
(4) ⚁ ⚁ □   (9) ⚂ □ ⚁ □ ⚀ □
(5) ⚂ □ □ □   (10) ⚀ □ ⚁ □ ⚂ □

III. Express in the Hindu-Arabic numeration system each of the base five numerals in Exercise II.

IV. Using the base five numeration system, express in powers of five each of the numerals in Exercise II [for example, ⚂ □ ⚀ = ⚂(⚀ □)⬚ + □(⚀ □)⬚ + ⚀].

V. Using the Hindu-Arabic numeration system, express in powers of five each of the numerals in Exercise II [for example, ⚂ □ ⚀ = $3(5^2) + 0(5^1) + 1$].

VI. Using the Hindu-Arabic numeration system, express in powers of five each of the following Hindu-Arabic numerals [for example, $131 = 1(5^3) + 0(5^2) + 1(5^1) + 1$].

(1) 11   (6) 632
(2) 22   (7) 138
(3) 27   (8) 200
(4) 29   (9) 627
(5) 122   (10) 629

VII. Using the base five numeration system, express in powers of five each of the Hindu-Arabic numerals in Exercise VI (see Exercise IV).

VIII. Write in base five each of the Hindu-Arabic numerals in Exercise VI.

IX. Compute each of the following sums (in base five).

(1) ⊡ ⊡ + ⊞ ⊡
(2) ⊡ ⊡ + ⊡ ⊞
(3) ⊡ ⊡ + ⊡ ⊡
(4) ⊡ ⊡ + ⊡ ⊞
(5) ⊡ ⊡ ⊞ + ⊡ ⊞ ⊡
(6) ⊡ ⊡ ⊡ + ⊡ ⊞ ⊞
(7) ⊡ ⊡ ⊡ ⊡ + ⊞ ⊞ □
(8) ⊡ ⊞ □ + ⊞ ⊞ ⊡ □
(9) ⊞ ⊡ □ ⊞ + ⊡ ⊡ ⊞ □
(10) ⊡ ⊡ ⊞ ⊡ □ ⊡ + ⊞ ⊡ ⊞

X. Justify the algorithm for addition of the following.

(1) □ ⊞ + ⊞ ⊡ □
(2) ⊞ ⊡ + ⊡ ⊡ ⊞
(3) ⊡ ⊞ + ⊞ ⊡
(4) ⊞ ⊡ + ⊡ ⊞

4.8   Base Five Numeration System (Continued)

In this section we shall continue the study of the base five numeration system, including the multiplication of counting numbers. Although the symbols □, ⊡, ⊡, ⊞, ⊞ are quite satisfactory for our purposes, they are not as easy to write as the symbols in the Hindu-Arabic system. For this reason we shall replace the symbols □, ⊡, ⊡, ⊞, ⊞ of the base five numeration system by the symbols 0, 1, 2, 3, 4, respectively, and shall write all numerals of the base five numeration system in terms of these symbols. For example, the numeral ⊡ □ ⊞ ⊡ will now be written 2031, and the numeral ⊡ ⊡ will be written 11. Although the use of the Hindu-Arabic symbols simplifies the writing, it creates a new problem; namely, any base five numeral of two or more digits represents a counting number which is different from the counting number represented by a base ten numeral of the same digits. For example, the numeral 11 in the base five numeration system represents the number *six*, whereas the numeral 11 in the Hindu-Arabic numeration system represents the number *eleven*. Thus if the base is not ten, we must be careful to specify the base. The numeral 11 in the base five numeration system should not be read *eleven* but should be read *one-one* (base five). Similarly the base five numeral 2031 should be read *two-zero-three-one* (base five). Obviously, the symbols of the preceding section did not present this problem. To indicate that the numeral 1004 is written in base five, we may write 1004_5. Notice that the subscript 5 is written in the Hindu-Arabic numeration system (base ten). Whenever the context makes it clear that the base is five, we may omit the subscript 5 from the numeral.

With this change in symbols the addition table of Figure 4.5 is as shown in Figure 4.6.

+	0	1	2	3	4
0	0	1	2	3	4
1	1	2	3	4	10
2	2	3	4	10	11
3	3	4	10	11	12
4	4	10	11	12	13

FIGURE 4.6

Consequently we may compute the sum $4432_5 + 1213_5$ as follows:

$$\begin{array}{r} 4432_5 \\ + \ \ 1213_5 \\ \hline 11200_5 \end{array}$$

Now let us represent in powers of five in base *five* the numerals 4432_5, 1213_5, and 11200_5.

$4432_5 = 4(\text{five}^3) + 4(\text{five}^2) + 3(\text{five}) + 2$
$$= 4(10^3) + 4(10^2) + 3(10) + 2,$$
$1213_5 = 1(\text{five}^3) + 2(\text{five}^2) + 1(\text{five}) + 3$
$$= 1(10^3) + 2(10^2) + 1(10) + 3,$$
$11200_5 = 1(\text{five}^4) + 1(\text{five}^3) + 2(\text{five}^2) + 0(\text{five}) + 0$
$$= 1(10^4) + 1(10^3) + 2(10^2) + 0(10) + 0.$$

Next we represent the numerals 4432_5, 1213_5, and 11200_5 in base *ten*:

$4432_5 = 4(5^3) + 4(5^2) + 3(5) + 2 = 500 + 100 + 15 + 2 = 617$
$1213_5 = 1(5^3) + 2(5^2) + 1(5) + 3 = 125 + 50 + 5 + 3 = 183$
$11200_5 = 1(5^4) + 1(5^3) + 2(5^2) + 0(5) + 0$
$$= 625 + 125 + 50 + 0 + 0 = 800$$

Notice that the 10^4, 10^3, 10^2, and 10^1 are powers of five written in base *five*, whereas the 5^4, 5^3, 5^2, and 5^1 are powers of five written in base *ten.* Thus $4432_5 = 617$, $1213_5 = 183$, and $11200_5 = 800$. Since $617 + 183 = 800$, we have a base ten check for the base five addition.

Now that we have developed a method for converting the base five numeral for a counting number into the corresponding base ten numeral for the same counting number, we may wonder if there is a general method for converting the base ten numeral for a counting number into the base five numeral for the same counting number. In Exercise 4.7–VIII, you were asked to convert base ten numerals to base five numerals. Although it was possible for you to do the conversions by inspection, the inspection method is unsuitable when the numbers are large. We shall postpone the development of a general method until subtraction and division have been studied. By inspection, we note that $56 = 50 + 5 + 1 = 2(5^2) + 1(5) + 1 = [2(10^2) + 1(10) + 1]$ (base five). Thus $56 = 211_5$. Similarly $142 = 125 + 15 + 2 = 1(5^3) + 0(5^2) + 3(5) + 2 = [1(10^3) + 0(10^2) + 3(10) + 2]$(base five). Thus $142 = 1032_5$.

The base five multiplication table is shown in Figure 4.7.

·	0	1	2	3	4		·	0	1	2	3	4
0	0						0	0	0	0	0	0
1	0	1					1	0	1	2	3	4
2	0	2	4				2	0	2	4	11	13
3	0	3	11	14			3	0	3	11	14	22
4	0	4	13	22	31		4	0	4	13	22	31
	(a)							(b)				

FIGURE 4.7

As in the Hindu-Arabic numeration system, we may multiply any two counting numbers by use of the multiplication facts in Figure 4.7 and the place value concept. For example $2_5 \cdot 123_5$ may be computed in base five as follows:

$$
\begin{aligned}
2 \cdot 123 &= 2[1(10^2) + 2(10) + 3] \\
&= 2(10^2) + 4(10) + 11 \\
&= 2(10^2) + 4(10) + 10 + 1 \\
&= 2(10^2) + (4+1)(10) + 1 \\
&= 2(10^2) + (10)(10) + 1 \\
&= 2(10^2) + 1(10^2) + 1 \\
&= (2+1)(10^2) + 1 \\
&= 3(10^2) + 0(10) + 1 \\
&= 301.
\end{aligned}
$$

It should be emphasized that all numerals in the above computation are written in base five. The computation may be arranged in compact form as follows:

$$
\begin{array}{r}
123 \\
\times \quad 2 \\
\hline
301
\end{array}
$$

Thus we have justified the base five algorithm for multiplying a counting number by a one-digit counting number: *multiply digit-by-digit and "carry" whenever necessary*. The base five algorithm for multiplying any two counting numbers may be justified by means of the above algorithm. The procedure, which is analogous to that in the Hindu-Arabic numeration system, is given below.

$$
\begin{aligned}
(4032)(413) &= (4032)[4(10^2) + 1(10) + 3] \\
&= (4032)[4(10^2)] + (4032)[10] + (4032)[3] \\
&= [(4032)(4)](10^2) + 4032(10) + (4032)(3) \\
&= 31233(10^2) + (4032)(10) + 22201 \\
&= 3123300 + 40320 + 22201 \\
&= 3241321.
\end{aligned}
$$

The following computation illustrates the algorithm:

$$
\begin{array}{r}
4032 \\
\times \quad 413 \\
\hline
22201 \\
4032 \\
31233 \\
\hline
3241321
\end{array}
$$

Notice the reason for "shifting" the second partial product one place to the left and the third partial product two places to the left. The second partial product is really not 4032 but 40320 [that is, 4032(10)] and the third partial product is really not 31233 but 312300 [that is, 4032(400)]. The algorithm is really a contracted form of the actual computation. However, when we use the algorithm we should realize the important role of the generalized commutative and associative, and the generalized distributive properties. Also, you will notice that the only addition and multiplication facts needed are those in the tables of Figures 4.6 and 4.7. However, if the only addition facts to be used are those in Figure 4.6, it may sometimes be necessary to add the partial products two at a time (by the associative property) as in the following example:

```
      4344
 ×    423
    24142 ─────────────────────────→  24142
    14243 ─────────────────────────→ + 142430
                                        222122
    34041 ─────────────────────────→ + 3404100
  4131222 ←─────────────────────────  4131222
```

Notice that all additions and multiplications were performed in base *five*. You should perform all operations in base five rather than convert the base five numerals to the corresponding base ten numerals. In this way you will have a better understanding of the base five numeration system.

Exercise 4.8

I. Write each of the following sets of base ten numerals as a set of numerals in base five.

(1) {23, 24, 25, 26, 27}
(2) {123, 124, 125, 126, 127}
(3) {624, 625, 626}
(4) {98, 99, 100, 101}

II. Write each of the following numerals in terms of units, fives, twenty-fives, etc.

(1) 201_5 (6) 2014_5'
(2) 402_5 (7) 230340_5
(3) 324_5 (8) 423010_5
(4) 432_5 (9) 340200_5
(5) 1043_5 (10) 423000_5

III. Express in the Hindu-Arabic numeration system each of the base five numerals in Exercise II.

IV. Using the base five numeration system, express in powers of five each of the numerals in Exercise II [for example, $2301 = 2(10^3) + 3(10^2) + 0(10) + 1$].

V. Using the Hindu-Arabic numeration system, express in powers of five each of the numerals in Exercise II [for example, $2301 = 2(5^3) + 3(5^2) + 0(5^1) + 1$].

VI. Using the Hindu-Arabic numeration system, express in powers of five each of the following Hindu-Arabic numerals [for example, $131 = 1(5^3) + 0(5^2) + 1(5^1) + 1$].

(1) 10
(2) 15
(3) 27
(4) 29
(5) 135

(6) 140
(7) 126
(8) 124
(9) 624
(10) 3124

VII. Write in base five each of the Hindu-Arabic numerals in Exercise VI.

VIII. Compute each of the following sums in base five. (All numerals are written in base five.)

(1) 301 + 112
(2) 123 + 301
(3) 3 + 13
(4) 24 + 3
(5) 34 + 14

(6) 23 + 32
(7) 333 + 222
(8) 312 + 243
(9) 4301 + 1034
(10) 1004 + 4002

IX. Compute each of the following products by first expressing the base five numerals in powers of five (as in Exercise IV).

(1) 23(10)
(2) 43(10)
(3) 14(10^2)
(4) 41(10^2)

(5) 110(10^3)
(6) 310(10^3)
(7) 11(10^4)
(8) 31(10^4)

X. Justify the base five algorithm for multiplication of two counting numbers in each of the following.

(1) $(234_5)(2_5)$
(2) $(421_5)(3_5)$
(3) $(123_5)(42_5)$
(4) $(231_5)(32_5)$

XI. Compute each of the following products in base five. (All numerals are written in base five.)

(1) 221(2)
(2) 122(2)
(3) 123(3)
(4) 212(4)
(5) 3214(23)

(6) 2341(32)
(7) 2113(123)
(8) 3211(213)
(9) 3412(304)
(10) 4023(403)

XII. (1) Write the largest five-digit numeral possible in base five.
(2) Write the smallest six-digit numeral possible in base five.
(3) Write the smallest two-digit numeral possible in base five.
(4) Write the largest one-digit numeral possible in base five.
(5) Write the largest three-digit numeral possible in base eight.
(6) Write the smallest four-digit numeral possible in base eight.

4.9   Other Numeration Systems

In the preceding sections we learned that the basic principles of the base ten numeration system are ten distinct *symbols* (for face value) and *position* of each symbol (for place value). Similarly the basic principles of the base five numeration system are five distinct symbols (for face value) and position of each symbol (for place value). We learned that the place value of the digit 4 in the numeral 2403_5 is twenty-five, whereas the place value of the digit 4 in the numeral 2403_{10} is one hundred, and similarly for the digits of any numeral. Any numeration system of base b similar to the Hindu-Arabic numeration system should consist of b distinct symbols and a corresponding concept of place value. The place value of any digit should be b times the place value of the digit immediately to the right. In this section we study the binary numeration system (base two) and the duodecimal numeration system (base twelve). In the exercises we shall investigate some numeration systems with other bases.

In the binary numeration system we need two distinct symbols to indicate face value. As the choice of the symbols is arbitrary, we could choose the symbols $\bigcirc$ and $\odot$ to represent the number zero and the number one, respectively. However, as 0 and 1 are easier to write, we shall choose the symbol 0 to represent the number *zero* and the symbol 1 to represent the number *one*. Thus, as in base five, any numeral of two or more digits represents a counting number different from the counting number represented by a base ten numeral of the same digits. For example, the numeral 11 in the binary system represents the number *three*. We have already seen that the numeral 11 in the base five system represents the number *six* and that the numeral 11 in the Hindu-Arabic numeration system represents the number *eleven*. For this reason we should not read 11 (base two) as *eleven* but as *one-one* (*base two*). As in base five, we may indicate that the base is *two* by writing the subscript 2 (in Hindu-Arabic notation). For example, we may write 101_2 and read *one-zero-one* (*base two*). Whenever the context makes it clear that the base is two, we may omit the subscript 2.

The base two numerals for the first twenty counting numbers are written as follows: 0, 1, 10, 11, 100, 101, 110, 111, 1000, 1001, 1010,

+	0	1
0	0	1
1	1	10

(*a*)

·	0	1
0	0	0
1	0	1

(*b*)

FIGURE 4.8

1011, 1100, 1101, 1110, 1111, 10000, 10001, 10010, and 10011. The addition and multiplication tables are shown in Figure 4.8.

As in the Hindu-Arabic numeration system, we may add or multiply any two counting numbers written in base two by use of the addition and multiplication facts from Figure 4.8, the place value concept, and the appropriate algorithm. The following examples illustrate the algorithm for computing the sum of two counting numbers expressed in base two.

Example 1.
```
    1001
+    110
    1111
```

Example 2.
```
   101001
+   10110
   111111
```

Example 3.
```
    10110
+    1101
   100011
```

Example 4.
```
    11001
+    1101
   100110
```

Example 5.
```
   10011111
+  11111001
  110011000
```

The following examples illustrate the algorithm for computing the product of any two counting numbers expressed in base two.

Example 6.
```
      1010
×       11
      1010
     1010
     11110
```

Example 7.
```
      11001
×      1011
      11001
     11001
    00000
   11001
  100010011
```

Example 8.
```
      11111
×       111
      11111 ──────────────────→   11111
      11111 ──────────────────→ +  111110
                                  1011101
     11111 ───────────────────→ + 1111100
   11011001 ←───────────────────  11011001
```

The following examples illustrate a method of converting a base two numeral to a base ten numeral.

Example 9. $101_2 = [1(10^{10}) + 0(10^1) + 1](\text{base two}) = [1(2^2) + 0(2^1) + 1](\text{base ten}) = [4 + 1](\text{base ten}) = 5.$

Example 10. $110110_2 = [1(2^5) + 1(2^4) + 0(2^3) + 1(2^2) + 1(2^1) + 0(1)](\text{base ten}) = [32 + 16 + 0 + 4 + 2 + 0](\text{base ten}) = 54.$

The following examples illustrate a method of converting a base ten numeral to a base two numeral.

Example 11. $7 = [4 + 2 + 1](\text{base ten}) = [1(2^2) + 1(2^1) + 1](\text{base ten}) = [1(10^{10}) + 1(10^1) + 1](\text{base two}) = 111_2.$

Example 12. $18 = [16 + 2](\text{base ten}) = [1(2^4) + 0(2^3) + 0(2^2) + 1(2) + 0(1)](\text{base ten}) = 10010_2.$

The Duodecimal Society of America is an organization which is dedicated to the change of base in the Hindu-Arabic numeration system from ten to twelve. The basic principles of the numeration system advocated by this Society are twelve distinct symbols (for face value) and position of each symbol (for place value). The place value of any digit is twelve times the place value of the digit immediately to the right. The reason for the name *duodecimal* numeration system for the base twelve system is that the Hindu-Arabic numeration system (base ten) is also known as the *decimal* numeration system, and the base twelve numeration system has *two* more distinct symbols than the decimal system; that is, twelve symbols.

In the duodecimal system we could choose any twelve distinct symbols to indicate the counting numbers zero, one, two, ... , eleven. In order to avoid learning new symbols and to facilitate the writing, we shall use the symbols of the decimal system to represent the first ten counting numbers zero through nine: 0, 1, 2, 3, 4, 5, 6, 7, 8, 9. Since we cannot use the two-digit symbols 10 and 11 to represent ten and eleven, respectively, we must invent or choose two other symbols to represent ten and eleven. For this purpose we choose the initials of ten and eleven; namely, *t* and *e*. Thus the first twenty-five counting numbers may be represented 0, 1, 2, 3, 4, 5, 6, 7, 8, 9, t, e, 10, 11, 12, 13, 14, 15, 16, 17, 18, 19, 1t, 1e, 20 in the duodecimal system. Note that the numerals 10 and 20 represent the numbers *twelve* and *twenty-four*, respectively, not *ten* and *twenty*. We may indicate that these numerals are written in base twelve by the subscript 12; for example, 10_{12} and 20_{12} represent twelve and twenty-four, respectively. As you can see, the *subscript* which indicates the base of the numeration system is always written in the *decimal system*, regardless of the base.

As in the decimal system, we may add any two counting numbers

+	0	1	2	3	4	5	6	7	8	9	t	e
0	0	1	2	3	4	5	6	7	8	9	t	e
1	1	2	3	4	5	6	7	8	9	t	e	10
2	2	3	4	5	6	7	8	9	t	e	10	11
3	3	4	5	6	7	8	9	t	e	10	11	12
4	4	5	6	7	8	9	t	e	10	11	12	13
5	5	6	7	8	9	t	e	10	11	12	13	14
6	6	7	8	9	. t	e	10	11	12	13	14	15
7	7	8	9	t	e	10	11	12	13	14	15	16
8	8	9	t	e	10	11	12	13	14	15	16	17
9	9	t	e	10	11	12	13	14	15	16	17	18
t	t	e	10	11	12	13	14	15	16	17	18	19
e	e	10	11	12	13	14	15	16	17	18	19	1t

FIGURE 4.9

written in the duodecimal system by the use of the addition facts from Figure 4.9, the place value concept, and the appropriate algorithm. The following examples illustrate the algorithm for computing the sum of two counting numbers in the duodecimal system.

Example 13.

$$345$$
$$+ \ \ 1t6$$
$$\overline{52e}$$

Example 14.

$$\overset{1\ 1}{27t}$$
$$+ \ \ e43$$
$$\overline{1201}$$

The multiplication table for the duodecimal numeration system is shown in Figure 4.10.

·	0	1	2	3	4	5	6	7	8	9	t	e
0	0	0	0	0	0	0	0	0	0	0	0	0
1	0	1	2	3	4	5	6	7	8	9	t	e
2	0	2	4	6	8	t	10	12	14	16	18	1t
3	0	3	6	9	10	13	16	19	20	23	26	29
4	0	4	8	10	14	18	20	24	28	30	34	38
5	0	5	t	13	18	21	26	2e	34	39	42	47
6	0	6	10	16	20	26	30	36	40	46	50	56
7	0	7	12	19	24	2e	36	41	48	53	5t	65
8	0	8	14	20	28	34	40	48	54	60	68	74
9	0	9	16	23	30	39	46	53	60	69	76	83
t	0	t	18	26	34	42	50	5t	68	76	84	92
e	0	e	1t	29	38	47	56	65	74	83	92	t1

FIGURE 4.10

We may multiply any two counting numbers written in the duodecimal system by use of the multiplication facts from Figure 4.10, the addition facts from Figure 4.9, the place value concept, and the appropriate algorithm. The following examples illustrate the algorithm for computing the product of two counting numbers expressed in the duodecimal system.

Example 15.

$$\begin{array}{r} \overset{1\ 1}{276} \\ \times\ \ 2 \\ \hline 530 \end{array}$$

Example 16.

$$\begin{array}{r} 3076 \\ \times\ \ 5et \end{array}$$

$$\begin{array}{rcl} 26630 & \longrightarrow & 26630 \\ 296t6 & \longrightarrow & +\ \ 296t60 \\ \hline & & 301490 \\ 13316 & \longrightarrow & +\ 1331600 \\ \hline 1632t90 & \longleftarrow & 1632t90 \end{array}$$

The following examples illustrate a method of converting a base twelve numeral to the corresponding base ten numeral.

Example 17.

$$\begin{aligned} 987_{12} &= [9(10^2) + 8(10^1) + 7]\,(\text{base twelve}) \\ &= [9(12^2) + 8(12^1) + 7]\,(\text{base ten}) \\ &= [9(144) + 8(12) + 7]\,(\text{base ten}) \\ &= 1296 + 96 + 7 \ (\text{base ten}) \\ &= 1399 \ (\text{base ten}). \end{aligned}$$

Example 18.

$$\begin{aligned} t9e6_{12} &= [t(10^3) + 9(10^2) + e(10) + 6]\,(\text{base twelve}) \\ &= [10(12^3) + 9(12^2) + 11(12) + 6]\,(\text{base ten}) \\ &= [10(1728) + 9(144) + 11(12) + 6]\,(\text{base ten}) \\ &= 17{,}280 + 1296 + 132 + 6 \ (\text{base ten}) \\ &= 18{,}714 \ (\text{base ten}). \end{aligned}$$

The following examples illustrate a method of converting a base ten numeral to the corresponding base twelve numeral.

Example 19.

$$\begin{aligned} 296 &= [2(144) + 8]\,(\text{base ten}) \\ &= [2(12^2) + 0(12) + 8]\,(\text{base ten}) \\ &= [2(10^2) + 0(10) + 8]\,(\text{base twelve}) \\ &= 208_{12}. \end{aligned}$$

Example 20.

$$1791 = [1728 + 60 + 3] \text{(base ten)}$$
$$= [1(12^3) + 0(12^2) + 5(12) + 3] \text{(base ten)}$$
$$= [1(10^3) + 0(10^2) + 5(10) + 3] \text{(base twelve)}$$
$$= 1053_{12}.$$

Exercise 4.9

I. Write each of the following sets of base ten numerals as a set of numerals in base two.

(1) {21, 22, 23, 24, 25, 26, 27, 28, 29, 30, 31, 32, 33, 34}

(2) {64, 65, 66, 67, 68, 69, 70, 71, 72, 73, 74, 75}

II. Write each of the following sets of Hindu-Arabic numerals as a set of numerals in base twelve.

(1) {31, 32, 33, 34, 35, 36, 37, 38, 39, 40}

(2) {144, 145, 146, 147, 148, 149, 150, 151, 152, 153, 154, 155}

III. Compute each of the following sums in base two. All given numerals are written in base two.

(1)	101	(2)	1101	(3)	10010
+	1000	+	111	+	1110

(4)	11011	(5)	1110001	(6)	1000110
+	1010	+	1011011	+	1001101

IV. Convert each of the base two numerals in Exercise III to base ten numerals. Add (in base ten) the numerals of each problem and convert this sum to base two. Use this sum to check the result of each problem of Exercise III.

V. Compute each of the following products in base two. All given numerals are written in base two.

(1)	101	(2)	1101	(3)	111
×	11	×	101	×	11

(4)	11101	(5)	111	(6)	1011
×	1101	×	111	×	1011

VI. Compute each of the following sums in base twelve. All given numerals are written in base twelve.

(1)	18	(2)	237	(3)	1te
+	3	+	16	+	513

$$
\begin{array}{r} (4) \quad 24t \\ + \ 17e \\ \hline \end{array}
\qquad
\begin{array}{r} (5) \quad 119 \\ + \ 1t3 \\ \hline \end{array}
\qquad
\begin{array}{r} (6) \quad 235 \\ + \ 987 \\ \hline \end{array}
$$

VII. Convert each of the base twelve numerals in Exercise VI to base ten numerals. Add (in base ten) the numerals of each problem and convert this sum to base twelve. Use this sum to check the result of each problem of Exercise VI.

VIII. Compute each of the following products in base twelve. All given numerals are written in base twelve.

$$
\begin{array}{r} (1) \quad 25 \\ \times \quad 2 \\ \hline \end{array}
\qquad
\begin{array}{r} (2) \quad 35 \\ \times \quad 2 \\ \hline \end{array}
\qquad
\begin{array}{r} (3) \quad 35 \\ \times \quad 10 \\ \hline \end{array}
$$

$$
\begin{array}{r} (4) \quad 1te \\ \times \quad 2t \\ \hline \end{array}
\qquad
\begin{array}{r} (5) \quad 30e \\ \times \quad t0 \\ \hline \end{array}
\qquad
\begin{array}{r} (6) \quad 610 \\ \times \quad t0e \\ \hline \end{array}
$$

IX. Express the first fifty counting numbers in the base eight numeration system.

X. Make an addition table for the base eight numeration system.

XI. Make a multiplication table for the base eight numeration system.

XII. Compute each of the following sums in base eight. All given numerals are written in base eight.

$$
\begin{array}{r} (1) \quad 35 \\ + \ 22 \\ \hline \end{array}
\qquad
\begin{array}{r} (2) \quad 53 \\ + \ 15 \\ \hline \end{array}
\qquad
\begin{array}{r} (3) \quad 55 \\ + \ 34 \\ \hline \end{array}
$$

$$
\begin{array}{r} (4) \quad 236 \\ + \ 143 \\ \hline \end{array}
\qquad
\begin{array}{r} (5) \quad 207 \\ + \ 316 \\ \hline \end{array}
\qquad
\begin{array}{r} (6) \quad 1007 \\ + \ 6771 \\ \hline \end{array}
$$

XIII. Convert each of the base eight numerals in Exercise XII to base ten numerals. Add (in base ten) the numerals of each problem of Exercise XII and convert this sum to base eight. Use this sum to check the result of each problem in Exercise XII.

XIV. Compute each of the following products in base eight. All given numerals are written in base eight.

$$
\begin{array}{r} (1) \quad 12 \\ \times \quad 3 \\ \hline \end{array}
\qquad
\begin{array}{r} (2) \quad 12 \\ \times \quad 4 \\ \hline \end{array}
\qquad
\begin{array}{r} (3) \quad 134 \\ \times \quad 5 \\ \hline \end{array}
$$

$$
\begin{array}{r} (4) \quad 203 \\ \times \quad 34 \\ \hline \end{array}
\qquad
\begin{array}{r} (5) \quad 345 \\ \times \ 107 \\ \hline \end{array}
\qquad
\begin{array}{r} (6) \quad 217 \\ \times \ 3070 \\ \hline \end{array}
$$

XV. Justify the base eight addition algorithm for each of the following. All given numerals are written in base eight.

(1) 35 + 22
(2) 257 + 26

(3) 273 + 716
(4) 705 + 610

XVI. Justify the base eight multiplication algorithm for each of the following. All of the given numerals are written in base eight.

(1) (105)(3)
(2) (105)(43)

(3) (105)(63)
(4) (105)(123)

Chapter 5

SUBTRACTION AND THE SET OF INTEGERS

5.1 Subtraction of Counting Numbers and Addition of Integers

When a young child has five pieces of candy and his mother orders him to give two pieces to his brothers when they return home, he begins to wonder how many pieces he will have left. So he places the five pieces on the table, forming a set of 5 elements, and removes two pieces and puts these aside. Now he has two sets, the first one of 3 elements and the second one of 2 elements. Immediately he realizes that he will have 3 pieces of candy left after he has given away the 2 pieces to his two brothers.

A child's original concept of subtraction is "take away"; that is, if he is asked the question "what is b take away a?" he may form a set of b elements and remove a elements from this set. The answer to the question is the number of elements remaining. He usually does this on his fingers. For example, if he is asked "what is 5 take away 2?" he puts up 5 fingers, covers 2 of these fingers with his other hand, and observes that there are 3 fingers remaining. He does not realize that he has solved a mathematical problem by actually using a physical model of the problem. The two numbers 5 and 2 have been combined by means of the binary operator "take away" to form a new number 3. Mathematicians use the term *minus* instead of the child's terminology "take away." Thus we say "5 minus 2 equals three" and write "$5 - 2 = 3$."

There are several possible ways in which the operation of subtraction can be defined. One way is to use the child's concept of "take away." The following definition of the binary operator minus $(-)$, the binary operation *subtraction*, and the difference is based on this concept. In the

150

definition, $B \setminus A = \{x : x \in B \wedge x \notin A\}$. The symbol $B \setminus A$ is read B *slash A.*

DEFINITION 1.   The *difference* $b - a$ in the subtraction of the counting number a from the counting number b is the counting number $n(B \setminus A)$, in which $n(A) = a$, $n(B) = b$ and $A \subset B$ [that is, $b - a = n(B) - n(A) = n(B \setminus A)$].

For example, if $A = \{1, 3, 5, 7\}$ and $B = \{1, 2, 3, 4, 5, 6, 7, 8, 9\}$, then $A \subset B$, $n(A) = 4$, $n(B) = 9$, $B \setminus A = \{2, 4, 6, 8, 9\}$, and $n(B \setminus A) = 5$. Hence $9 - 4 = 5$. The Venn diagram in Figure 5.1 illustrates this concept.

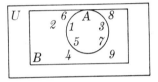

FIGURE 5.1

Observe that $b - a$ is not defined if $b < a$. An alternate way of defining subtraction is given in the following theorem. The notation $a \leq b$ is read *a is less than or equal to b* and means $a < b$ *or* $a = b$.

THEOREM 1.   If a and b are any counting numbers such that $a \leq b$, then the *difference* $b - a$ is the counting number c if and only if $b = a + c$. (That is, $b - a = c$ if and only if $b = a + c$.)

Proof.

$(\rightarrow)$ Let $b - a = c$. Then there exist finite sets A and B such that $n(A) = a$, $n(B) = b$, $A \subset B$, and $n(B) - n(A) = b - a = c$. But by Definition 1, $n(B) - n(A) = n(B \setminus A)$. Thus $n(B \setminus A) = c$. Since $A \cap (B \setminus A) = \phi$ and $B = A \cup (B \setminus A)$, it follows from Definition 2 of Chapter 3 that $n(B) = n(A) + n(B \setminus A)$. Hence $b = a + c$.

$(\leftarrow)$ Conversely, let $b = a + c$. Then by Definition 2 of Chapter 3, there exist sets A, B, and C such that $n(A) = a$,

$n(B) = b$, $n(C) = c$, $n(B) = n(A) + n(C)$, $A \cap C$ $= \phi$, and $A \cup C = B$. Since $A \cap C = \phi$ and $A \cup C$ $= B$, we see that $C = B \setminus A$ and $A \subset B$. (Illustrate this fact by means of a Venn diagram.) Hence by Definition 1, $n(B) - n(A) = n(B \setminus A)$; that is, $b - a = c$.

Thus $(b - a = c) \rightleftarrows (b = a + c).$ //

For example, in the subtraction $8 - 5$ we seek a counting number c such that $8 = 5 + c$. Since $8 = 5 + 3$, we see that $c = 3$ and hence that $8 - 5 = 3$. Since $13 = 9 + 4$, we see that $13 - 9 = 4$ and $13 - 4 = 9$. In general, by Theorem 1, in any subtraction problem $b - a$ we seek a counting number c such that $b = a + c$. This counting number c is the difference $b - a$; that is, $b - a = c$.

Thus we see that subtraction may be defined in terms of addition. If $a \leq b$, we can compute the difference $b - a$ by replacing the variable x in the open sentence $a + x = b$ by that counting number which converts the open sentence to a true sentence. For example, in the open sentence $5 + x = 9$ replacement of the variable x by the counting number 4 converts that open sentence to the true sentence $5 + 4 = 9$. Hence $9 - 5 = 4$. To convert the open sentence $5 + x = 5$ to a true sentence we replace the variable x by the counting number 0. Thus $5 + 0 = 5$ and $5 - 5 = 0$.

If we attempt to convert the open sentence $5 + x = 3$ to a true sentence by replacing the variable x by a counting number, we soon realize that the replacement of x by *any* counting number yields a false sentence. Thus the sentence "there exists a counting number x such that $5 + x = 3$" is false. Similarly, the open sentence $5 + x = 0$ cannot be converted to a true sentence by replacement of the variable by a counting number. The sentence "for no counting number x, $5 + x = 0$" is true, but the sentence "for some counting number x, $5 + x = 0$" is false. However, the sentence "for some counting number x, $0 + x = 0$" is true. We conclude that, for each counting number $a \neq 0$, there is no counting number x such that $a + x = 0$. This deficiency of the counting numbers is a serious one. While, at first glance, one might believe that this is not a serious deficiency, certain physical considerations demonstrate the desirability of creating a new set of numbers which includes the counting numbers as a proper subset and which eliminates this deficiency of the set of counting numbers. For example, the weather man reports that the temperature has risen $10°$ F during the past two hours and that the present reading is $0°$ F. What was the temperature two hours ago? To answer this question we attempt to convert the open sentence $x + 10 = 0$

to a true sentence by replacement of the variable x. There are many other physical problems involving negative numbers. For example, problems which involve velocity, acceleration, fluid flow, and gains and losses may involve negative numbers for their formulation and solution. After we have introduced the *negative integers*, we shall consider some physical applications. In order to create the new system of numbers, we consider the open sentence $x + 1 = 0$. As we have seen, $x + 1 = 0$ cannot be converted to a true sentence by replacement of the variable by a counting number. Consequently, we create a new number called the *negative of one* (or *negative one*, or in more advanced work *minus one*) and denoted by $^{-}1$, and we extend the binary operator $+$ so that $^{-}1 + 1 = 0$ and $1 + ^{-}1 = 0$. In a similar manner, from consideration of the open sentence $x + 2 = 0$, we create the *negative of two*, denote it by $^{-}2$, and extend the binary operator $+$ so that $^{-}2 + 2 = 0$ and $2 + ^{-}2 = 0$. In general, from consideration of the open sentence $x + a = 0$ for any counting number $a \neq 0$, we create the *negative of a*, denote it by ^{-}a, and extend the binary operator $+$ so that $^{-}a + a = 0$ and $a + ^{-}a = 0$. Thus we create the set $\{^{-}1, ^{-}2, ^{-}3, ^{-}4, \ldots\}$ with the property that $^{-}a + a = 0$ and $a + ^{-}a = 0$ for any counting number $a \neq 0$. The following definition gives a name to this new set of numbers.

DEFINITION 2. The *set of negative integers* is the set $\{^{-}1, ^{-}2, ^{-}3, ^{-}4, \ldots\}$.

Since no element of a set is repeated, it follows from Definition 2 that $^{-}a = ^{-}b$ if and only if $a = b$. To avoid confusion with the binary operator minus $(-)$ the symbol $^{-}$ to indicate a negative integer is raised. Throughout this text the set of negative integers will be denoted by I^{-}. Next we define the set of *integers*.

DEFINITION 3. The *set of integers* is the union of the set of counting numbers and the set of negative integers.

Throughout this text, the set of integers will be denoted by I. Thus $I = C_0 \cup I^{-}$. Now it is possible to convert the open sentence $x + a = 0$, for any integer a, to a true sentence by replacement of the variable by an integer. In other words, corresponding to any integer a, there exists an integer x such that $x + a = 0$.

So far we have defined the operator $+$ only between two counting numbers a and b and between the counting number a and the negative of a. Now that we have extended the set of counting numbers to the set of integers (that is, $C_0 \subset I$), we would like to extend the definition of $+$ so that it is defined between any two integers. The method of the extension will be motivated by our desire to retain the closure, commutative, associative, and identity properties for addition of the counting numbers.

The following examples illustrate the method of extension of the definition of $+$.

Example 1.   How should we define $^-3 + 5$ if the associative property is to be retained?

$^-3 + 5 = ^-3 + (3 + 2)$.
If the associative property is to be retained, $^-3 + (3 + 2)$
  must be equal to $(^-3 + 3) + 2$.
But $(^-3 + 3) + 2 = 0 + 2 = 2$.
Consequently we must define $+$ so that $^-3 + 5 = 2$.

Example 2.   How should we define $^-6 + ^-3$ if the associative property is to be retained?

$$(^-6 + ^-3) + 9 = ^-6 + (^-3 + 9) \qquad \text{(if the associative}$$
$$\text{property is to be retained)}$$
$$= ^-6 + [^-3 + (3 + 6)]$$
$$= ^-6 + [(^-3 + 3) + 6] \quad \text{(if the associative}$$
$$\text{property is to be retained)}$$
$$= ^-6 + [0 + 6]$$
$$= ^-6 + 6$$
$$= 0.$$

But $^-9 + 9 = 0$.
Consequently we must define $+$ so that $^-6 + ^-3$
  $= ^-(6 + 3) = ^-9$.

Example 3.   How should we define $^-9 + 3$ if the associative property is to be retained?

$$^-9 + 3 = (^-6 + ^-3) + 3 \qquad \text{(Example 2)}$$
$$= ^-6 + (^-3 + 3) \qquad \text{(if the associative property is}$$
$$\text{to be retained)}$$
$$= ^-6 + 0$$
$$= ^-6. \qquad \text{(if the identity property is retained)}$$
Consequently we must define $+$ so that $^-9 + 3 = ^-(6 + 3)$
  $+ 3 = ^-6$.

Example 4.   How should we define $^-5 + 0$ and $0 + ^-5$ if the identity property is to be retained?

$^-5 + 0 = {}^-5,$

$0 + {}^-5 = {}^-5.$

Consequently we must define $+$ so that $^-5 + 0 = {}^-5$ and $0 + {}^-5 = {}^-5.$

As we shall frequently refer to the set of nonzero counting numbers, we give this set a special name.

DEFINITION 4. The set of *positive integers* is the set $\{1, 2, 3, \ldots\}.$

Throughout this text the set of positive integers will be denoted by I^+. It is easy to see that $I = I^- \cup \{0\} \cup I^+$. We are now ready to give the definition of $+$ for any two integers.

DEFINITION 5. The *binary operator* $+$ is defined between any pair of integers as follows:

(a) If a and b are any counting numbers, then $a + b$ is as defined in Definition 2 of Chapter 3.

(b) If a is any positive integer, then $a + {}^-a = 0$ and $^-a + a = 0.$

(c) If a is any positive integer and ^-b is any negative integer and $b < a$ (that is, $a = c + b$ for some positive integer c), then $a + {}^-b = (c + b) + {}^-b = c$ and $^-b + a = {}^-b + (b + c) = c.$

(d) If a is any positive integer and ^-b is any negative integer and $a < b$ (that is, $b = c + a$ for some positive integer c), then $a + {}^-b = a + {}^-(c + a) = {}^-c$ and $^-b + a = {}^-(c + a) + a = {}^-c.$

(e) If ^-a and ^-b are any negative integers, then $^-a + {}^-b = {}^-(a + b).$

(f) If ^-a is any negative integer, then $^-a + 0 = 0 + {}^-a = {}^-a.$

Because of Definition 5, the *sum* of any two integers is defined. Furthermore, the sum is an integer, and $a + b = 0 \rightleftarrows b = {}^-a$ for any positive integer a. It may be proved from Definition 5 that the operation of addition of two integers satisfies the following properties.

CLOSURE PROPERTY FOR ADDITION

If a and b are any integers, then $a + b$ is a unique integer.

COMMUTATIVE PROPERTY FOR ADDITION

If a and b are any integers, then $a + b = b + a$.

ASSOCIATIVE PROPERTY FOR ADDITION

If a, b, and c are any integers, then $(a + b) + c = a + (b + c)$.

SIGN PROPERTY FOR ADDITION

If a and b are any integers, then $^-a + {}^-b = {}^-(a + b)$.

CANCELLATION PROPERTY FOR ADDITION

If a, b, and c are any integers and $a + b = a + c$, then $b = c$.

IDENTITY PROPERTY FOR ADDITION

If a is any integer, then $a + 0 = a$. Moreover, if $a + z = a$ for some integer a, then $z = 0$.

The proofs of all but the associative property for addition follow immediately from Definition 5. The associative property for addition may be proved by cases. The manner in which we defined the operator $+$ in Definition 5 set the stage so that the above properties, proved previously in Chapter 3 for the set of counting numbers, would be true for the set of integers. Of course, the *generalized commutative and associative property for addition of integers* may be proved as the corresponding property for the addition of counting numbers.

The introduction of the set of integers facilitates the formulation of mathematical models of many physical problems. For example, business gains and losses may be formulated in terms of the integers, the positive integers representing gains and the negative integers representing losses. A second application of negative integers is to temperature reading. A temperature of five degrees below zero would be formulated as $^-5$ degrees. Fluid flow problems provide a third application of negative integers as the following example illustrates.

Example 5.   Water is flowing into a tank at the rate of 1000 gallons per minute and flowing out at the rate of 1200 gallons per minute. If the tank contains 180,000 gallons at 9:00 A.M., at what time will the tank be empty?

The rate of flow into the tank is represented by 1000 gal/min, and the rate of flow out of the tank is represented by $^-1200$ gal/min. The net rate of flow $= 1000 + {}^-1200 = {}^-200$. Although you can probably solve problems of this type, we shall postpone solution until a later chapter.

In order to illustrate Definition 5, we shall establish a one-to-one correspondence between the set I^- and a subset of the number line. The number line studied in Chapter 3 is shown in Figure 5.2.

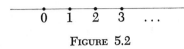

FIGURE 5.2

Now we label a subset of the points to the left of 0 with the symbols $^-1, ^-2, ^-3, \ldots$ for the negative integers, as shown in Figure 5.3.

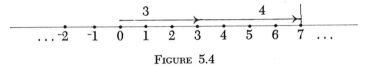

FIGURE 5.3

The set of negative integers is in one-to-one correspondence with the set of points labeled $^-1, ^-2, ^-3, \ldots$.

Recall the method of computing the sum of two counting numbers on the number line. For example, the sum of 3 and 4 is computed as shown in Figure 5.4.

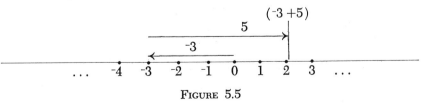

FIGURE 5.4

To illustrate $a + {}^-b$, where a and b are positive integers, we draw an arrow whose tail is at 0 and whose head is at a, and then draw an arrow whose tail is at a and whose head is b units to the left of a. The sum $a + {}^-b$ is determined by the head of the second arrow. The illustrations of $^-a + b$ and $^-a + {}^-b$ are similar, as shown in Figures 5.5 and 5.6.

We illustrate the addition of Example 1 on the number line, as shown in Figure 5.5.

FIGURE 5.5

Notice that the head of the topmost arrow indicates the sum $^-3 + 5$; that is, $^-3 + 5 = 2$. In any sum involving a negative integer, the arrow corresponding to that negative integer points to the left.

The addition in Example 2 is illustrated in Figure 5.6.

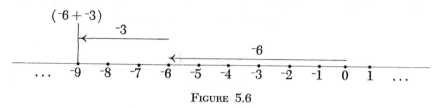

FIGURE 5.6

The addition in Example 3 is illustrated in Figure 5.7.

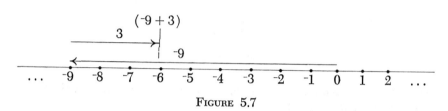

FIGURE 5.7

The addition in Example 4 is illustrated in Figure 5.8. Notice that the arrow corresponding to 0 is 0 unit in length. Although it is pointing to the left, it could point to the right.

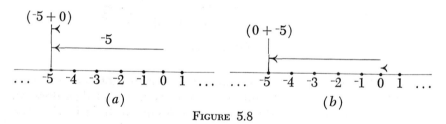

FIGURE 5.8

Exercise 5.1

I. State the negative of each of the following counting numbers.

(1) 7   (4) $(3 + 5)$
(2) 9   (5) $2 + (8 + 4)$
(3) 10   (6) $(2 + 8) + 4$

II. Compute each of the following sums.

(1) $^-3 + 3$ (6) $0 + 8 + {}^-8$
(2) $^-7 + 7$ (7) $^-11 + 13$
(3) $(^-7 + 7) + 3$ (8) $^-3 + 5$
(4) $^-7 + (7 + 3)$ (9) $^-a + a$
(5) $^-7 + 17$ (10) $^-a + (a + b)$

III. Illustrate each sum in Problem II on the number line.

IV. Compute each of the following sums. The letters a and b represent positive integers.

(1) $^-3 + {}^-5$

(2) $^-5 + {}^-3$

(3) $^-5 + {}^-4 + {}^-3$

(4) $^-9 + {}^-1 + 3$

(5) $a + b + {}^-a$

(6) $a + ({}^-b + {}^-a)$

(7) $^-5 + 3 + 2$

(8) $5 + 3$

(9) $3 + a + {}^-a$

(10) $0 + b + 3 + 0 + {}^-b$

(11) $6 + {}^-2$

(12) $^-15 + 7$

(13) $^-3 + {}^-7$

(14) $^-27 + 23$

(15) $^-6 + 23$

V. Compute each of the following differences and verify by use of Theorem 1.

(1) $5 - 3$

(2) $8 - 5$

(3) $2 - 2$

(4) $2 - 0$

(5) $5 - 4$

(6) $7 - 6$

(7) $11 - 10$

(8) $10 - 9$

(9) $9 - 9$

(10) $9 - 0$

(11) $0 - 0$

(12) $4 - 2$

(13) $1 - 1$

(14) $1 - 0$

(15) $7 - 4$

VI. Convert each of the following open sentences to a true sentence by replacement of the variable by an integer.

(1) $x + 5 = 0$

(2) $x + 17 = 0$

(3) $x + 0 = 0$

(4) $x + {}^-9 = 0$

(5) $x + {}^-1 = 0$

(6) $5 + x = {}^-9$

(7) $9 - x = 5$

(8) $11 + x = {}^-3$

(9) $0 + x = 7$

(10) $^-3 + x = {}^-8$

(11) $3 - x = 2$

(12) $^-3 + x = {}^-3$

(13) $^-9 + x = {}^-7$

(14) $^-5 + x = {}^-7$

(15) $x + {}^-3 = {}^-3$

VII. Discuss the relationship between the binary operator $+$ of Definition 5 and the binary operator $+$ of Definition 2 of Chapter 3.

5.2 Subtraction of Integers and Additive Inverses

In Section 5.1 we defined subtraction of counting numbers. In fact, by Theorem 1 if a and b are any counting numbers and $a \leq b$, then $b - a = c$ if and only if $b = a + c$. However, we still cannot subtract a from b if $b < a$; that is, subtraction of any counting number from any other counting number is not defined. Moreover, we have not defined subtraction of any integer from any integer. Subtraction of any integer b (positive, 0, or negative) from any integer a (positive, 0, or negative) is defined below.

DEFINITION 6. For any integers a and b, the *difference* in the subtraction of b from a, written $a - b$, is the integer c if and only if $a = b + c$ (that is, $a - b = c$ if and only if $a = b + c$).

Note that Definition 6 is consistent with Theorem 1 and is an extension of Theorem 1. Note also that the symbols a, b, and c represent any integers (positive, 0, or negative). Moreover, from Definition 6 and the cancellation property for addition, we see that the *difference* of any two integers is unique. The following examples illustrate Definition 6.

Example 1. $4 - 6 = {}^-2$ because $4 = 6 + {}^-2$.

Example 2. ${}^-5 - 3 = {}^-8$ because ${}^-5 = 3 + {}^-8$.

Example 3. ${}^-5 - {}^-3 = {}^-2$ because ${}^-5 = {}^-3 + {}^-2$.

Example 4. $6 - {}^-3 = 9$ because $6 = {}^-3 + 9$.

Example 5. ${}^-3 - {}^-7 = 4$ because ${}^-3 = {}^-7 + 4$.

Although we may compute $a - b$ for any integers a and b by applying Definition 5 and Definition 6, we shall introduce an alternate method for computing $a - b$. As the alternate method involves the concept of *additive inverse*, we shall first discuss and define additive inverse.

By Definition 5 if c is any positive integer, then $c + {}^-c = {}^-c + c = 0$. The integer ${}^-c$ is called the *additive inverse* of the positive integer c. In particular, the additive inverse of 7 is ${}^-7$. Since ${}^-7 + 7 = 0$, we say that the additive inverse of ${}^-7$ is 7. In Definition 7, the concept of additive inverse of an integer is defined.

DEFINITION 7. The integer b is said to be an *additive inverse* of the integer a if and only if $a + b = 0$.

Definition 7 does not guarantee that each integer has an additive inverse. However, part (b) of Definition 5 does guarantee that every integer has an additive inverse. It is easy to see that each integer a has exactly one additive inverse. Since no integer can have two additive inverses, we speak of *the* additive inverse and denote the additive inverse of the integer a by the symbol ^-a and read it *the negative of* a. Since $0 + 0 = 0$, we see that the additive inverse of 0 is 0; that is, $^-0 = 0$.

Notice that the additive inverse of the negative integer $^-3$ is $^-(^-3)$. Since $^-3 + 3 = 0$, we see that the additive inverse of $^-3$ is 3; that is $^-(^-3) = 3$. A more general result is stated in the following theorem.

THEOREM 2.   If a is any integer, then $^-(^-a) = a$.

Proof.   By Definition 7, $a + ^-a = 0$.

By the commutative property for addition, $^-a + a = 0$.

Thus the additive inverse of ^-a is a.

But the additive inverse of ^-a is $^-(^-a)$.

Since the additive inverse of any integer is unique, we see that $^-(^-a) = a.//$

For example, $^-(^-3) = 3$ and $^-(^-10) = 10$.

THEOREM 3.   If a and b are any integers, then $^-(a + b) = ^-a + ^-b$.

Proof.   The additive inverse of $(a + b)$ is $^-(a + b)$.

$$\text{Moreover, } (a + b) + (^-a + ^-b) = (a + ^-a) + (b + ^-b)$$
$$= 0 + 0$$
$$= 0.$$

Thus $(^-a + ^-b)$ is the additive inverse of $a + b$.

Hence $^-(a + b) = ^-a + ^-b.//$

The important properties in Theorems 2 and 3 deserve special names.

DOUBLE NEGATIVE PROPERTY FOR INTEGERS
If a is any integer, then $^-(^-a) = a$.

SIGN PROPERTY FOR ADDITION OF INTEGERS
If a and b are any integers, then $^-(a + b) = ^-a + ^-b$.

For example, $^-(3 + 5) = ^-3 + ^-5$, and $^-(3 + ^-5) = ^-3 + ^-(^-5) = ^-3 + 5$.

Notice that the sign property for addition of integers is not included in Definition 5. Definition 5 applies only to the case $^-a + ^-b$ in which both a and b are positive integers. Theorem 3 applies to all pairs of integers a and b.

The following theorem, which relates subtraction to the additive inverse, is an alternate method for computing $a - b$.

THEOREM 4.   If a and b are any integers, then $a - b = a + {}^-b$.

Proof.   Now $b + (a + {}^-b) = b + ({}^-b + a) = (b + {}^-b) + a$
$= 0 + a = a$.
Hence by Definition 6, $(a + {}^-b) = a - b.$ //

Note that $a + {}^-b$ plays the role of c in Definition 6. Moreover, in Theorem 4 we have proved an additional property of the integers; namely, the closure property for subtraction of integers.

CLOSURE PROPERTY FOR SUBTRACTION OF INTEGERS
If a and b are any integers, then $a - b$ is a unique integer.

Recall that the set of counting numbers is *not* closed under subtraction. The introduction of negative integers made it possible for us to define subtraction so that the set of *integers* would be closed under subtraction. You may be tempted to conclude that $a - b = b - a$ for all integers a and b. However, it is easy to see that $5 - 2 \neq 2 - 5$. Thus there is no commutative property for subtraction. Similarly, since $(8 - 5) - 2 = 1$ and $8 - (5 - 2) = 5$, we see that there is no associative property for subtraction. The cancellation property for subtraction of integers is an immediate consequence of Theorem 4 and the cancellation property for addition of integers.

Example 6. $7 - 4 = 7 + {}^-4 = (3 + 4) + {}^-4 = 3 + (4 + {}^-4) = 3 + 0$
$= 3.$

Example 7. $6 - {}^-5 = 6 + {}^-({}^-5) = 6 + 5 = 11.$

Example 8. ${}^-8 - 3 = {}^-8 + {}^-3 = {}^-(8 + 3) = {}^-11.$

Example 9. ${}^-7 - {}^-5 = {}^-7 + {}^-({}^-5) = {}^-7 + 5 = {}^-(2 + 5) + 5 =$
$({}^-2 + {}^-5) + 5 = {}^-2 + ({}^-5 + 5) = {}^-2 + 0 = {}^-2.$

Example 10. $2 - 7 = 2 + {}^-7 = 2 + {}^-(2 + 5) = 2 + ({}^-2 + {}^-5) =$
$(2 + {}^-2) + {}^-5 = 0 + {}^-5 = {}^-5.$

Exercise 5.2

I. State the additive inverse of each of the following integers.

(1) 7

(2) 9

(3) 0

(4) $^-3$

(5) $^-9$

(6) $^-3 + 2$

(7) $3 + {}^-2$

(8) a

(9) $a + b$

(10) $a + {}^-b$

II. Compute each of the following differences by means of Definition 6. The letter a represents any counting number.

(1) $5 - 3$

(2) $5 - 5$

(3) $6 - 0$

(4) $5 - 7$

(5) $5 - {}^-7$

(6) $^-5 - 8$

(7) $^-3 - {}^-5$

(8) $0 - 0$

(9) $^-8 - {}^-8$

(10) $^-5 - {}^-4$

(11) $^-7 - 4$

(12) $a - {}^-a$

(13) $a - a$

(14) $(a + 3) - 3$

(15) $(a + 7) - 5$

(16) $(a - 4) - 3$

(17) $a - (4 + 3)$

(18) $a - (4 - 3)$

(19) $5a - 2a$

(20) $3a - a$

III. Compute each difference in Exercise II by means of Theorem 4.

IV. On the number line illustrate each difference in Exercise II.

V. Convert each of the following differences to a sum by means of Theorem 4 and then illustrate each on the number line.

(1) $5 - 2$

(2) $8 - 3$

(3) $3 - 7$

(4) $1 - 4$

(5) $3 - {}^-2$

(6) $3 - {}^-4$

(7) $^-3 - 4$

(8) $^-5 - {}^-2$

(9) $3 - 0$

(10) $0 - 7$

VI. If possible, convert each of the following open sentences to a true sentence by replacement of the variable by an integer.

(1) $x + {}^-5 = 2$

(2) $x - 7 = {}^-2$

(3) $x - 0 = 4$

(4) $0 - x = 7$

(5) $^-7 - x = {}^-3$

(6) $^-7 - x = {}^-4$

(7) $4 - x = {}^-3$

(8) $4 - x = {}^-2$

(9) $4 - x = {}^-4$

(10) $^-4 - x = 6$

(11) $^-4 - x = {}^-6$

(12) $^-5 - {}^-x = {}^-2$

(13) $^-5 - {}^-x = 2$

(14) $^-x + 3 = 4$

(15) $(^-x + 2 = 3) \vee (x + 2 = 3)$

(16) $(x - 2 = 3) \vee (x - 3 = 2)$

(17) $(5 - x = 7) \wedge (6 + x = {}^-7)$

(18) $(2x - 9 = 1) \wedge (3x - 9 = 3)$

(19) $3x - 2 = 5$

(20) $x = 2 - x$

5.3 Multiplication of Integers

In the two preceding sections we learned that the closure, commutative, associative, cancellation, and identity properties for the addition of integers are valid and that only the closure property and the cancellation property for subtraction of integers are valid.

In this section we define multiplication of any two integers a and b. As multiplication of any two counting numbers was defined in Definition 3 of Chapter 3, the definition in this section must not conflict with Definition 3 of Chapter 3. Moreover, the definition will be motivated by our desire to retain all of the multiplication and addition properties of the set of counting numbers. Thus we shall define the operator $\cdot$ between any two integers so that the closure property for multiplication, commutative property for multiplication, associative property for multiplication, identity property for multiplication, zero property for multiplication, and distributive property previously proved for the set of counting numbers will be valid for the set of integers.

The following examples illustrate the manner in which the definition of the binary operator $\cdot$ will be extended.

Example 1.   If the temperature changes $^-4°$ per hour during a 5-hour period, what is the total change in temperature? Since the change during the 5 hours is $^-4$ degrees per hour, we see that the total change is $^-4 + {}^-4 + {}^-4 + {}^-4 + {}^-4$ degrees. We would like a mathematical model such that $5(^-4)$ represents the total change. For this reason, we should define $5(^-4)$ such that $5(^-4) = {}^-4 + {}^-4 + {}^-4 + {}^-4 + {}^-4$. Another reason for defining $5(^-4)$ in this manner is our desire to retain the distributive property. If the distributive property is to be retained, then $5(^-4 + 4)$ must be equal to $5(^-4) + 5(4)$. But $5(^-4 + 4) = 5(0) = 0$. Thus $5(^-4) + 5(4) = 0$; that is, $5(^-4) + 20 = 0$. But $^-20 + 20 = 0$. Hence $5(^-4) = {}^-20$

$\qquad\qquad = {}^-4 + {}^-4 + {}^-4 + {}^-4 + {}^-4$ (if the distributive property is to be retained).

Example 2.   How should we define $^-4(5)$ if the commutative property is to be retained? Obviously, if we are to retain the commutative property, then $^-4(5)$ must be equal to $5(^-4)$, which is equal to $^-20$ from Example 1. Thus we define $^-4(5) = 5(^-4)$.

Example 3.   How should we define $^-4(^-5)$ if the distributive property is to be retained? If we are to retain the distributive

property, then $^-4(5 + ^-5)$ must be equal to $^-4(5) + ^-4(^-5)$. But $^-4(5 + ^-5) = ^-4(0) = 0$. (Why?)
Hence $^-4(5) + ^-4(^-5) = 0$; that is, $^-20 + ^-4(^-5) = 0$.
But $^-20 + 20 = 0$.
Hence $^-4(^-5) = 20$, if the distributive property is to be retained. Thus we must define $^-4(^-5)$ such that $(^-4)(^-5) = 4(5)$.
We are now ready to give the definition of $\cdot$ for any two integers.

DEFINITION 8. The *binary operator* $\cdot$ is defined between any pair of integers as follows:

(a) If a and b are any counting numbers, then $a \cdot b$ is defined as in Definition 3 of Chapter 3.

(b) If ^-b is any negative integer, then $0 \cdot ^-b = 0$ and $^-b \cdot 0 = 0$.

(c) If a is any positive integer and ^-b is any negative integer, then $a \cdot ^-b = \underbrace{^-b + ^-b + \ldots + ^-b}_{a \text{ summands}} = ^-(ab)$.

(d) If ^-a is any negative integer and b is any positive integer, then $^-a \cdot b = b \cdot ^-a$.

(e) If ^-a is any negative integer and ^-b is any negative integer, then $^-a \cdot ^-b = ab$.

Because of Definition 8, the product of any two integers is defined. Moreover, the product is a unique integer. It may be proved from Definition 8 that the operation of multiplication of integers satisfies the following properties. In fact, Definition 8 was motivated by our desire to retain these properties which were proved in Chapter 3 for the counting numbers.

CLOSURE PROPERTY FOR MULTIPLICATION
If a and b are any integers, then ab is a unique integer.

COMMUTATIVE PROPERTY FOR MULTIPLICATION
For all integers a and b, $ab = ba$.

SIGN PROPERTY FOR MULTIPLICATION
For all integers a and b,

(1) $a \cdot ^-b = ^-(ab)$,
(2) $^-a \cdot b = ^-(ab)$,
(3) $a \cdot ^-b = ^-a \cdot b$,
(4) $^-a \cdot ^-b = ab$.

MULTIPLICATION PROPERTY OF ZERO
For all integers a and b, $ab = 0$ if and only if $a = 0$ or $b = 0$.

CANCELLATION PROPERTY FOR MULTIPLICATION
For all integers a, b, and c, if $a \neq 0$ and $ab = ac$, then $b = c$.

ASSOCIATIVE PROPERTY FOR MULTIPLICATION
For all integers a, b, and c, $a(bc) = (ab)c$.

IDENTITY PROPERTY FOR MULTIPLICATION
If a is any integer, then $a \cdot 1 = a$. Moreover if $au = a$ for some integer $a \neq 0$, then $u = 1$.

DISTRIBUTIVE PROPERTY
For all integers a, b, and c, $a(b + c) = ab + ac$.

The closure property for multiplication of integers is an immediate consequence of Definition 8.

To prove the commutative property for multiplication, we consider the various cases. In all cases, a and b are counting numbers.

Case 1. $ab = ba$ [part (a) of Definition 8]

Case 2. $0 \cdot {}^-b = 0 = {}^-b \cdot 0$ [part (b) of Definition 8]

Case 3. $a \cdot {}^-b = {}^-b \cdot a$ [part (d) of Definition 8]

Case 4. ${}^-a \cdot b = b \cdot {}^-a$ [part (d) of Definition 8]

Case 5. ${}^-a \cdot {}^-b = ab$ [part (e) of Definition 8]
          $= ba$ [part (a) of Definition 8]
          $= {}^-b \cdot {}^-a$ [part (e) of Definition 8]

Notice that Cases 3 and 4 could be combined into a single case. In all cases, $ab = ba$; that is, if a and b are any integers, then $ab = ba$.

Although we may think that the sign property for multiplication of integers is given in parts (c), (d), (e) of Definition 8, Definition 8 applies only to the cases in which a and b are positive integers. The sign property applies to all integers a and b. For example, by the sign property, $3 \cdot {}^-x = {}^-(3x)$ even if $x \in I^-$. However by Definition 8, $3 \cdot {}^-x = {}^-(3x)$ only if $x \in I^+$. Without the sign property, it would be impossible to perform certain algebraic manipulations that will be necessary later. In order to prove that $a \cdot {}^-b = {}^-(ab)$ for all integers a and b, we consider the various special cases.

Case 1. $a = 0$ or $b = 0$.
               $a \cdot {}^-b = 0 = {}^-(ab)$.

Case 2. $a \in I^+, b \in I^+$
               $a \cdot {}^-b = {}^-(ab)$ [part (c) of Definition 8].

Case 3. $a \in I^-, b \in I^+$
               There exists $c \in I^+$ such that $a = {}^-c$.
               Thus $a \cdot {}^-b = {}^-c \cdot {}^-b$
                         $= cb$ [part (e) of Definition 8]
                         $= bc$ [commutative property]
                         $= {}^-[{}^-(bc)]$ [Theorem 2]
                         $= {}^-[b \cdot {}^-c]$ [part (c) of Definition 8]
                         $= {}^-[{}^-c \cdot b]$ [commutative property]
                         $= {}^-[ab]$.

Case 4. $a \in I^+, b \in I^-$
               There exists $c \in I^+$ such that $b = {}^-c$.
               $a \cdot {}^-b = a \cdot {}^-({}^-c)$
                      $= a \cdot c$ [Theorem 2)
                      $= {}^-[{}^-(ac)]$ [Theorem 2]
                      $= {}^-[a \cdot {}^-c]$ [part (c) of Definition 8]
                      $= {}^-(ab)$.

Case 5. $a \in I^-, b \in I^-$
               There exist $c, d \in I^+$ such that $a = {}^-c$ and $b = {}^-d$.
               $a \cdot {}^-b = ({}^-c) \, {}^-({}^-d)$
                      $= {}^-c \cdot d$ [Theorem 2]
                      $= d \cdot {}^-c$ [commutative property]
                      $= {}^-(dc)$ [part (c) of Definition 8]
                      $= {}^-(cd)$ [commutative property]
                      $= {}^-({}^-c \cdot {}^-d)$ [part (e) of Definition 8]
                      $= {}^-(ab)$.

Thus for all integers a and b, $a \cdot {}^-b = {}^-(ab)$.

The following proof of part (2) of the sign property for multiplication depends on the commutative property and part (1) of the sign property for multiplication.

     ${}^-a \cdot b = b \cdot {}^-a$ [commutative property for multiplication]
           $= {}^-(ba)$ [part (1) of the sign property for multiplication]
           $= {}^-(ab)$ [commutative property for multiplication]
Hence for all integers a and b, ${}^-ab = {}^-(ab)$.
In particular, ${}^-1b = {}^-(1b) = {}^-b$ for any integer b.

Part (3) of the sign property for multiplication follows immediately from parts (1) and (2).

We now prove part (4) of the sign property for multiplication.

$$^-a \cdot {}^-b = {}^-(^-a \cdot b) \text{ [part (1) of the sign property for multiplication]}$$
$$= {}^-[^-(ab)] \text{ [part (2) of the sign property for multiplication]}$$
$$= ab \text{ [Theorem 2]}$$

Thus for all integers a and b, $^-a \cdot {}^-b = ab$.

Hence all four parts of the sign property for multiplication have been proved.

To prove the multiplication property of zero for the set of integers [that is, $(a \cdot b = 0) \rightleftarrows (a = 0 \lor b = 0)$, for all integers a and b], we consider the various cases.

Case 1. $a, b \in C_0$.
            The multiplication property of zero in this case was proved in Chapter 3.

Case 2. $a \in I^-, \ b \in C_0$.
            Then there exists $c \in I^+$ such that $a = {}^-c$.
            $$ab = 0 \rightleftarrows {}^-c \cdot b = 0$$
            $$\rightleftarrows {}^-(cb) = 0$$
            $$\rightleftarrows cb = 0$$
            $$\rightleftarrows c = 0 \text{ or } b = 0$$
            $$\rightleftarrows {}^-a = 0 \text{ or } b = 0$$
            $$\rightleftarrows a = 0 \text{ or } b = 0.$$

Case 3. $a \in C_0, b \in I^-$
            The proof in this case is similar to that in Case 2.

Case 4. $a \in I^-, b \in I^-$
            Then $ab \in I^+$
            Hence $ab \neq 0$
            Thus $ab = 0 \rightleftarrows a = 0$ or $b = 0$ in this case.

Hence, in all cases $ab = 0 \rightleftarrows a = 0$ or $b = 0$.

The cancellation property for multiplication of integers follows immediately from the multiplication property of zero as shown below.

$$[a \neq 0 \land ab = ac] \rightleftarrows ab + {}^-(ac) = 0$$
$$\rightleftarrows ab + a(^-c) = 0$$
$$\rightleftarrows a(b + {}^-c) = 0$$
$$\rightleftarrows b + {}^-c = 0$$
$$\rightleftarrows (b + {}^-c) + c = c$$
$$\rightleftarrows b = c.$$

The associative property for multiplication may be proved from the sign property for multiplication. As in the proof of the sign property, one must consider the various cases. The following examples illustrate the method of proof.

Example 4. $(3 \cdot 4) \cdot 7 = 3 \cdot (4 \cdot 7)$ [associative property for multiplication of counting numbers]

Example 5. $(3 \cdot {}^-4) \cdot 7 = {}^-(3 \cdot 4) \cdot 7$ [sign property (1)]
$= {}^-[(3 \cdot 4) \cdot 7]$ [sign property (2)]
$= {}^-[3 \cdot (4 \cdot 7)]$ [associative property for multiplication of counting numbers]
$= 3 \cdot {}^-(4 \cdot 7)$ [sign property (1)]
$= 3 \cdot ({}^-4 \cdot 7)$ [sign property (2)]

Example 6. $(3 \cdot {}^-4) \cdot {}^-7 = {}^-(3 \cdot 4) \cdot {}^-7$ [sign property (1)]
$= (3 \cdot 4) \cdot 7$ [sign property (4)]
$= 3 \cdot (4 \cdot 7)$ [associative property for multiplication of counting numbers]
$= 3 \cdot ({}^-4 \cdot {}^-7)$ [sign property (4)]

To prove the identity property for multiplication of integers, we employ the identity property for multiplication of counting numbers. If $a \in C_0$, then $a \cdot 1 = 1 \cdot a = a$. If $a \in I^-$, then there exists $b \in I^+$ such that $a = {}^-b$. Then $a \cdot 1 = {}^-b \cdot 1 = {}^-(b \cdot 1) = {}^-(b) = {}^-b$. Thus if a is any integer, then $a \cdot 1 = a$.

The proof of the second part of the identity property for multiplication follows from the first part, the multiplication property of zero, and the definition of additive inverse.

$au = a, \quad a \neq 0$
$au + {}^-a = 0,$
$({}^-a \cdot {}^-u) + {}^-a = 0,$
${}^-a({}^-u + 1) = 0,$
${}^-u + 1 = 0,$
$u = 1.$

Finally, we prove that $a(b + c) = ab + ac$ for any integers a, b, and c.

Case 1. $a = 0, b \in I, c \in I.$
Then $a(b + c) = 0(b + c) = 0.$
Moreover, $ab + ac = 0b + 0c = 0 + 0 = 0.$
Hence $a(b + c) = ab + ac.$

Case 2. $a \in I^+, b \in I, c \in I.$

$$a(b + c) = \underbrace{(b + c) + (b + c) + \ldots + (b + c)}_{a \text{ summands}}$$

[Theorem 2 of Chapter 3 and Definition 8(c)]

$$= \underbrace{(b + b + \ldots + b)}_{a \text{ summands}} + \underbrace{(c + c + \ldots + c)}_{a \text{ summands}}$$

(GCAAPA)

$= ab + ac.$ [Theorem 2 of Chapter 3 and Definition 8(c)]

Case 3. $a \in I^-, b \in I, c \in I.$
Then there exists $d \in I^+$ such that $a = {}^-d.$
Thus $a(b + c) = {}^-d(b + c)$
$\qquad\qquad\quad = d \cdot {}^-(b + c)$ [sign property (3) for multiplication]
$\qquad\qquad\quad = d({}^-b + {}^-c)$ [sign property for addition]
$\qquad\qquad\quad = d({}^-b) + d({}^-c)$ [Case 2]
$\qquad\qquad\quad = {}^-db + {}^-dc$ [sign property (3) for multiplication]
$\qquad\qquad\quad = ab + ac.$

Since these three cases exhaust all possibilities, we have proved the distributive property. That is, if a, b, and c are any integers, then $a(b + c) = ab + ac.$

The reader should realize that Definition 8 set the stage so that the above properties of the integers would be true. The generalized commutative and associative property for multiplication and the generalized distributive property, studied in Chapter 3 for the set of counting numbers, are true also for the set of integers. For example, ${}^-3(5 + {}^-6 + 2 + {}^-9)$ $= {}^-3(5) + {}^-3({}^-6) + {}^-3(2) + {}^-3({}^-9) = 18 + 27 + {}^-6 + {}^-15.$

The following examples illustrate the properties studied in this section.

Example 7. ${}^-1 \cdot ({}^-3 + 5) = 1 \cdot {}^-({}^-3 + 5) = {}^-({}^-3 + 5) = 3 + {}^-5 = {}^-2.$

Example 8. $5({}^-4 + {}^-3 + 2) = 5({}^-4) + 5({}^-3) + 5(2) = {}^-20 + {}^-15 + 10$
$= {}^-35 + 10 = {}^-25.$

Example 9. ${}^-a(2x + {}^-3y + 4z) = {}^-a(2x) + {}^-a({}^-3y) + {}^-a(4z) = {}^-2ax$
$+ 3ay + {}^-4az = 3ay + {}^-2ax + {}^-4az = 3ay - 2ax - 4az.$

Example 10. ${}^-3 \cdot ({}^-5 \cdot 7) = ({}^-3 \cdot {}^-5) \cdot 7 = 15 \cdot 7 = 105.$

Example 11. $^-3 \cdot (^-5 \cdot 7) = ^-3 \cdot ^-35 = 3 \cdot 35 = 105.$

Example 12. $^-(2 + ^-3 + ^-5a + ^-b) = ^-2 + 3 + 5a + b = 1 + 5a + b.$

Example 13. $3 - (4 + ^-3a) = 3 + ^-(4 + ^-3a) = 3 + ^-4 + 3a = ^-1 + 3a$
                $= 3a + ^-1 = 3a - 1.$

Example 14. $^-(a + b + c) = ^-a + ^-b + ^-c = ^-1 \cdot a + ^-1 \cdot b + ^-1 \cdot c$
                $= ^-1(a + b + c).$

Exercise 5.3

I. Compute each of the following.

(1) $5(^-3)$
(2) $^-3(5)$
(3) $^-5(3)$
(4) $^-5(^-3)$
(5) $5(3)$
(6) $^-7(^-3 \cdot ^-2)$
(7) $(^-7 \cdot ^-3)(^-2)$
(8) $3(^-5 + 2)$
(9) $4(5 + ^-3)$
(10) $3(^-5 + ^-2)$
(11) $7(5 + 3)$
(12) $^-7(5 + ^-4)$
(13) $^-3(^-5 + ^-2)$

(14) $^-3(^-5) + ^-3 \cdot ^-2$
(15) $^-7(5) + ^-7(^-4)$
(16) $4(5) + 4(^-3)$
(17) $^-3(^-2 + 5 + ^-6)$
(18) $^-3(^-2) + ^-3(5) + ^-3(^-6)$
(19) $^-5(1) + ^-7(1) + 3(1)$
(20) $2(7) + 7(^-2)$
(21) $^-3 + 0$
(22) $^-3(0)$
(23) $0(3) + 2$
(24) $0(3 + 2)$
(25) $a(3)(^-2).$

II. Convert each of the following open sentences to a true sentence by replacement of the variable by an integer.

(1) $3x = 12$
(2) $3x = ^-12$
(3) $^-3x = 12$
(4) $^-3x = ^-12$
(5) $2x - 5 = 9$
(6) $^-2x + 5 = ^-9$
(7) $^-3x + ^-7 = ^-1$
(8) $^-3x + 7 = ^-2$
(9) $5x = 7(^-5)$
(10) $5(x + ^-3) = 35$
(11) $^-5(x - 3) = ^-35$
(12) $^-17x = 51$
(13) $17x = ^-51$

(14) $13x = ^-39$
(15) $^-11x = 77$
(16) $^-11x = ^-88$
(17) $11x = 88$
(18) $11(x + 3) = 0$
(19) $11(x + 3) = 55$
(20) $11x = 0$ or $11x = 44$
(21) $^-3x + 2 = ^-1$ or $2(^-x) = ^-2$
(22) $^-5x = ^-15$ or $^-5x = 15$
(23) $5(^-3)(2x) = ^-60$
(24) $3x = x$
(25) $3(^-x) = ^-3x$

III. Prove the associative property for multiplication of integers in each of the following cases.

(1) $a \in C_0, b \in C_0, c \in C_0$
(2) $a \in I^-, b \in I^+, c \in I^+$
(3) $a \in I^+, b \in I^-, c \in I^+$
(4) $a \in I^+, b \in I^+, c \in I^-$
(5) $a \in I^+, b \in I^-, c \in I^-$
(6) $a \in I^-, b \in I^-, c \in I^-$

IV. What cases were not considered in Exercise III?

V. Prove that each of the following open sentences may be converted to a true sentence by replacement of each variable by *any* integer.

(1) $^-3(x + 2a + ^-4) = ^-3x + ^-6a + 12$
(2) $5(a + 2b - 3c) = ^-15c + 10b + 5a$
(3) $a(b + ^-3c) = ab - 3ac$
(4) $5 + ^-3b + ^-6c + ^-7^-c = 5 + 7c + ^-3(b + 2c)$
(5) $2abxy(4z) = 8abxyz$
(6) $x(a - b + c - d) = xa - xb + xc - xd$

VI. Discuss the relationship between the binary operator • defined between any pair of integers in Definition 8 and the binary operator • of Definition 3 in Chapter 3.

VII. Prove each of the following.

(1) If a, b, and c are any integers, then $(b + c)a = ba + ca$.
(2) If a, b, c, and d are any integers, then $(b + c + d)a = ba + ca + da$.

5.4   Order Properties of the Set of Integers

In Section 3.5 we studied the order properties of the set of counting numbers. In this section we extend the concept of order to the set of integers. According to Theorem 7 of Chapter 3, if a and b are any counting numbers, then $a < b$ if and only if there exists a positive integer k such that $a + k = b$. Now we define the order relation $<$ between any pair of *integers*. Our definition is motivated by our desire for an order relation between any pair of integers which agrees with the order relation between any pair of *counting numbers*. Accordingly we make the following definition.

DEFINITION 9. The integer a *is less than* the integer b (written $a < b$) if and only if there exists a positive integer k such that $a + k = b$ (that is, $a < b$ if and only if $a + k = b$ for some positive integer k).

Notice that this definition agrees with Theorem 7 of Chapter 3 if a and b are counting numbers. If a or b is a negative integer, Theorem 7 of Chapter 3 does not apply. However, Definition 9 applies in this case. For example, if $a = ^-3$ and $b = 2$, then $a < b$ because there exists a positive integer $k = 5$ such that $a + k = b$; that is, $^-3 + 5 = 2$. Similarly, $^-8 < ^-5$ because $^-8 + 3 = ^-5$. Moreover, $^-7 < 0$ because $^-7 + 7 = 0$. It follows immediately from Definition 9 that any negative integer is less than zero.

Observing that $5 < 8$ and $^-8 < ^-5$, and other similar examples, we are led to the following theorem.

THEOREM 5.   If a and b are any integers, then $a < b$ if and only if $^-b < ^-a$.

Proof.
$(\rightarrow)$ Let $a < b$. Then there exists a *positive* integer k such that $a + k = b$.
Thus $^-(a + k) = ^-b$,
$\quad ^-a + ^-k = ^-b$,
$\quad (^-a + ^-k) + k = ^-b + k$,
$\quad ^-a = ^-b + k$,
$\quad ^-b + k = ^-a$.
Hence $^-b < ^-a$ (since k is a positive integer).

$(\leftarrow)$ Conversely, let $^-b < ^-a$. Then there exists a *positive* integer k such that $^-b + k = ^-a$.
Thus $^-a = ^-b + k$,
$\quad ^-a + ^-k = ^-b + k + ^-k$,
$\quad ^-(a + k) = ^-b$,
$\quad a + k = b$.
Hence $a < b$ (since k is a positive integer).$/\!/$

Theorem 5 enables us to conclude from $3 < 7$, for example, that $^-7 < ^-3$.

Now that we have proved Theorem 5 we are prepared to prove the following theorem for the set of integers.

THEOREM 6.   If a and b are any two distinct integers, then $a < b$ or $b < a$ (but not both).

Proof.

Case 1.   If a and b are counting numbers, then $a < b$ or $b < a$ (but not both) by Theorem 6 of Chapter 3.

Case 2.   If $a \in I^-$ and $b \in C_0$, then $a < b$.

Case 3.   If $a \in C_0$ and $b \in I^-$, then $b < a$.

Case 4.   If $a \in I^-$ and $b \in I^-$, then $^-a \in I^+$ and $^-b \in I^+$.
               By Theorem 6 of Chapter 3, $^-a < {}^-b$ or $^-b < {}^-a$ (but not
               both).
               Hence by Theorem 5, $b < a$ or $a < b$.//

Theorem 6 enables us to state the *trichotomy property* of the integers.

TRICHOTOMY PROPERTY
If a and b are any integers, then one and only one of the following is true:

(1) $a = b$,
(2) $a < b$,
(3) $b < a$.

The following theorems concerning order on I are proved in the same manner as are the corresponding theorems of Chapter 3.

THEOREM 7.   For all $a,b,c \in I$, if $a < b$, then $c + a < c + b$.

THEOREM 8.   (a) For all $a,b,c \in I$, if $a < b$ and $0 < c$, then $ca < cb$.
                (b) For all $a,b,c \in I$, if $a < b$ and $c < 0$, then $cb < ca$.

THEOREM 9.   For all $a,b,c \in I$, if $a < b$ and $b < c$, then $a < c$ (transitive property for $<$).

Although the well-ordering property is true for the set C_0, it is not true for the set I. For example, the subset I^- of I does not contain a least element.

We shall not restate the Archimedean property for the set I.

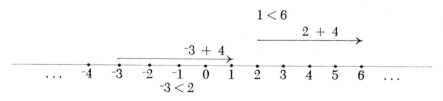

FIGURE 5.9

If $a < b$, then the point labeled a on the number line is to the left of the point labeled b. For example, $^-3 < 2$ and the point $^-3$ is to the left of the point 2 on the number line. By Theorem 7, $4 + ^-3 < 4 + 2$; that is, $1 < 6$. Thus the point 1 on the number line is to the left of the point 6. Theorem 7 is illustrated on the number line in Figure 5.9.

Exercise 5.4

I. By means of Definition 9, determine whether each of the following inequalities is a true sentence.

(1) $3 < ^-8$	(6) $0 < ^-1$
(2) $3 < 7$	(7) $^-7 < ^-8$
(3) $^-3 < 1$	(8) $^-8 < ^-7$
(4) $^-5 < 0$	(9) $4 < 3$
(5) $^-6 < ^-6$	(10) $^-4 < ^-3$

II. Without use of the number line illustrate the transitive property for order in each of the following.

(1) $a = ^-3, b = 0, c = 3$.
(2) $a = ^-5, b = ^-2, c = 0$.
(3) $a = ^-6, b = ^-1, c = 1$.
(4) $a = ^-1, b = 1, c = 5$.
(5) $a = ^-8, b = ^-5, c = ^-3$.

III. Illustrate each part of Exercise II on the number line.

IV. Illustrate each of the following on the number line.

(1) $^-5 + ^-3$	(6) $5 \cdot ^-3$
(2) $5 + ^-3$	(7) $5 \cdot 3$
(3) $^-5 + 3$	(8) $^-5(^-2 + 5)$
(4) $5 + 3$	(9) $^-5 + 0 + 2$
(5) $^-5 \cdot 3$	(10) $1 \cdot ^-6$

5.5 Subtraction Algorithm

In this section we justify the usual algorithm for the subtraction of a positive integer from a larger positive integer. First we justify the algorithm in the decimal system. Later we show that the same general principles are applicable to other numeration systems. The difference $768 - 245$ is usually computed as follows:

$$\begin{array}{r} 768 \\ - 245 \\ \hline 523 \end{array}$$

Subtraction and the Set of Integers

This procedure may be justified as follows:

$$768 - 245 = 768 + {}^-245$$
$$= [7(10^2) + 6(10) + 8] + {}^-[2(10^2) + 4(10) + 5]$$
$$= [7(10^2) + 6(10) + 8] + [{}^-2(10^2) + {}^-4(10) + {}^-5]$$
$$= 7(10^2) + {}^-2(10^2) + 6(10) + {}^-4(10) + 8 + {}^-5$$
$$= (7 + {}^-2)(10^2) + (6 + {}^-4)(10) + (8 + {}^-5)$$
$$= 5(10^2) + 2(10) + 3$$
$$= 523.$$

Notice that the above procedure justifies our subtracting the units digit 5 from the units digit 8 to obtain the units digit 3 of the difference, subtracting the tens digit 4 from the tens digit 6 to obtain the tens digit 2 of the difference, and subtracting the hundreds digit 2 from the hundreds digit 7 to obtain the hundreds digit 5 of the difference. The computation may be arranged as follows:

$$768 = 7(10^2) + 6(10) + 8$$
$${}^-245 = {}^-2(10^2) + {}^-4(10) + {}^-5$$
$$\overline{523 = 5(10^2) + 2(10) + 3}$$

The next example involves a difference in which one must "borrow." The difference $735 - 453$ is usually computed as follows:

$$\overset{1}{7}35$$
$$- 453$$
$$\overline{282}$$

The procedure may be justified as follows:

$$735 - 453 = 735 + {}^-453$$
$$= [7(10^2) + 3(10) + 5] + {}^-[4(10^2) + 5(10) + 3]$$
$$= [6(10^2) + 1(10^2) + 3(10) + 5] + [{}^-4(10^2) + {}^-5(10) + {}^-3]$$
$$= [6(10^2) + 10(10) + 3(10) + 5] + [{}^-4(10^2) + {}^-5(10) + {}^-3]$$
$$= [6(10^2) + 13(10) + 5] + [{}^-4(10^2) + {}^-5(10) + {}^-3]$$
$$= [6(10^2) + {}^-4(10^2)] + [13(10) + {}^-5(10)] + [5 + {}^-3]$$
$$= (6 + {}^-4)(10^2) + (13 + {}^-5)(10) + (5 + {}^-3)$$
$$= 2(10^2) + 8(10) + 2$$
$$= 282.$$

The computation may be arranged as follows:

$$735 = 7(10^2) + 3(10) + 5 = 6(10^2) + 13(10) + 5$$
$${}^-453 = {}^-4(10^2) + {}^-5(10) + {}^-3 = {}^-4(10^2) + {}^-5(10) + {}^-3$$
$$\overline{282} \qquad\qquad\qquad\qquad\qquad = 2(10^2) + 8(10) + 2$$

Since each digit has a place value as well as a face value, when we "borrow" 1 from the 7, we are really "borrowing" 10 tens and adding them to the 3 tens to get 13 tens. This justifies our placing a 1 to the left of the digit 3 and reading it 13. In general, whenever we "borrow" 1 from any digit, we are really "borrowing" ten times the place value of the digit immediately to the right. Actually, the traditional word "borrow" adds nothing to the understanding. The word "reorganize" would be a better word.

The algorithm for subtraction in base 5, base 12, or any other base is similar to that in base 10. For example, the difference $421_5 - 213_5$ may be computed as follows:

$$
\begin{array}{r}
421 = 4(10^2) + 2(10) + 1 = 4(10^2) + 1(10) + 11 \;(\text{all} \\
-213 = {}^-2(10^2) + {}^-1(10) + {}^-3 = {}^-2(10^2) + {}^-1(10) + {}^-3 \quad \text{base} \\
\hline
203 \qquad\qquad = 2(10^2) + 0(10) + 3 \quad \text{five})
\end{array}
$$

The difference $9t27_{12} - 6874_{12}$ may be computed as follows:

$$
\begin{array}{r}
9t27 = 9(10^3) + t(10^2) + 2(10) + 7 = 9(10^3) + 9(10^2) + 12(10) + 7 \\
-6874 = {}^-6(10^3) + {}^-8(10^2) + {}^-7(10) + {}^-4 = {}^-6(10^3) + {}^-8(10^2) + {}^-7(10) + {}^-4 \\
\hline
3173 \qquad\qquad\qquad = 3(10^3) + 1(10^2) + 7(10) + 3 \\
(\text{all base 12})
\end{array}
$$

Exercise 5.5

I. (1) Give a detailed justification of the subtraction algorithm for $421_5 - 213_5$

(2) Give a detailed justification of the subtraction algorithm for $9t27_{12} - 6874_{12}$.

II. Compute each of the following differences in base 5. All given numerals are written in base 5.

(1) $3412 - 2303$ (4) $3422 - 1423$
(2) $3421 - 3212$ (5) $3333 - 2243$
(3) $4312 - 1234$ (6) $4213 - 3434$

III. Convert each of the base five numerals in Exercise II to base ten numerals. Compute each difference in base ten, convert this difference to base five, and check each result of Exercise II.

IV. Compute each of the following differences in base 12. All given numerals are written in base 12.

(1) $9t5 - 895$ (5) $t0e - t0t$
(2) $te0 - 9t0$ (6) $9te - 7tt$
(3) $tet - 99t$ (7) $973 - 664$
(4) $tte - 99t$ (8) $960 - 273$

V. Convert each of the base twelve numerals in Exercise IV to base ten numerals. Compute each difference in base ten, convert this difference to base twelve, and check each result of Exercise IV.

VI. Compute each of the following differences in base 2. All given numerals are written in base 2.

(1) 1101 − 101   (4) 10101 − 1010
(2) 1010 − 1001   (5) 11110 − 10111
(3) 1101 − 1011   (6) 10001 − 1111

VII. Convert each of the base two numerals in Exercise VI to base ten numerals. Compute each difference in base ten, convert this difference to base two, and check each result of Exercise VI.

VIII. Compute each of the following products.

(1) 240 · ⁻3 (base 5)
(2) ⁻134 · 4 (base 5)
(3) 11 · ⁻10 (base 2)
(4) ⁻101 · ⁻11 (base 2)
(5) 76 · ⁻67 (base 12)
(6) ⁻3t · 91 (base 12)
(7) 702 · 57 (base 8)
(8) 407 · 75 (base 8)
(9) (2106)(⁻6) (base 7)
(10) (⁻3056)(⁻5) (base 7)

Chapter 6

ELEMENTARY NUMBER THEORY

6.1 Divisors and Multiples

In the preceding chapters we developed the operations of addition, multiplication, and subtraction and their associated properties. Moreover, we observed that subtraction is the inverse operation of addition. In this chapter we develop the properties of the relation *divides* and the inverse operation of multiplication; namely, the operation of *division*. Our development will be guided by the concept and properties of the relation *divides*.

DEFINITION 1. *The integer b divides the integer a* (written $b \mid a$) if and only if there exists an integer k such that $a = bk$.

DEFINITION 2. The integer b is said to be a *divisor* (or *factor*) of the integer a if and only if $b \mid a$.

DEFINITION 3. The integer a is said to be a *multiple* of the integer b if and only if b is a *divisor* of a.

DEFINITION 4. The integer a is said to be *divisible by* the integer b if and only if a is a multiple of b.

Example 1. $3 \mid 15$ because $3 \cdot 5 = 15$. Thus 3 is a divisor of 15, and 15 is a multiple of 3.

Example 2. $^-3 \mid 15$ because $^-3 \cdot {}^-5 = 15$. Thus $^-3$ is a divisor of 15, and 15 is a multiple of $^-3$.

179

Example 3. $7 \mid ^-56$ because $7 \cdot ^-8 = ^-56$. Thus 7 is a divisor of $^-56$, and $^-56$ is a multiple of 7.

Example 4. $^-7 \mid 0$ because $^-7 \cdot 0 = 0$. Thus $^-7$ is a divisor of 0, and 0 is a multiple of $^-7$.

Example 5. $0 \mid 0$ because $0 \cdot k = 0$ for any integer k. Thus 0 is a divisor of 0, and 0 is a multiple of 0.

Example 6. $0 \nmid 7$ because $0 \cdot k \neq 7$ for any integer k.

Example 7. $3 \nmid 8$ because $3 \cdot k \neq 8$ for any integer k.

Example 8. $12 \nmid 4$ because $12 \cdot k \neq 4$ for any integer k.

Since $b \mid a$ is really a *sentence* (which is either true or false but not both) rather than a *number*, we see that "divides" expresses a *relation* rather than a binary *operation*. Thus, although $2 \cdot 6$ is a number, $2 \mid 6$ is *not* a number but a sentence expressing a relationship between the integers 2 and 6. We should exercise care not to write $2 \mid 6 = 3$.

Since $\mid$ is a relation on the set of integers, it is natural to wonder whether it is an equivalence relation. To determine whether $\mid$ is an equivalence relation, we check the reflexive, symmetric, and transitive properties. Since $a = a \cdot 1$ for any integer a, we see that $a \mid a$. Thus the relation $\mid$ is reflexive. Since $2 \mid 6$ but $6 \nmid 2$, we see that the relation $\mid$ is not symmetric. Consequently, the relation $\mid$ is not an equivalence relation. The following theorem states that $\mid$ is transitive.

THEOREM 1.   If a, b, c are any integers and if $c \mid b$ and $b \mid a$, then $c \mid a$.

Proof.   Let $c \mid b$ and $b \mid a$.
Then there exist integers k_1 and k_2 such that $ck_1 = b$ and $bk_2 = a$.
Thus $a = bk_2$
$= (ck_1)k_2$
$= c(k_1k_2)$
$= ck$ (since k_1k_2 is an integer).
Hence $c \mid a. /\!/$

Example 9. $3 \mid 6$ and $6 \mid 24$. Hence $3 \mid 24$.

Example 10. $7 \mid 21$ and $21 \mid 84$. Hence $7 \mid 84$.

Theorem 1 enables us to conclude, for example, that any integer divisible by 10 is divisible by 2 and 5. Notice that, by Theorem 1, if $b \mid a$, then $b \mid ac$.

The following theorems are used frequently in mathematics.

THEOREM 2.   If a, b, c are any integers such that $c \mid a$ and $c \mid b$, then $c \mid (a + b)$.

Proof.   Let $c \mid a$ and $c \mid b$.
                 Then there exist integers k_1 and k_2 such that $ck_1 = a$ and $ck_2 = b$.
                 Hence $ck_1 + ck_2 = a + b$.
                 Thus $c(k_1 + k_2) = (a + b)$ (by the distributive property).

                 But $k_1 + k_2$ is an integer k (by the closure property for addition of integers).

                 Hence $c \mid (a + b)$ (by Definition 1).//

It follows immediately from Theorem 2 and the definition of subtraction that, if $c \mid a$ and $c \mid b$, then $c \mid (a - b)$. Although the following result is also an immediate consequence of Theorem 2 and of Theorem 4 of Chapter 5, we state it as a theorem.

THEOREM 3.   If a, b, c are any integers such that $c \mid (a + b)$ and $c \mid a$, then $c \mid b$.

Proof.   Let $c \mid (a + b)$ and $c \mid a$.
                 Then $c \mid [(a + b) - a]$.
                 Hence $c \mid b$.//

Recall from Definition 4 that a is *divisible* by b if and only if $b \mid a$. A simple test for divisibility by 4 is an immediate consequence of Theorem 2. According to this test, a number is divisible by 4 if and only if the number represented by the last two digits is divisible by 4. For example, the number 14,324 is divisible by 4. The reason for this is that 14,300 is divisible by 4 and 24 is divisible by 4, and hence by Theorem 2 (14,300 + 24) is divisible by 4; that is, $4 \mid (14{,}300 + 24)$. Similarly, since $4 \mid 137{,}700$ and $4 \mid 72$, it follows from Theorem 2 that 4 divides their sum; that is, $4 \mid 137{,}772$. On the other hand, $4 \mid 137{,}700$ but $4 \nmid 27$. Hence by Theorem 3, $4 \nmid 137{,}727$.

Another divisibility test states that a number is divisible by 5 if and only if its last digit is 0 or 5. For example, by Theorem 1, $5 \mid 3230$

because 5 | 10 and 10 | 3,230. Similarly by Theorem 2, 5 | 62,765 because 5 | 62,760 and 5 | 5.

Although it appears obvious, the following important theorem is stated and proved for future reference. We have already proved that $a \mid a$ for any integer a.

THEOREM 4.   (a) If a is any integer, then $a \mid a$, $a \mid -a$, and $-a \mid a$.
(b) If a is any integer, then $1 \mid a$ and $-1 \mid a$.
(c) If a is any positive integer, then a is the largest integer which divides a.
(d) If a is any counting number and b is any positive integer such that $a < b$ and $b \mid a$, then $a = 0$.

Proof.   (a) Left to you as an exercise.
(b) Left to you as an exercise.
(c) Let a be a positive integer. By Part (a), $a \mid a$.
Let $b \in I^+$ and $b \mid a$. Then there exists $k \in I^+$ such that $bk = a$.
Moreover, $bk = b + b(k - 1)$.
Thus $a = b + b(k - 1)$.
If $k = 1$, then $a = b$.
If $k \neq 1$, then $b(k - 1) \in I^+$ and $b < a$ by Definition 9 of Chapter 5.
Hence $b \leq a$; that is, a is the largest integer which divides a.
(d) Let $a \in C_0$, $b \in I^+$, $a < b$, and $b \mid a$.
Assume $a \neq 0$. Then $a \in I^+$.
By Part (c), a is the largest integer which divides a; that is, $b \leq a$.
But, by hypothesis, $a < b$.
Hence $(a < b) \wedge (b \leq a)$.
Because of this contradiction, the assumption that $a \neq 0$ is false.
Hence $a = 0.\,/\!/$

Although Definition 1 asserts the existence of an integer k such that $bk = a$ whenever the integer b divides the integer a, it does not assert that k is unique. The following theorem clarifies this point.

THEOREM 5.   If a and b are any integers such that $b \mid a$ and $b \neq 0$, then there exists a unique integer k such that $bk = a$.

Proof.   Let $b \mid a$ and $b \neq 0$.

By Definition 1, there exists an integer k_1, such that $bk_1 = a$.

Assume there exists a second integer k_2 such that $bk_2 = a$.

Then $bk_1 = bk_2$.

Since $b \neq 0$, it follows from the cancellation property that $k_1 = k_2$.

Thus the integer k of Definition 1 is unique.//

Theorem 5 asserts the uniqueness of the integer k of Definition 1 whenever $b \neq 0$. However, if $b = 0$, and $b \mid a$, then by Definition 1 $0k = a$ and hence $a = 0$. Since $0k = 0$ for any integer k, we see that there are many integers in this case; that is, k is *not* unique whenever $b = 0$ and $b \mid a$.

Now $3 \mid 15$ because $3 \cdot 5 = 15$. Similarly $5 \mid 35$ because $5 \cdot 7 = 35$. Thus we can define the binary operator $\div$ in such a manner that $15 \div 3 = 5$ and $35 \div 5 = 7$; that is, if $b \mid a$ and $b \neq 0$, then there exists a unique integer k such that $bk = a$. Thus we define $a \div b = k$. However, if $b \nmid a$, then we cannot define $a \div b$ to be a unique integer k such that $bk = a$. For example, since $3 \nmid 8$, there is no integer k such that $8 \div 3 = k$. This fact is a serious deficiency of the *set of integers;* that is, we cannot define a binary operator $\div$ such that $a \div b$ is a unique integer k for any integer a and any nonzero integer b.

In the following definition, the binary operator $\div$ and the binary operation *division* are defined for *certain pairs* of integers.

DEFINITION 5.   For all integers a and $b \neq 0$ such that $b \mid a$, *a divided by b* (written $a \div b$) is the unique integer k such that $a = bk$.

Thus $a \div b = k$ if and only if $a = kb$ and $b \neq 0$. The reason for the use of the word *unique* in Definition 5 is that Theorem 5 guarantees that k is unique. The reason for the restriction on b is that Definition 1 does not exclude the case in which $a = 0$ and $b = 0$. However, in this case the integer k is not unique. If $a \neq 0$ and $b = 0$, then there is no integer k such that $a = bk$. Hence in both cases (that is, $b = 0$) we do not define $a \div b$. That is, $a \div 0$ is *undefined and therefore meaningless.* It follows immediately from Definition 5 that $15 \div 3 = 5$, $21 \div 7 = 3$, but $21 \div 5$ is undefined.

In Chapter 7 we shall extend the set of integers so that $a \div b$ will be defined for any integer a and any nonzero integer b. In addition, all of the properties previously proved for the set of integers will be true for the extended set of numbers. Moreover, we shall discover that there are some additional properties of the extended set. In the remainder of this chapter we shall pursue some more of the elementary properties of the integers. The branch of mathematics which studies integers and their properties is known as *number theory*. If you wish to pursue the study further than in this chapter you should consult any of the well-known texts on number theory.

Exercise 6.1

I. Test each of the following pairs of integers to determine whether $b \mid a$. If $b \mid a$, compute $a \div b$.

(1) $b = 3, a = 21$.

(2) $b = 7, a = 21$.

(3) $b = -5, a = 35$.

(4) $b = -5, a = -50$.

(5) $b = 5, a = -50$.

(6) $b = 5, a = 51$.

(7) $b = 1, a = 6$.

(8) $b = -1, a = -6$.

(9) $b = 2, a = -9$.

(10) $b = 3, a = -9$.

(11) $b = 0, a = 3$.

(12) $b = 0, a = -3$.

(13) $b = 0, a = 0$.

(14) $b = 15, a = -5$.

(15) $b = -3, a = 0$.

(16) $b = 17, a = 0$.

(17) $b = 20, a = -2$.

(18) $b = 10, a = -5$.

(19) $b = -20, a = 20$.

(20) $b = 19, a = -19$.

II. By means of Theorems 1 through 3, decide which of the following integers divides 6758. In each case specify the theorem(s) used.

(1) 2

(2) -2

(3) 4

(4) -4

(5) 8

(6) -8

(7) 5

(8) -5

(9) 10

(10) -10

III. By means of Theorems 1 through 3, decide which of the integers in Exercise II divides -596,732. In each case specify the theorem(s).

IV. Prove that if a, b, c, d are integers and $d \mid a$, $d \mid b$, and $d \mid c$, then $d \mid (a + b + c)$.

V. (1) Prove that 1, -1, 5, and -5 are the only integers which divide 5.

(2) Prove that 1, -1, 7, and -7 are the only divisors of 7.

VI. (1) List the first 10 positive multiples of 3.

(2) List the first 6 positive multiples of 3.

(3) List the first 15 positive multiples of 1.

(4) List the first 10 positive multiples of 50.

(5) List 10 positive multiples of ⁻5.

(6) List 10 negative multiples of ⁻5.

VII. List all divisors (positive and negative) of each of the following integers.

(1) 1   (7) ⁻22

(2) ⁻3   (8) 13

(3) 4   (9) 28

(4) 6   (10) 32

(5) ⁻9   (11) 0

(6) 21   (12) ⁻31

VIII. If the hypotheses of Theorem 5 are satisfied, compute the unique integer k such that $bk = a$ in each part of Exercise I.

IX. (1) Prove Part (a) of Theorem 4.

(2) Prove Part (b) of Theorem 4.

X. (1) By means of Definition 1, define an even integer.

(2) By means of Definition 1, define an odd integer.

(3) By means of Definition 1, define a multiple of 3.

(4) By means of Definition 1, define a multiple of 5.

XI. (1) Prove that if a is any odd integer, then a^2 is an odd integer.

(2) Prove that if a is any even integer, then a^2 is an even integer.

(3) Prove that if a is any integer and b is any even integer, then ab is an even integer.

(4) Prove that if a is any odd integer and b is any odd integer, then ab is an odd integer.

(5) Prove that if a, b, and c are any integers and $b \mid a$, then $b \mid ac$.

(6) Prove that if c is any integer such that $10 \mid c$, then $2 \mid c$ and $5 \mid c$.

(7) Prove that if a, b, and c are any integers such that $c \mid a$ and $c \mid b$, then $c \mid (a - b)$.

XII. Illustrate the proof of Theorem 1 by proving each of the following.

(1) If $2 \mid 6$ and $6 \mid 48$, then $2 \mid 48$.

(2) If $5 \mid 15$ and $15 \mid 75$, then $5 \mid 75$.

6.2 The Division Algorithm

If a and b are integers, $b \neq 0$, and $b \mid a$, then there exists a unique integer k such that $bk = a$. For example, if oranges cost 7 cents each and you have 35 cents, then you can buy exactly 5 oranges because $7 \cdot 5 = 35$; that is, $7 \mid 35$. If bananas cost 5 cents each and you have 35 cents, then you can buy exactly 7 bananas because $5 \cdot 7 = 35$; that is, $5 \mid 35$. If you have 38 cents, then you can still buy 7 bananas but you will have 3 cents change left. The reason for this is that $5 \nmid 38$. However, even in this case, we can write $38 = 5 \cdot 7 + 3$. Of course you can buy 6 bananas, if you prefer, and have 8 cents change remaining. Thus $38 = 5 \cdot 6 + 8$. However, we are interested in determining the *largest* number of 5-cent bananas one can purchase for 38 cents. Thus we write $38 = 5 \cdot 7 + 3$. Notice that $3 < 5$ but that $8 \not< 5$. This example leads us to conjecture that, for any pair of positive integers a and b such that $b < a$, there exist a unique positive integer q and a unique counting number $r < b$ such that $a = bq + r$. We shall actually state and prove a theorem which tells us that our conjecture is true. First, however, we shall give an intuitive justification of the theorem.

Let a and b be positive integers and let $b < a$. On the number line the point b is to the left of the point a, as shown in Figure 6.1. By the trichotomy property, $a < 2b$ or $a = 2b$ or $2b < a$. If $a < 2b$, as shown in Figure 6.1, then $q = 1$ and $r = a - b$. Thus $a = bq + r$, and $0 < r < b$.

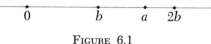

FIGURE 6.1

If $a = 2b$, then $a = b \cdot 2 + 0$. That is $q = 2$, $r = 0$, and $r < b$.

If $2b < a$, as shown in Figure 6.2, we determine whether $a < 3b$ or $a = 3b$ or $3b < a$.

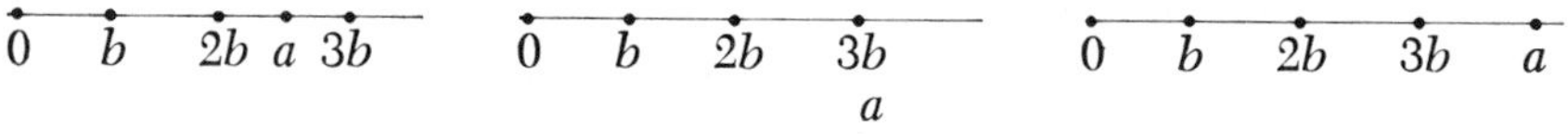

0   b   2b a 3b   0   b   2b   3b   0   b   2b   3b   a

                                          a

FIGURE 6.2

If $a < 3b$, then $q = 2$ and $r = a - 2b$. Thus $a = bq + r$, and $0 < r < b$.

If $a = 3b$, then $a = b \cdot 3 + 0$. That is $q = 3$, $r = 0$, and $r < b$.

If $3b < a$, as shown in Figure 6.3, we determine whether $a < 4b$ or $a = 4b$ or $4b < a$.

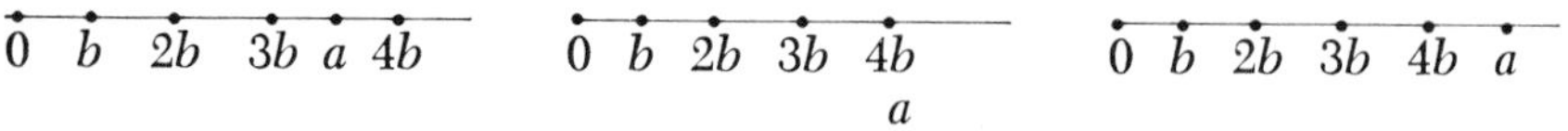

0   b   2b   3b a 4b   0   b   2b   3b   4b   0   b   2b   3b   4b   a

                                          a

FIGURE 6.3

Continuing in this manner, we eventually get an integer q such that $a = bq$ or $bq < a < b(q + 1)$. If $a = bq$, then $r = 0$ and $a = bq + r$. If $bq < a < b(q + 1)$, then there exists a counting number $r = a - bq$. Thus $a = bq + r$ and $r < b$, as shown in Figure 6.4.

FIGURE 6.4

Consider the previous example of the 5-cent bananas and the 38 cents. In this example, $a = 38$ and $b = 5$. The above procedure is illustrated in Figure 6.5. We see that $q = 7$ and $r = 3$.

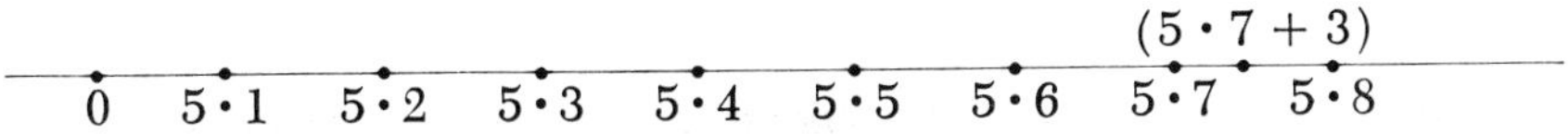

FIGURE 6.5

In all cases we desire the largest integer q such that $bq \leq a$. When q has been computed in this manner, the integer r will be 0 or a positive integer less than b.

The following theorem is a statement of the *division algorithm*. Its proof depends upon the Archimedean property and the well-ordering property.

THEOREM 6.   If a and b are any positive integers and $b < a$, then there exist a unique positive integer q and a unique counting number r such that $a = bq + r$ and $0 \leq r < b$.

Proof.   Consider the set K of positive integers defined by $K = \{k: a < bk\}$.

By the Archimedean property, we know that there exists k_1 such that $a < bk_1$.

Hence $K \neq \phi$.

By the well-ordering property, K contains a least element k_0.

Since $k_0 \in I^+$, there exists $q \in C_0$ such that $k_0 = q + 1$.

Now $q < q + 1 = k_0$.

Hence $q < k_0$.

Consequently $q \notin K$ (since k_0 is the least element of K).

By Definition of K, $q \in K$ if and only if $a < bq$.

Thus $a \not< bq$.

Hence $bq \leq a$ (by the trichotomy property).

Now $a = bq + (a - bq)$.

Since $bq \leq a$, we see that $0 \leq a - bq$.

Hence $a - bq \in C_0$.

Let $r = a - bq$.

Then $a = bq + r$ and $r \in C_0$.

We now know that $0 \le r$.

Now we shall prove that $r < b$.

Since $k_0 = q + 1$ and k_0 is the least element of K, we see
that $q + 1 \in K$ and $a < b(q + 1)$; that is, $a < bq + b$.

Thus $a - bq < b$; that is, $r < b$ (since $r = a - bq$).

Hence $0 \le r < b$.

To prove that q and r are unique, we assume that there also exist
q_1 and r_1 such that $a = bq_1 + r_1$, $0 \le r_1 < b$.

Thus $a = bq + r$ and $a = bq_1 + r_1$.

Hence $bq + r = bq_1 + r_1$.

Case 1. $r \le r_1$.

Then $0 \le r_1 - r$.

Now $bq - bq_1 = r_1 - r$ (since $bq + r = bq_1 + r_1$).

Thus $b(q - q_1) = r_1 - r$.

Hence $b \mid (r_1 - r)$ (by Definition 1).

But $0 \le r_1 - r < b$ (because $0 \le r \le r_1 < b$).

Thus $r_1 - r = 0$; that is, $r_1 = r$ (by Theorem 4(d)).

Then $bq + r = bq_1 + r$.

Hence $bq = bq_1$ and $b \ne 0$.

Thus $q = q_1$.

Case 2. $r_1 \le r$.

The proof is similar to that of Case 1.

In both cases, $r_1 = r$ and $q_1 = q$; that is, the integers r
and q are unique. $/\!/$

If a and b are specified, how are q and r computed? One method is
inspection. A second method is the computational device commonly
called *long division*, which is taught in the elementary schools. Although
this device is called long division and the word *division* is used in the
division algorithm, the operation *division* is not defined unless $r = 0$. In
fact, the operation division is the combining of two integers a and $b \ne 0$
by means of the operator $\div$ to produce a third integer q, which is $a \div b$.
Of course, there is a close analogy between the operation of division and
the division algorithm, which is more general than division. In the
special case of the division algorithm in which $r = 0$, division is actually
defined. In the last section of this chapter, we shall justify the device of
long division. In the meantime, we shall use this device whenever it is
convenient to do so.

Exercise 6.2

I. Compute the integers q and r of the division algorithm ($a = bq + r$, $0 \le r < b$) corresponding to each of the following pairs of integers a and b.

(1) $a = 7, b = 2$.
(2) $a = 20, b = 3$.
(3) $a = 20, b = 2$.
(4) $a = 105, b = 21$.
(5) $a = 105, b = 5$.

(6) $a = 367, b = 7$.
(7) $a = 28, b = 6$.
(8) $a = 28, b = 7$.
(9) $a = 983, b = 29$.
(10) $a = 897, b = 51$.

II. Formulate each of the following in terms of positive integers and apply the division algorithm to compute the largest number of articles which can be purchased and the change in each case. Ignore all sales taxes.

(1) Shirts sell for $5 each. Toby has $26.
(2) Ties sell for $2 each. Paul has $11.
(3) Belts sell for $4 each. Ralph has $9.
(4) Socks sell for $1 per pair. Ed has $6.
(5) Cuff links sell for $4 per pair. Lloyd has $11.
(6) Cigars sell for $4 per box. John has $10.
(7) Pens sell for $2 each. Jack has $9.
(8) Shoes sell for $20 per pair. Dave has $31.
(9) Sport coats sell for $45 each. Maurice has $57.
(10) Sweaters sell for $9 each. Trev has $21.

III. Name the remainder in each part of Exercise II.

IV. Supply the proof of Case 2 of Theorem 6.

V. Formulate each of the following by means of the division algorithm.

(1) Seven boys wish to divide 23 apples without cutting any of the apples.
(2) Three boys wish to divide 23 apples without cutting any of the apples.
(3) Thirty students wish to divide $97 (in $1 bills) without making change.
(4) Five children wish to divide 17 suckers without breaking or cutting any of the suckers.
(5) Twenty-three children wish to divide 25 easter eggs without cutting or breaking any of the easter eggs.
(6) Six thousand students wish to divide 6,000 tickets.

VI. Compute the integers q and r of the base five division algorithm $(a = bq + r, 0 \leq r < b)$ corresponding to each of the following pairs of base five integers a and b.

(1) $a = 12, b = 2$.	(4) $a = 44, b = 2$.
(2) $a = 40, b = 3$.	(5) $a = 43, b = 4$.
(3) $a = 40, b = 2$.	(6) $a = 41, b = 3$.

6.3 Primes and Composites, Greatest Common Divisor

In Section 6.1 we defined *divisor* and *multiple* and proved some of the fundamental divisibility properties. In Section 6.2 we proved the division algorithm. The purpose of this section is to introduce the concept of *prime number*, which plays an important role in mathematics, especially in arithmetic. As we proceed, the reason for the importance of prime numbers will become apparent. Because of Theorem 4, we can restrict the discussion of primes and composites to the set of positive integers.

DEFINITION 6. The positive integer p is said to be a *prime number* (or simply a *prime*) if and only if $p \neq 1$ and the only positive divisors of p are 1 and p.

According to Definition 6, 1 is *not* a prime. Moreover, 4, 6, 8, 9, 10, and 15 are not primes. The first ten primes are 2, 3, 5, 7, 11, 13, 17, 19, 23, 29. Observe that some odd numbers are not primes. The following definition gives a name to an integer such as 15 which is *not* a prime.

DEFINITION 7. The positive integer c is said to be a *composite number* (or simply a *composite*) if and only if $c \neq 1$ and c is not a prime.

The first 10 composites are 4, 6, 8, 9, 10, 12, 14, 15, 16, 18.

It follows from Definitions 6 and 7 that 1 is neither prime nor composite. This choice is arbitrary. We *could* have defined the words *prime* and *composite* so that 1 would be prime. However, in more advanced mathematics time is saved in statements and proofs of theorems if 1 is not considered prime. In the following definition we give a special name to the integer 1.

DEFINITION 8. The positive integer 1 is called a *unit*.

For centuries mathematicians have been fascinated by many interesting questions concerning primes. Although many of these questions have been answered, some of them remain unanswered even today. Many problems in number theory are easily stated but not easily solved. In fact, most problems on the list of unsolved problems are so easily stated that the average high school student can understand them. However, their solutions have evaded the most eminent mathematicians. Later in this chapter we shall consider some of these problems, both solved and unsolved. In particular, we shall prove that every composite number may be written as a product of primes. The importance of this latter result cannot be over-estimated. We now proceed to lay the foundation upon which the proof of this important result is based.

DEFINITION 9. The positive integer c is said to be a *common divisor* of the integers a and b if and only if $c \mid a$ and $c \mid b$.

For example, 5 is a common divisor of 20 and 30 because $5 \mid 20$ and $5 \mid 30$. Other common divisors of 20 and 30 are 1, 2, and 10. Definition 9 is easily extended to include a common divisor of more than two integers; any common divisor is a divisor of each of the integers.

Since 1 divides every positive integer, we see that 1 is a common divisor of any two positive integers a and b. That is, if a and b are any positive integers, then there exists a common divisor of a and b.

Now let us consider the set of all common divisors of a and b. Since any common divisor of a and b divides a, we see that the set of all common divisors of a and b is a subset of $\{1, 2, 3, \ldots, a\}$. Thus the set of all common divisors of a and b is a finite set. Hence it contains a largest element. In Definition 10, we give a name to the element.

DEFINITION 10. The largest member of the set of all common divisors of the positive integers a and b is called the *greatest common divisor* (*gcd*) of a and b.

The gcd of a and b is denoted by (a, b). For example, the set of all common divisors of 210 and 20 is equal to $\{1, 2, 5, 10\}$. Thus the gcd of 210 and 20 is equal to 10. Notice that every element of $\{1, 2, 5, 10\}$ divides 10. This example and other similar ones lead us to suspect that the greatest common divisor of any two positive integers a and b is divisible by every common divisor of a and b. In the following theorem, usually called the *Euclidean algorithm*, some properties of the gcd of a and b are stated.

THEOREM 7. If a and b are any positive integers and $d = (a, b)$, then there exist integers j and k such that $d = ja + kb$. Moreover, if c is any common divisor of a and b, then $c \mid d$.

Proof.   If $a = b$, the theorem is obvious. Without loss of generality, we assume that $b < a$.

By the division algorithm, there exist integers q and r such that $a = bq + r, 0 \leq r < b$.

If $r = 0$, then $a = bq$ and the desired integer d is b; that is, $b = 0a + 1b$.

If $r \neq 0$, we reapply the division algorithm until we obtain a remainder of 0 as follows:

$a = bq + r, 0 \leq r < b$
$b = rq_1 + r_1, 0 \leq r_1 < r$
$r = r_1q_2 + r_2, 0 \leq r_2 < r_1$
$r_1 = r_2q_3 + r_3, 0 \leq r_3 < r_2$
$r_2 = r_3q_4 + r_4, 0 \leq r_4 < r_3$

$\cdots$

$r_{m-2} = r_{m-1}q_m + r_m, 0 \leq r_m < r_{m-1}$
$r_{m-1} = r_mq_{m+1}.$

Eventually there must be a remainder of 0 because $0 \leq r_m < r_{m-1} < r_{m-2} < \ldots < r_1 < r < b$, and there are only a finite number of positive integers less than b.

Now we shall prove that r_m is a common divisor of a and b. Since $r_{m-1} = r_mq_{m+1}$, we see that $r_m \mid r_{m-1}$. Hence, by Theorem 1, $r_m \mid r_{m-1}q_m$. Thus by Theorem 2, r_m divides $r_{m-1}q_m + r_m$; *that is, $r_m \mid r_{m-2}$.* Proceeding in this manner, we see that $r_m \mid r_{m-3}, r_m \mid r_{m-4}, \ldots, r_m \mid r_1, r_m \mid r, r_m \mid b$, and $r_m \mid a$. Thus r_m is a common divisor of a and b.

Although we could prove that there exist integers j and k such that $r_m = ja + kb$, we shall not actually prove this fact here. Instead, we illustrate the proof in Examples 1 through 4.

To prove that r_m is the gcd of a and b, we let c be any common divisor of a and b and prove that $c \mid r_m$.

Now $c \mid a$ and $c \mid b$,
$c \mid ja$ and $c \mid kb$ (by Theorem 1),
$c \mid (ja + kb)$ (by Theorem 2),
$c \mid r_m$ (since $r_m = ja + kb$).
Hence r_m is the gcd of a and b [by Theorem 4(c)].
Thus $r_m = d$ and there exist integers j and k such that $d = ja + kb.\mathbin{/\!/}$

Theorem 7 is extremely useful in number theory and enables us to prove that any composite may be written as a product of primes.

The following examples illustrate a procedure for computing (a, b) and the integers j and k of Theorem 7. In Section 6.5 we shall give an alternate method for computing (a, b).

Example 1.   Compute $(294, 273)$ and express it in the form $j(294) + k(273)$.

$294 = 273(1) + 21$
$273 = 21(13).$
Hence $(294, 273) = 21.$
Now $21 = 294 - 273(1)$
$\qquad = 1(294) + {}^-1(273).$
Thus $(294, 273) = 1(294) + {}^-1(273)$, and $j = 1$ and $k = {}^-1.$

Example 2.   Compute $(364, 154)$ and express it in the form $j(364) + k(154)$.

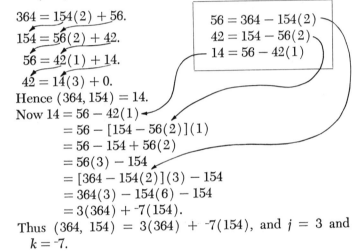

$364 = 154(2) + 56.$
$154 = 56(2) + 42.$
$56 = 42(1) + 14.$
$42 = 14(3) + 0.$
Hence $(364, 154) = 14.$

$$56 = 364 - 154(2)$$
$$42 = 154 - 56(2)$$
$$14 = 56 - 42(1)$$

Now $14 = 56 - 42(1)$
$\qquad = 56 - [154 - 56(2)](1)$
$\qquad = 56 - 154 + 56(2)$
$\qquad = 56(3) - 154$
$\qquad = [364 - 154(2)](3) - 154$
$\qquad = 364(3) - 154(6) - 154$
$\qquad = 3(364) + {}^-7(154).$
Thus $(364, 154) = 3(364) + {}^-7(154)$, and $j = 3$ and $k = {}^-7.$

Example 3.   Compute $(526, 72)$ and express it in the form $j(526) + k(72)$.

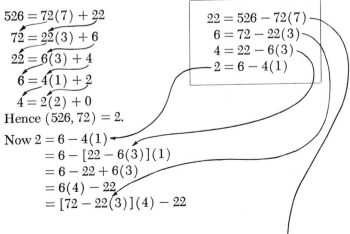

$526 = 72(7) + 22$
$72 = 22(3) + 6$
$22 = 6(3) + 4$
$6 = 4(1) + 2$
$4 = 2(2) + 0$
Hence $(526, 72) = 2.$

$$22 = 526 - 72(7)$$
$$6 = 72 - 22(3)$$
$$4 = 22 - 6(3)$$
$$2 = 6 - 4(1)$$

Now $2 = 6 - 4(1)$
$\qquad = 6 - [22 - 6(3)](1)$
$\qquad = 6 - 22 + 6(3)$
$\qquad = 6(4) - 22$
$\qquad = [72 - 22(3)](4) - 22$

$$= 72(4) - 22(12) - 22$$
$$= 72(4) - 22(13)$$
$$= 72(4) - [526 - 72(7)](13)$$
$$= 72(4) - 526(13) + 72(91)$$
$$= 72(95) + 526(^-13)$$
$$= ^-13(526) + 95(72).$$

Thus $(526, 72) = ^-13(526) + 95(72)$, and $j = ^-13$ and $k = 95$.

Example 4.   Compute $(63, 44)$ and express it in the form $j(63) + k(44)$.

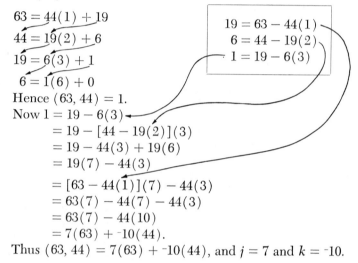

$$63 = 44(1) + 19$$
$$44 = 19(2) + 6$$
$$19 = 6(3) + 1$$
$$6 = 1(6) + 0$$

Hence $(63, 44) = 1$.

Now
$$1 = 19 - 6(3)$$
$$= 19 - [44 - 19(2)](3)$$
$$= 19 - 44(3) + 19(6)$$
$$= 19(7) - 44(3)$$
$$= [63 - 44(1)](7) - 44(3)$$
$$= 63(7) - 44(7) - 44(3)$$
$$= 63(7) - 44(10)$$
$$= 7(63) + ^-10(44).$$

Thus $(63, 44) = 7(63) + ^-10(44)$, and $j = 7$ and $k = ^-10$.

Notice that the integers j and k are not unique. For example, $1 = 7(63) + ^-10(44) = 51(63) + ^-73(44)$. Thus $j = 7$ and $k = ^-10$, or $j = 51$ and $k = ^-73$. In fact, there are infinitely many pairs of integers j and k such that $(63, 44) = j(63) + k(44)$.

DEFINITION 11.   The positive integers a and b are said to be *relatively prime* if and only if $(a, b) = 1$.

For example, 63 and 44 are relatively prime. Similarly 5 and 12 are relatively prime. Obviously, any two primes are relatively prime.

Exercise 6.3

I. (1) List all primes less than 100.
    (2) List all composites less than 100.
    (3) List all primes less than 3.
    (4) List all odd composites between 7 and 59.

II. (1) Form the union of the sets in Exercises I(1) and I(2).

    (2) Form the union of the sets in Exercises I(3) and I(4).

    (3) Form the intersection of the sets in Exercises I(1) and I(2).

    (4) Form the intersection of the sets in Exercises I(3) and I(4).

III. (1) List all even primes.

    (2) Use Definition 7 to prove that 51 is composite.

    (3) List all composites less than 100 which are of the form $4k + 1$, where k is a counting number.

IV. List all divisors of each of the following integers.

(1) 23

(2) 25

(3) 6

(4) 16

(5) 24

(6) 28

(7) 64

(8) 1

(9) 0

(10) $4p$, where p is a prime

V. (1) List all integers each of which has exactly two divisors.

    (2) List all integers each of which has infinitely many divisors.

    (3) List five integers each of which has exactly four divisors.

    (4) List five integers each of which has exactly six divisors.

    (5) List five odd integers each of which has exactly six divisors.

VI. Compute each of the following.

(1) $(105, 30)$

(2) $(36, 24)$

(3) $(11, 3)$

(4) $(796, 21)$

(5) $(875, 651)$

(6) $(150, 57)$

(7) $(10, 18)$

(8) $(15, 25)$

(9) $(14, 21)$

(10) $(60, 84)$

VII. For each pair of numbers a and b in Exercise VI compute j and k such that $(a, b) = ja + kb$.

VIII. Extend the definition of gcd to more than two integers and compute $(48, 42, 66)$.

IX. Let a and b be positive integers and $b < a$. Suppose repeated application of the division algorithm yields the following result:

$a = bq + r, 0 < r < b$

$b = rq_1 + r_1, 0 < r_1 < r$

$r = r_1q_2 + r_2, 0 < r_2 < r_1$

$r_1 = r_2q_3.$

    (1) Without use of Theorem 7, prove that $(a, b) = r_2$.

    (2) Express (a, b) in the form $ja + kb$.

6.4   Prime Factorization

In this section we prove that every positive integer may be written as a product of primes. In order to prove this important theorem, we need the following theorem, which depends on the Euclidean algorithm.

THEOREM 8.   If p is any prime and a_1 and a_2 are any positive integers such that $p \mid a_1 a_2$, then $p \mid a_1$ or $p \mid a_2$.

Proof.   If $a_1 = 1$, the theorem is obvious. Without loss of generality, we assume that $a_1 \neq 1$.

Since $p \mid a_1$ or $p \nmid a_1$, we must consider two cases.

Case 1. $p \mid a_1$.
Then $p \mid a_1$ or $p \mid a_2$ (By Section 1.9, $r \to r \vee s$).

Case 2. $p \nmid a_1$.
In this case, we must prove that $p \mid a_2$.
Since p is a prime and $a_1 \neq 1$, it follows that $a_1 \nmid p$.
Now $p \nmid a_1 \wedge a_1 \nmid p \to (a_1, p) = 1$.
Hence $(a_1, p) = 1$.
By Theorem 7, there exist integers j and k such that
$1 = ja_1 + kp$.
Hence $1 \cdot a_2 = (ja_1 + kp)a_2$; that is, $a_2 = ja_1 a_2 + kpa_2$.
By hypothesis, $p \mid a_1 a_2$.
Thus $p \mid ja_1 a_2$ and $p \mid kpa_2$ [By Theorem 1 or problem XI(6) of Section 6.1].
Hence $p \mid ja_1 a_2 + kpa_2$)   (By Theorem 2).
Therefore $p \mid a_2$ (since $a_2 = ja_1 a_2 + kpa_2$).
Hence $p \mid a_1$ or $p \mid a_2$.//

The following examples illustrate Theorem 8.

Example 1.   Given that $7 \mid 16(3710)$, we know that 7 *must* divide 3710.

Example 2.   Since $5 \nmid 2357$ and $5 \nmid 983$, we see that $5 \nmid (2357)(983)$. The proof is based on the contrapositive of Theorem 8; namely, if $p \nmid a_1$ and $p \nmid a_2$, then $p \nmid a_1 a_2$.

Example 3.   Although $6 \mid (15)(2)$, we see that $6 \nmid 15$ and $6 \nmid 2$. The reason that the conclusion of Theorem 8 is not true in this example is that the hypothesis is not true; that is, 6 is not prime. We cannot guarantee the conclusion of a theorem unless the hypothesis is true.

Example 4. $6 \mid (4)(12)$
$6 \nmid 4$ but $6 \mid 12$
Although 6 is not a prime, and hence the hypothesis is false, the conclusion is true.

Example 5. Observe that $7 \mid (41)(309)(38,500)$,
$7 \nmid 41$, $7 \nmid 309$, and $7 \mid 38,500$.

Example (5) is an *extension* of Theorem 8. Although Theorem 8 is stated for the product of two positive integers a_1 and a_2, it may be generalized to include the case in which p divides the product of any numbe of positive integers. The more general theorem is stated below.

THEOREM 9. If p is any prime and a_1, a_2, . . . , a_k are any positive integers such that $p \mid (a_1 \cdot a_2 \cdot \ldots a_k)$, then $p \mid a_1$ or $p \mid a_2$ or . . . or $p \mid a_k$.

Proof. If $k = 2$; that is, if $p \mid a_1 a_2$, then $p \mid a_1$ or $p \mid a_2$ (By Theorem 8).

If $k = 3$; that is, if $p \mid a_1 a_2 a_3$, then $p \mid (a_1 a_2)a_3$.

By Theorem 8, $p \mid (a_1 a_2)$, or $p \mid a_3$.

Applying Theorem 8 again, we see that $p \mid a_1$ or $p \mid a_2$, or $p \mid a_3$.

By repeated application of Theorem 8, we see that $p \mid a_1$ or $p \mid a_2$ or $p \mid a_3$ or . . . or $p \mid a_k$.//

The above proof of Theorem 9 is more of a plausible explanation than a rigorous proof. The rigorous proof of Theorem 9 depends on the *postulate of finite induction*, which we shall not include in this text. The proofs of the generalized commutative, associative, and distributive properties of the integers also are based on the postulate of finite induction.

Recall from Definition 2 that b is called a factor of a if and only if $a = bk$ for some integer k. By this same definition we see that k is also a factor of a. When an integer has been written as a product of factors, we say that it has been *factored*. Thus a has been factored into its factors b and k. In particular, 21 may be factored as $3 \cdot 7$, and 30 may be factored as $6 \cdot 5$. Since $6 = 2 \cdot 3$, we can factor 30 into a product of three factors; thus $30 = 2 \cdot 3 \cdot 5$. Notice that the three factors of 30 are

Elementary Number Theory

primes. Thus 30 has been written as a product of prime factors. Similarly, when we write $21 = 3 \cdot 7$, we are writing 21 as a product of prime factors.

DEFINITION 12. (a) The integer a is said to be *factored* if and only if it is written as a product of factors.

(b) The integer a is said to be *factored into prime factors* if and only if it is written as a product of prime factors.

(c) A *prime factorization* of the integer a is any product of primes $p_1 p_2 \ldots p_k$ such that $a = p_1 p_2 \ldots p_k$.

Thus $2 \cdot 3 \cdot 5$ is a prime factorization of 30. Other prime factorizations of 30 are $2 \cdot 5 \cdot 3$, $3 \cdot 5 \cdot 2$, $3 \cdot 2 \cdot 5$, $5 \cdot 2 \cdot 3$, and $5 \cdot 3 \cdot 2$. The only difference between any two of these prime factorizations of 30 is the *order* in which the prime factors are written. If we disregard the order, we see that there is *exactly one* prime factorization of 30.

Now we are ready to prove the important result mentioned in the beginning of this section. This result, known as the *unique prime factorization theorem* (or *fundamental theorem of arithmetic*) is stated below.

THEOREM 10. (a) If a is any composite, then a may be written as a product of primes; $a = p_1 p_2 \ldots p_k$.

(b) Except for the order in which the primes are written, the prime factorization of a is unique; that is, if $a = p_1 p_2 \ldots p_i$ and $a = q_1 q_2 \ldots q_j$, then $p_1, p_2, \ldots, p_i$ are the same primes as $q_1, q_2, \ldots, q_j$.

Proof.   (a) Let a be a composite.

By Definition 7, there exist positive integers b and c such that $a = bc$, $1 < b < a$, and $1 < c < a$.

If b and c are primes, then a has been factored into prime factors.

If b or c is a composite, then it can be factored into two or more smaller factors.

Continuing in this manner, we eventually factor any composite factor into prime factors.

Thus we conclude that a can be written as a product of primes; that is, $a = p_1 p_2 \ldots p_k.\mathbin{/\!/}$

However, we have not proved that this prime factorization is unique; that is, we have not proved that two different procedures will yield the same prime factorization, except for order. It is important to investigate this because we know that a number may have two different factorizations if the factors are composite. For example, $60 = 5 \cdot 12$ and $60 = 6 \cdot 10$.

(b) To prove that the prime factorization is unique, we assume that there are two prime factorizations of a; that is, we assume that $a = p_1 p_2 \ldots p_i$ and $a = q_1 q_2 \ldots q_j$.

Then $p_1 p_2 \ldots p_i = q_1 q_2 \ldots q_j$.

By Definition 1, $p_1 \mid (q_1 q_2 \ldots q_j)$.

By Theorem 9, $p_1 \mid q_1$ or $p_1 \mid q_2$ or $\ldots$ or $p_1 \mid q_j$.

Thus there exists an integer s such that $p_1 \mid q_s$ and $1 \leq s \leq j$.

By the generalized commutative property, we may rearrange the subscripts on the primes $q_1, q_2, \ldots, q_j$ such that $p_1 \mid q_1$.

But p_1 and q_1 are primes.

Therefore $p_1 = q_1$.

By the cancellation property for multiplication, $p_2 p_3 \ldots p_i = q_2 q_3 \ldots q_j$.

Continuing the above procedure, we see that $p_2 = q_2$, $p_3 = q_3, \ldots, p_i = q_j$, and $i = j.//$

One of the main applications of the unique prime factorization theorem is to the addition of fractions. In order to add two or more fractions we first compute the least common denominator. In the next section we shall develop a method for computing the least common denominator based on the unique prime factorization theorem. It is interesting to note that the techniques employed in the addition of algebraic fractions are generalizations of the techniques employed in the addition of numerical fractions. The unique prime factorization theorem has been proved for the set of positive integers.

Examples 6 through 9 illustrate the theorem. In Example 10 we investigate a system which does not have a unique prime factorization theorem.

Example 6.   Exhibit the unique prime factorization of 1430.
$$1430 = 2(715) = 2(5)(143) = 2(5)(11)(13).$$

Example 7.   Factor 495 into a product of primes.
$$495 = 3(165) = 3(3)(55) = 3(3)(5)(11) = 3^2(5)(11).$$

Example 8.   Express 625 as a product of primes.
$$625 = 5(125) = 5(5)(25) = 5(5)(5)(5) = 5^4.$$

Example 9.   Write 13,328 as a product of primes.

$$13{,}328 = 2(6{,}664) = 2(2)(3332) = 2(2)(2)(1666)$$
$$= 2(2)(2)(2)(833) = 2(2)(2)(2)(7)(119)$$
$$= 2(2)(2)(2)(7)(7)(17) = 2^4(7^2)(17).$$

Notice that we have extracted the prime factors in numerical order. First we determine whether 2 is a factor and, if it is, we write it as many times as it appears. Next we try 3, then 5, then 7, then 11, et cetera, until the number has been expressed as a product of primes. Observe that the prime factors of a number are not necessarily distinct.

Example 10.   Let the universe be the set $\{1, 5, 9, 13, 17, 21, \ldots\}$; that is, $U = \{4k + 1: k \in C_0\}$. Any number p of U is said to be a *prime* if and only if its only divisors (in U) are 1 and p. In the following list of the first 25 elements of U, the primes are underlined.

<u>1</u> <u>5</u> <u>9</u> <u>13</u> <u>17</u> <u>21</u> 25 <u>29</u> <u>33</u> <u>37</u> <u>41</u> 45 <u>49</u> <u>53</u>
<u>57</u> <u>61</u> 65 <u>69</u> <u>73</u> <u>77</u> 81 85 <u>89</u> <u>93</u> 97

Since every composite in the partial list above can be factored uniquely into a product of primes of U, one might conjecture that every composite in U has a unique prime factorization. However, the number 693, which is an element of U, can be written as a product of primes of U in two different ways:

$$693 = 9 \cdot 77$$
$$693 = 21 \cdot 33$$

Thus there is no unique prime factorization theorem in the set U.

The above example should caution you not to assert a general theorem from a few, or even many, cases. This is a good illustration of the necessity of a general proof of Theorem 10. No matter how many composite numbers of I^+ we manage to factor uniquely into prime factors, it is still necessary to give a general proof of the unique prime factorization theorem.

Exercise 6.4

I. Express each of the following as a product of primes.

(1) 126   (3) 500
(2) 120   (4) 578

(5) 240	(8) 480
(6) 2115	(9) 960
(7) 3115	(10) 238

II. In each of the following express a and b as products of primes.

(1) $a = 30, b = 525$.	(5) $a = 40, b = 21$.
(2) $a = 14, b = 21$.	(6) $a = 39, b = 33$.
(3) $a = 75, b = 10$.	(7) $a = 6, b = 6$.
(4) $a = 60, b = 24$.	(8) $a = 8, b = 15$.

III. In each part of Exercise II, compute the largest integer d such that $d \mid a$ and $d \mid b$.

IV. In each part of Exercise II, compute the smallest positive integer m such that $a \mid m$ and $b \mid m$.

V. Prove each of the following.

(1) If $(a, b) = 1$ and $a \mid bc$, then $a \mid c$.

(2) If $1 = ja + kb$, for some integers j and k, then $(a, b) = 1$.

(3) If $3 = ja + kb$, for some integers j and k, then $(a, b) = 1$ or 3.

(4) If p is a prime and $p \mid abc$, then $p \mid a$, or $p \mid b$, or $p \mid c$.

(5) If $d = (a, b)$, then there exist integers a_1 and b_1 such that $a = a_1 d$, $b = b_1 d$, and $(a_1, b_1) = 1$.

6.5 Least Common Multiple

By Definition 3, a is a multiple of b if and only if b is a divisor of a. Thus 35 is a multiple of 5 because 5 is a divisor of 35; that is, $35 = 5(7)$. We see also that $7 \mid 35$ and that 35 is a multiple of 7. Some multiples of 9 are 9, 18, 27, 36, 45, 54, 63, 72, and some multiples of 12 are 12, 24, 36, 48, 60, 72. From these two sets of multiples we see that 36 and 72 are multiples of 9 and of 12; that is, 36 is a *common multiple* of 9 and 12, and so is 72. In the following definition and throughout the remainder of this chapter, unless otherwise specified, the letters a, b, c, ... will represent positive integers.

DEFINITION 13. The positive integer c is said to be a *common multiple* of the positive integers a and b if and only if c is a multiple of a and c is a multiple of b.

For any pair of positive integers a and b we know that a common multiple exists: namely, ab. In fact, for any positive integer k, kab is a common multiple of a and b. Thus, since 36 is a common multiple of 9 and 12, we see that $2(36)$, $3(36)$, $4(36)$, ... are also common multiples of 9 and 12. The set $M = \{m_1, m_2, \ldots\}$ of all common multiples of a and b is a subset of C_0. By the well-ordering property, there is a least element m of M. For example, the set $\{36, 72, 108, 144, \ldots\}$ of all common multiples of 9 and 12 contains the least element 36. For this reason we say that 36 is the *least common multiple* of 9 and 12.

DEFINITION 14. The *least common multiple* (*lcm*) of a and b is the least element m of the set of all common multiples of a and b.

The least common multiple of a and b is written $[a, b]$. Thus $[9, 12] = 36$ and $[5, 7] = 35$. It is worth mentioning again that the lcm is a useful concept in the addition of fractions, as we shall see in the next chapter.

We may employ the unique prime factorization theorem to compute the lcm of any two positive integers. For convenience, we define $a^0 = 1$ for any nonzero integer a. Later in Chapter 8, we shall define a^0 for any nonzero real number a and discuss the advantages of the notation.

Example 1.   Compute $[12, 9]$.
$12 = 2 \cdot 2 \cdot 3$.
$9 = 3 \cdot 3$.
Since 12 divides $[12, 9]$, we see that $[12, 9]$ must contain the factor $2 \cdot 2 \cdot 3$. Since 9 divides $[12, 9]$, we see that $[12, 9]$ must contain the factor $3 \cdot 3$. Clearly, the smallest positive integer containing these factors is $2 \cdot 2 \cdot 3 \cdot 3$. Hence $[12, 9] = 36$.

Example 2.   Compute $[360, 84]$.
$360 = 2^3 \cdot 3^2 \cdot 5 = 2^3 \cdot 3^2 \cdot 5^1 \cdot 7^0$.
$84 = 2^2 \cdot 3 \cdot 7 = 2^2 \cdot 3^1 \cdot 5^0 \cdot 7^1$.
Thus $[360, 84] = 2^3 \cdot 3^2 \cdot 5^1 \cdot 7^1$.

Example 3.   Compute $[40320, 2376]$.
$40320 = 2^7 \cdot 3^2 \cdot 5 \cdot 7 = 2^7 \cdot 3^2 \cdot 5^1 \cdot 7^1 \cdot 11^0$.
$2376 = 2^3 \cdot 3^3 \cdot 11 = 2^3 \cdot 3^3 \cdot 5^0 \cdot 7^0 \cdot 11^1$.
Thus $[40320, 2376] = 2^7 \cdot 3^3 \cdot 5 \cdot 7 \cdot 11$.

Example 4.   Compute $[105, 22]$.
$105 = 3 \cdot 5 \cdot 7 = 2^0 \cdot 3^1 \cdot 5^1 \cdot 7^1 \cdot 11^0$.
$22 = 2 \cdot 11 = 2^1 \cdot 3^0 \cdot 5^0 \cdot 7^0 \cdot 11^1$.
Thus $[105, 22] = 2^1 \cdot 3^1 \cdot 5^1 \cdot 7^1 \cdot 11^1$.

The following theorem justifies the procedure for computing the lcm of any two positive integers a and b. In the exercises you are asked to supply the proof.

THEOREM 11. If a and b are any positive integers such that $a = p_1^{s_1}p_2^{s_2} \ldots p_k^{s_k}$, $b = p_1^{t_1}p_2^{t_2} \ldots p_k^{t_k}$, and the primes $p_1, p_2, \ldots, p_k$ are all distinct, then $[a, b] = p_1^{w_1}p_2^{w_2} \ldots p_k^{w_k}$, where w_1 is the maximum of s_1 and t_1, w_2 is the maximum of s_2 and $t_2, \ldots$, and w_k is the maximum of s_k and t_k.

The reader should notice that some of the exponents may be 0.

To illustrate again the notation of Theorem 11, we reconsider Example 3. In Example 3, $a = 40320 = 2^7 \cdot 3^2 \cdot 5^1 \cdot 7^1 \cdot 11^0$, $p_1 = 2$, $s_1 = 7$, $p_2 = 3$, $s_2 = 2$, $p_3 = 5$, $s_3 = 1$, $p_4 = 7$, $s_1 = 1$, and $p_5 = 11$, $s_5 = 0$. Similarly, $b = 2376 = 2^3 \cdot 3^3 \cdot 5^0 \cdot 7^0 \cdot 11^1$, $t_1 = 3$, $t_2 = 3$, $t_3 = 0$, $t_4 = 0$, and $t_5 = 1$. Thus $w_1 = 7 =$ maximum of 7 and 3, $w_2 = 3 =$ maximum of 2 and 3, $w_3 = 1 =$ maximum of 1 and 0, $w_4 = 1 =$ maximum of 1 and 0, and $w_5 = 1 =$ maximum of 0 and 1. Consequently $[40320, 2376] = 2^7 \cdot 3^3 \cdot 5^1 \cdot 7^1 \cdot 11^1$.

Similarly, we may employ the unique prime factorization theorem to compute the gcd of any two positive integers. The following examples illustrate the method.

Example 5.   Compute $(12, 9)$.

$12 = 2 \cdot 2 \cdot 3$

$9 = 3 \cdot 3$

Since $(12, 9) \mid 12$, we see that $(12, 9)$ must be a factor of 12.

Since $(12, 9) \mid 9$, we see that $(12, 9)$ must be a factor of 9. Clearly, the largest positive integer which is a factor of *both* 12 and 9 is 3.

Hence $(12, 9) = 3$.

Example 6.   Compute $(360, 84)$.

$360 = 2^3 \cdot 3^2 \cdot 5 = 2^3 \cdot 3^2 \cdot 5^1 \cdot 7^0$.

$84 = 2^2 \cdot 3 \cdot 7 = 2^2 \cdot 3^1 \cdot 5^0 \cdot 7^1$.

Thus $(360, 84) = 2^2 \cdot 3^1 \cdot 5^0 \cdot 7^0$

$\qquad\qquad\qquad = 2^2 \cdot 3^1$

$\qquad\qquad\qquad = 12$.

Example 7.   Compute $(40320, 2376)$.

$40320 = 2^7 \cdot 3^2 \cdot 5 \cdot 7 = 2^7 \cdot 3^2 \cdot 5^1 \cdot 7^1 \cdot 11^0$.

$2376 = 2^3 \cdot 3^3 \cdot 11 = 2^3 \cdot 3^3 \cdot 5^0 \cdot 7^0 \cdot 11^1.$

Thus $(40320, 2376) = 2^3 \cdot 3^2 \cdot 5^0 \cdot 7^0 \cdot 11^0$

$$= 2^3 \cdot 3^2$$
$$= 72.$$

Example 8.   Compute $(105, 22)$.

$105 = 3 \cdot 5 \cdot 7 = 2^0 \cdot 3^1 \cdot 5^1 \cdot 7^1 \cdot 11^0.$

$22 = 2 \cdot 11 = 2^1 \cdot 3^0 \cdot 5^0 \cdot 7^0 \cdot 11^1.$

Thus $(105, 22) = 2^0 \cdot 3^0 \cdot 5^0 \cdot 7^0 \cdot 11^0$

$$= 1.$$

The following theorem justifies the procedure for computing the gcd of any two positive integers a and b. In the exercises you are asked to supply the proof.

THEOREM 12.   If a and b are any positive integers such that $a = p_1^{s_1}p_2^{s_2} \ldots p_k^{s_k}$, $b = p_1^{t_1}p_2^{t_2} \ldots p_k^{t_k}$, and the primes $p_1, p_2, \ldots, p_k$ are all distinct, then $(a, b) = p_1^{v_1}p_2^{v_2} \ldots p_k^{v_k}$, where v_1 is the minimum of s_1 and t_1, v_2 is the minimum of s_2 and t_2, $\ldots$, and v_k is the minimum of s_k and t_k.

The reader should notice that some of the exponents may be 0. In Example 7 above, $p_1 = 2$, $p_2 = 3$, $p_3 = 5$, $p_4 = 7$, $p_5 = 11$; $s_1 = 7$, $s_2 = 2$, $s_3 = 1$, $s_4 = 1$, $s_5 = 0$; $t_1 = 3$, $t_2 = 3$, $t_3 = 0$, $t_4 = 0$, $t_5 = 1$; $v_1 = 3$, $v_2 = 2$, $v_3 = 0$, $v_4 = 0$, $v_5 = 0$.

Exercise 6.5

I.   (1) Compute the multiples of 5 which are less than 101.
     (2) Compute the multiples of 5 which are less than 100.
     (3) Compute the multiples of 2 which are less than 50.
     (4) Compute the multiples of 4 which are less than 50.
     (5) Compute the multiples of 10 which are less than 100.

II. Compute the lcm of each of the following pairs of numbers.

(1) 2 and 3.	(6) 630 and 84.
(2) 10 and 15.	(7) 84 and 630.
(3) 9 and 6.	(8) 98 and 56.
(4) 22 and 77.	(9) 55 and 22.
(5) 630 and 42.	(10) 7 and 15.

III. Compute the gcd of each pair of numbers in Exercise II.

IV. Observe from Exercises II and III that $ab = (a, b) [a, b]$.

   (1) Prove that $ab = (a, b) [a, b]$ for any positive integers a and b.

   (2) Prove that if a and b are relatively prime, then $[a, b] = ab$.

V. (1) Formulate a definition for $[a, b, c]$.

   (2) State a theorem for computing $[a, b, c]$.

   (3) State a theorem for computing (a, b, c).

VI. Compute the lcm of each of the following number triplets.

   (1) 12, 15, and 33.   (4) 50, 125, and 8.

   (2) 12, 6, and 18.   (5) 77, 121, and 49.

   (3) 12, 21, and 77.   (6) 24, 16, and 9.

VII. Compute the gcd of each number triplet in Exercise VI.

VIII. (1) Prove Theorem 11.

     (2) Prove Theorem 12.

6.6 Classical Problems

Since every composite number can be written as a product of primes, we see that the primes are the building blocks of the set of positive integers. This is one of the reasons mathematicians are interested in studying facts concerning the primes. In this section we state some of the well-known theorems and conjectures about primes. Some of the unproved conjectures have occupied mathematicians' attention for centuries. The first theorem we state and prove is one that has probably already occurred to you; namely, the set of primes is an infinite set.

THEOREM 13.   The set of primes is an infinite set.

Proof.   Assume that the set of primes is a finite set.
Then the set may be written $\{p_1, p_2, \ldots, p_k\}$.
Let $a = 1 + p_1 p_2 \ldots p_k$.
Then $p_1 < a, p_2 < a, \ldots, p_k < a$.
Either a is prime or a is composite.

Case 1. a is prime.
Then a is a prime which is different from any of the primes $p_1, p_2, \ldots, p_k$.
Thus $\{p_1, p_2, \ldots, p_k\}$ cannot be the set of all primes.
But $\{p_1, p_2, \ldots, p_k\}$ is the set of all primes.
Consequently, we have derived a contradiction.

Case 2. a is composite.
Then there exists a prime q such that $q \mid a$.
If $q = p_1$, then $q \mid p_1 p_2 \ldots p_k$ and $q \mid a$.
Hence $q \mid (a - p_1 p_2 \ldots p_k)$ (By Theorem 2).
But $a - p_1 p_2 \ldots p_k = 1$.
Thus $q \mid 1$.
But $q \nmid 1$ (Since the only positive divisor of 1 is 1).
Hence $q \mid 1 \wedge q \nmid 1$.
Contradiction.
Hence $q \neq p_1$.
Similarly, $q \neq p_2, q \neq p_3, \ldots, q \neq p_k$.
Hence q is a prime which is different from any of the
primes $\{p_1, p_2, \ldots, p_k\}$.
Thus $\{p_1, p_2, \ldots, p_k\}$ cannot be the set of all primes.
But $\{p_1, p_2, \ldots, p_k\}$ is the set of all primes.
Consequently, we have derived a contradiction.

In each case, we have derived a contradiction.

Hence the assumption that the set of primes is a finite set is a false
assumption.

Thus the set of primes is an infinite set.//

This interesting theorem was proved by Euclid over 2,000 years ago.

Now that we know that the set of primes is infinite, we would like
to develop a systematic procedure for computing all primes less than any
given positive integer k. The following device, known as the *sieve of
Eratosthenes*, enables us to compute the set of all primes less than any
specific positive integer. We shall compute the set of primes less than 50
by use of the sieve. First we list the integers 1, 2, 3, . . . , 50.

We circle 1 to indicate that 1 is *not* a prime. Since 2 is a prime, we
do not circle 2. However, every multiple of 2, except 2, is composite;
hence we circle all multiples of 2, except 2. The list appears as shown
in Figure 6.6.

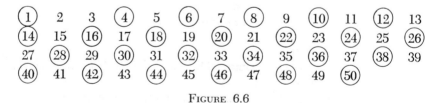

FIGURE 6.6

Notice that the first number following 2 which has not been circled
is 3, a prime. Since the multiples of 3, except 3 itself, are composite, we

circle them. The list appears in Figure 6.7. Observe that some of the multiples of 3 were circled as multiples of 2.

(1) 2 3 (4) 5 (6) 7 (8) (9) (10) 11 (12) 13
(14) (15) (16) 17 (18) 19 (20) (21) (22) 23 (24) 25 (26)
(27) (28) 29 (30) 31 (32) (33) (34) 35 (36) 37 (38) (39)
(40) 41 (42) 43 (44) (45) (46) 47 (48) 49 (50)

FIGURE 6.7

Notice that the first number following 3 which has not been circled is 5, a prime. Since the other multiples of 5 are composite, we circle them. The list appears in Figure 6.8.

(1) 2 3 (4) 5 (6) 7 (8) (9) (10) 11 (12) 13
(14) (15) (16) 17 (18) 19 (20) (21) (22) 23 (24) (25) (26)
(27) (28) 29 (30) 31 (32) (33) (34) (35) (36) 37 (38) (39)
(40) 41 (42) 43 (44) (45) (46) 47 (48) 49 (50)

FIGURE 6.8

Observe that the next prime is 7. Since the multiples of 7, except 7 itself, are composite, we circle them. The list appears in Figure 6.9.

(1) 2 3 (4) 5 (6) 7 (8) (9) (10) 11 (12) 13
(14) (15) (16) 17 (18) 19 (20) (21) (22) 23 (24) (25) (26)
(27) (28) 29 (30) 31 (32) (33) (34) (35) (36) 37 (38) (39)
(40) 41 (42) 43 (44) (45) (46) 47 (48) (49) (50)

FIGURE 6.9

Of course, the next step is to circle the multiples of 11, except 11, then the multiples of 13, et cetera. However, you will notice that these have *already* been circled as multiples of the smaller primes. You may wonder when you can stop the circling procedure and be certain that all uncircled numbers are primes. You may terminate the circling procedure after you have circled all composites which are multiples of the largest prime p such that $p^2 \le k$. In the above illustration, $k = 50$ and $p = 7$. Thus $p^2 = 49 < 50$. It is *not* necessary to continue the process beyond $p = 7$, because $11^2 = 121$ and 121 is larger than 50. This fact is very useful when we are trying to ascertain whether a given positive integer k is a prime. We determine whether each prime $p_1, p_2, \ldots, p_m$, such that $p_1^2 < k, p_2^2 < k, \ldots, p_m^2 < k$, divides k. The integer k is prime if and only if $p_1 \nmid k$, $p_2 \nmid k$, . . . , $p_m \nmid k$. For example, 53 is prime because $2 \nmid 53$, $3 \nmid 53$, $5 \nmid 53$, and $7 \nmid 53$, and $7^2 \le 53 < 11^2$.

From the sieve of Eratosthenes, we list the following primes less than 50.

2, 3, 5, 7, 11, 13, 17, 19, 23, 29, 31, 37, 41, 43, 47.

Observe that 3 and 5 differ by 2, 5 and 7 differ by 2, 11 and 13 differ by 2, 17 and 19 differ by 2, 29 and 31 differ by 2, and 41 and 43 differ by 2. Any pair of consecutive primes which differ by 2 is called a pair of *twin primes*. Thus each pair listed above is a pair of twin primes. It appears that the set of all pairs of twin primes is infinite. However, no one knows for certain whether the set is finite or infinite. Although many mathematicians have tried to prove that this set is infinite, and much progress has been made, no one has been able to construct a valid proof.

An eighteenth century mathematician named Charles Goldbach conjectured that every even number larger than 4 is the sum of two primes (not necessarily distinct). For example, $6 = 3 + 3$ and $8 = 3 + 5$. This conjecture, known as *Goldbach's conjecture*, has been *verified* for all even integers to 100,000. However, it has never been *proved*.

In 1637 the great French mathematician Pierre Fermat, the father of number theory, wrote in the margin of his copy of Bachet's edition of Diophantus's *Aritmetica* "and I have assuredly found an admirable proof of this, but the margin is too narrow to contain it." Fermat was referring to a famous conjecture now known as *Fermat's Last Theorem*. Essentially, Fermat's conjecture states that the open sentence $x^n + y^n = z^n$ cannot be converted to a true sentence by replacement of the variables x, y, and z by nonzero integers if $2 < n$. Over three centuries of sustained efforts by some of history's greatest mathematicians have failed to produce a proof. However, various special cases have been verified.

The main purpose of this section has been to convince you that not all mathematical problems have been solved. Not only are there many stated problems which remain unsolved but, also, there are many problems which must be formulated and solved. The forthcoming solutions of these problems will vary in difficulty. Some of these solutions will greatly influence mathematics and science, while others will only satisfy the curiosity of many people.

You may wonder why the subject of number theory is studied. Although applications of advanced number theory to the physical world are rare, the subject has greatly influenced the development of more advanced branches of pure mathematics by stimulating the development of general methods and by providing a source of ideas and inspiration. For example, attempts to solve Fermat's Last Theorem led to the investigation of the theory of algebraic numbers, which generated some of the guiding concepts in modern algebra. These concepts, in turn, have greatly influenced modern physics. Looking back, we see that the study is worth-while. However, man's past interest in arithmetical questions and his present interest in number theory were not motivated by these developments. What, then, is the driving force which compels man to study number theory? His insatiable curiosity, his fervent desire to know and to do are whetted by the diversity and unexpected difficulty of number theory and are rewarded by the beauty and elegance of the surprising results. One of the world's greatest mathematicians, Carl Friedrich Gauss (1777–1855), was so impressed by the beauty of number theory that he called it the *Queen of mathematics.*

If you look through the *Mathematical Reviews* under the subject of *number theory,* you will observe that researchers are making many new discoveries about primes.

Exercise 6.6

I. Apply the sieve of Eratosthenes to each of the following.

(1) $k = 25$ (3) $k = 100$
(2) $k = 75$ (4) $k = 150$

II. Verify Goldbach's conjecture for every number between 5 and 31.

III. (1) Prove that 127 is a prime by proving that 2, 3, 5, 7, 11 do not divide 127.

(2) Prove that q is a prime if and only if $p \nmid q$ for all primes p such that $p^2 \leq q$.

(3) Prove that there are only two *consecutive* positive integers which are prime.

IV. Prove that 3, 5, 7 is the only prime triplet.

V. From the *Mathematical Reviews* make a list of recent articles in number theory.

6.7 Analysis of Long Division

Recall from Section 6.1 that *divides* is a relation rather than an operation. Although we have already developed the *division algorithm,* we have not defined the operation of division between all pairs of integers. In elementary school when a child works a long division problem, he is really not performing the operation of division (in fact, division may not even be defined at that point), but he is applying the division algorithm. For example, when he writes

$$9 \overline{)\begin{array}{r} 3 \\ 29 \\ \underline{27} \\ 2 \end{array}}$$

he has not really divided because 9 ∤ 29. He has merely applied the division algorithm to obtain 29 = 9(3) + 2. Of course, there is a very close analogy between the division algorithm and the operation of division, *when division is defined.* In fact, we cannot define an operation of division of integers such that the closure property for division of integers is satisfied. In the next chapter we extend the set of integers to the set of rational numbers in such a manner that the closure property for division of rational numbers, except for division by 0, will be satisfied.

In this section we justify the computational device for computing q and r in $a = bq + r$ such that $0 \le r < b$. As this device, known as *long division*, is familiar to you, it is not our objective to provide drill problems but rather to analyze the procedure with a view to complete understanding. In any long division problem involving two positive integers a and $b < a$, we seek the largest positive integer q such that $bq \le a$; that is, we seek the largest q such that $0 \le a - bq < b$. After we have succeeded in computing (or guessing) q, the *remainder* r will be less than b. Whenever a and b are sufficiently small, it is easy to guess q. If a and b are large, the device of long division as shown in Figure 6.10 is useful.

$$
\begin{array}{r}
136 \\
29\overline{)\,3969} \\
29 \\
\hline
106 \\
87 \\
\hline
199 \\
174 \\
\hline
25
\end{array}
$$

FIGURE 6.10

Before analyzing this procedure, we observe that it is equivalent to the forms in Figure 6.11, which are sometimes taught in the elementary school.

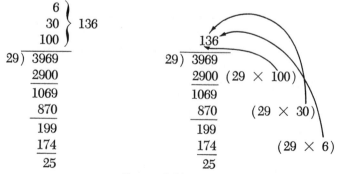

FIGURE 6.11

The form in Figure 6.10 is briefer and emphasizes place value. The forms in Figure 6.11 are often used to illustrate developmental stages prior to the presentation of the more concise form.

In Figure 6.10, for *hundreds*, we subtracted 29(1) *hundreds* from 39 *hundreds;* that is, 39 *hundreds* − 29 *hundreds* = 10 *hundreds.* Ten *hundreds,* or 100 *tens,* + 6 *tens* = 106 *tens.* Next, for *tens,* we subtracted 29(3) *tens* from 106 *tens;* that is, 106 *tens* − 87 *tens* = 19 *tens.* Nineteen *tens,* or 190 *ones,* + 9 *ones* = 199 *ones.* Next, for *ones,* we subtracted 29(6) *ones* from 199 *ones;* that is, 199 − 174 = 25. We can show the computation this way:

$$
\begin{aligned}
3969 - 29(100) - 29(30) - 29(6) &= 3969 + {}^-29(100) + {}^-29(30) + {}^-29(6) \\
&= 3969 + {}^-29(100 + 30 + 6) \\
&= 3969 + {}^-29(136) \\
&= 3969 - 29(136) \\
&= 25.
\end{aligned}
$$

Consequently, by the above analysis, we have shown that 3969 = 29 (136) + 25.

In Figure 6.10 notice that the 1 placed above the 9 (hundreds digit) really represents 100. Similarly, the 3 above the 6 in Figure 6.10 represents 30, and the 6 above the 9 represents 6. In Figure 6.11, left device, these numbers appear as 30 and 6, respectively.

In actual practice, as illustrated in Figure 6.12, students may use tables of multiples to compute the greatest multiple of 18 not exceeding 70 and the greatest multiple of 18 not exceeding 167.

$$
\begin{array}{r}
39 \\
18{\overline{)\,707}} \\
54 \\
\hline
167 \\
162 \\
\hline
5
\end{array}
$$

$18 \times 4 = 72$ $\Big\}$ Table of multiples to find the greatest multiple of 18 (≤ 70)
$18 \times 3 = 54$

$18 \times 9 = 162$ $\Big\}$ Table of multiples to find the greatest multiple of 18 (≤ 167)

FIGURE 6.12

Students soon abandon writing tables of multiples and then they determine the greatest multiple immediately. This saves time and writing as contrasted to a device, such as Figure 6.13, where failure to recognize immediately the greatest multiple leads to additional steps and greater probability of error.

$$\left.\begin{array}{r} 1 \\ 8 \\ 10 \\ 20 \end{array}\right\} 39$$

$$18)\overline{707} \\ \underline{360} \\ 347 \\ \underline{180} \\ 167 \\ \underline{144} \\ 23 \\ \underline{18} \\ 5$$

$$\left.\begin{array}{r} 9 \\ 30 \end{array}\right\} 39$$

$$18)\overline{707} \\ \underline{540} \\ 167 \\ \underline{162} \\ 5$$

FIGURE 6.13   FIGURE 6.14

As the student develops more skill in using the device in Figure 6.13, he progresses to the device in Figure 6.14, but he is not getting the advantage from the use of place value that is available through use of the device in Figure 6.10.

In the procedure of Figure 6.12 it is necessary to determine that the *tens* digit of the *quotient* is 3 before we can proceed. To do this, we think of the greatest multiple of 18 (≤ 70) (the number of tens). In $18)\overline{7073}$ it is necessary to determine the *hundreds* digit or, again, the greatest multiple of 18 (≤ 70) (the number of hundreds). Similarly, in $18)\overline{707,351}$ it is necessary to determine the *ten thousands* digit, or the greatest multiple of 18 (≤ 70). In any case, we must be careful not to obtain a negative remainder. If we do obtain a negative remainder, we must reduce the quotient sufficiently so that the remainder will be nonnegative and less than the divisor.

As we have seen, the division algorithm may be analyzed from two points of view. From one point of view, we compute the largest positive integer q such that $bq \leq a$. This point of view is illustrated in Figure 6.15 with $a = 17$ and $b = 3$. Also, this is the point of view we employ in short division.

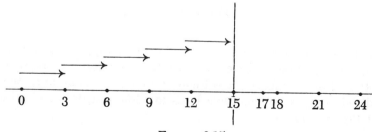

FIGURE 6.15

From the other point of view, we compute the largest positive integer q such that $0 \leq a - bq < b$. This point of view is illustrated in Figure 6.16 with $a = 17$ and $b = 3$. This is the point of view we employ in long division and is based on repeated subtraction.

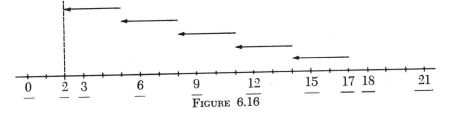

FIGURE 6.16

In long division we successively subtract multiples of b from a until we obtain a remainder less than b. That is, we first try q_1 and compute $a - bq_1$; if $0 \leq a - bq_1 < b$, then q_1 is the quotient. If $a - bq_1 < 0$, then q_1 is too large and we try a smaller q_1. If $b < a - bq_1$, then we try q_2 and compute $a - bq_1 - bq_2$; if $0 \leq a - bq_1 - bq_2 < b$, then $q_1 + q_2$ is the quotient. If $a - bq_1 - bq_2 < 0$, then q_2 is too large and we try a smaller q_2. If $b < a - bq_1 - bq_2$, then we continue the process until $0 \leq a - bq_1 - bq_2 - \ldots - bq_k < b$. Since $a - bq_1 - bq_2 - \ldots - bq_k = a + ^-bq_1 + ^-bq_2 + \ldots + ^-bq_k = a + ^-b(q_1 + q_2 + \ldots + q_k) = a - b(q_1 + q_2 + \ldots + q_k) < b$, we see that $q_1 + q_2 + \ldots + q_k$ is the quotient. In Figure 6.13, $a = 707$, $b = 18$, $q_1 = 20$, $q_2 = 10$, $q_3 = 8$, $q_4 = 1$, $r = 5$. Thus the quotient q is equal to $20 + 10 + 8 + 1 = 39$. In Figure 6.14 $q_1 = 30$ and $q_2 = 9$. Hence $q = 30 + 9$. The computational device and our knowledge of the decimal system enable us to make convenient choices of $q_1, q_2, \ldots, q_k$ and to *exhibit* these choices in a convenient form.

Exercise 6.7

I. In each of the following compute the quotient and the remainder as in Figure 6.13 and then as in Figure 6.14.

(1) $37 \overline{)\ 785\ }$ (4) $217 \overline{)\ 87{,}353\ }$

(2) $73 \overline{)\ 787\ }$ (5) $365 \overline{)\ 673{,}421\ }$

(3) $127 \overline{)\ 7873\ }$ (6) $452 \overline{)\ 534{,}673\ }$

II. Justify the procedure in each part of Exercise I.

III. On the number line illustrate both points of view of the division algorithm in each of the following.

(1) $a = 38, b = 11$.   (3) $a = 123, b = 12$.

(2) $a = 42, b = 13$.   (4) $a = 135, b = 13$.

IV. In each of the following design a base five computational device for computing q and r in $a = bq + r$, $0 \leq r < b$. All numbers are written in base five.

(1) $a = 32, b = 4$.
(2) $a = 40, b = 4$.
(3) $a = 324, b = 12$.
(4) $a = 432, b = 21$.

V. Justify the computational device used in Exercise IV.

VI. We may convert a base ten numeral to a base b numeral by means of a simple device. For example, to convert 934_{10} to base five, we apply the *division algorithm* successively as follows:

$934 = 5(186) + 4$
$186 = 5(37) + 1$
$37 = 5(7) + 2$
$7 = 5(1) + 2$
$1 = 5(0) + 1$

The first remainder is the units digit, the second remainder is the fives digit, the third remainder is the twenty-fives digit, etc. Thus $934_{10} = 12214_5$. Employ this device to convert 493_{10} to

(1) base 5   (4) base 12
(2) base 4   (5) base 2
(3) base 8   (6) base 3

VII. Prove that the device in Exercise VI is a valid procedure.

Chapter 7

THE RATIONAL NUMBERS

7.1 Fractions

In Chapter 6, we noted a serious defect of the integers; namely, the operation of division is not defined for some pairs of integers a and b. The following examples illustrate the type of problems which can be solved as well as the type which cannot.

Example 1.   Ralph, Ray, and Jim have 18 cookies which they wish to divide equally. How many cookies does each one receive? Since there are 3 boys to share 18 cookies, the mathematical model is $18 \div 3$. Thus each boy should receive 6 cookies.

Example 2.   Ralph, Ray, and Jim have 19 cookies which they wish to divide equally. How many cookies does each one receive? Since there are 3 boys to share 19 cookies, the mathematical model is $19 \div 3$. However, by Definition 1 and Definition 5 of Chapter 6, $19 \div 3$ is not defined. Thus there is no integer k such that $19 \div 3 = k$. However, by the division algorithm $19 = 3(6) + 1$. Thus if each boy receives 6 cookies, there will be 1 cookie remaining. The original problem was to divide the 19 cookies among the 3 boys with none remaining. One way to do this is to cut the left-over cookie into 3 equal pieces. We need a mathematical representation of 1 cookie divided into 3 equal parts, called thirds. Some symbols for *one-third* (one of the *three* equal parts) are $\frac{1}{3}$ and $(1, 3)$. If we adopt these symbols, we can say that each boy should receive 6 cookies and $\frac{1}{3}$ of a cookie, or 6 and $(1, 3)$ cookies.

In order to have a mathematical model to solve any problem in which a whole number of objects is divided equally among a (whole) number of individuals, we would like to have a number system which includes numbers of the type $\frac{1}{2}, \frac{1}{3}, \frac{1}{4}, \frac{1}{5}, \frac{2}{5}, \frac{3}{7}, \frac{4}{15}$, et cetera. If 2 cookies are divided equally among 3 boys, each boy receives $\frac{2}{3}$ cookie. However, if 3 cookies are divided equally between 2 boys, each boy receives $\frac{3}{2}$ cookies. These two examples should convince us that the order in which the integers of a *fraction* are written is important. This discussion motivates us to make the following definition of *fraction*.

DEFINITION 1. (a) A *fraction* is an ordered pair (a, b), in which a and b are integers and $b \neq 0$.
(b) The first member a of the ordered pair (a, b) is called the *numerator* of the fraction.
(c) The second member b of the ordered pair (a, b) is called the *denominator* of the fraction.

Since the symbol $\frac{a}{b}$ also specifies the order of a and b, we shall represent a fraction by $\frac{a}{b}$.

Now that we have defined *fraction*, how will this definition help us to solve problems of the type in Example 2? Notice that we have not defined addition, subtraction, multiplication, or division between two fractions. We could define the sum of any two fractions to be equal to zero. However, this would not help us solve the above type of problem. Although mathematics is really an abstract system, our definitions are motivated by our desire for mathematical models of physical problems. Our desire is to create a set of numbers and to define the operations so that the new system shall possess the properties proved previously for the integers and shall enable us to solve problems of the type in Example 2.

Since the fraction $\frac{1}{3}$ is an ordered pair of integers, we see that $\frac{1}{3}$ is a mathematical concept rather than a physical concept. This fraction $\frac{1}{3}$ is not a portion of a cookie, cake, apple, and so on. However, when we interpret the mathematical model in terms of the physical problem, the fraction $\frac{1}{3}$ may represent $\frac{1}{3}$ of a cookie, cake, or apple. It now appears that we are ready to define the operations of addition, subtraction, multiplication, and division. However, a moment's reflection reveals two main problems which must be resolved. (1) How is the set of integers related to the set of fractions? For example, how is the integer 3 related to the fraction $\frac{3}{1}$? The answer to the question will be postponed until Section 7.6. (2) How is the ordered pair $\frac{2}{4}$ related to the ordered pair $\frac{1}{2}$? We see from Definition 1 that $\frac{1}{2} \neq \frac{2}{4}$ because $1 \neq 2$ and $2 \neq 4$. In the physical world, $\frac{1}{2}$ of a cake is *one* of *two* equal parts into which a cake has been divided; $\frac{2}{4}$ of a cake is *two* of *four* equal parts into which a cake has been divided. Although $\frac{1}{2}$ of a cake is not the same as $\frac{2}{4}$ of a cake, one who has eaten $\frac{1}{2}$ of a cake has eaten the same amount of cake as one who has eaten $\frac{2}{4}$ of the same cake. From this point of view, we should say that $\frac{1}{2}$ and $\frac{2}{4}$ are the same. However, as Definition 1 says that $\frac{1}{2}$ and $\frac{2}{4}$ are *not* the same fraction, we have a problem which prevents us from continuing the development, unless we can first resolve this difficulty. Now consider the number line in Figure 7.1.

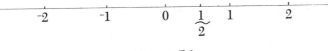

FIGURE 7.1

The point labeled $\frac{1}{2}$ is half-way between the point labeled 0 and the point labeled 1; that is, the point labeled $\frac{1}{2}$ is that point which divides the line segment from 0 to 1 into two segments of equal length. If the segment from 0 to 1 (called a *unit* segment because its length is 1) is divided into 6 segments of equal length, then the segment from 0 to $\frac{1}{6}$ is the first of these segments, the segment from $\frac{1}{6}$ to $\frac{2}{6}$ is the second segment, the segment from $\frac{2}{6}$ to $\frac{3}{6}$ is the third, and so on, as shown in Figure 7.2.

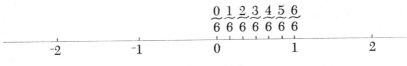

FIGURE 7.2

We see immediately that the point labeled $\frac{3}{6}$ coincides with the point labeled $\frac{1}{2}$, the point labeled $\frac{0}{6}$ coincides with the point labeled 0, and the point labeled $\frac{6}{6}$ coincides with the point labeled 1. To locate the point labeled $\frac{5}{6}$, we count the first 5 of the 6 segments from 0 to 1; the *right-end* point of the 5th segment is the point labeled $\frac{5}{6}$. In general, if a is any counting number and b is any positive integer, we divide each segment between each pair of consecutive counting numbers into b segments of equal length and then count the first a of these smaller segments to the right of 0. The *right-end* point of the ath segment is the point labeled $\frac{a}{b}$. For example, we locate the point labeled $\frac{11}{6}$ as shown in Figure 7.3

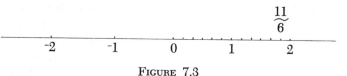

FIGURE 7.3

As the point labeled $\frac{1}{2}$ coincides with the points labeled $\frac{2}{4}$, $\frac{3}{6}$, $\frac{4}{8}$, ..., we see that there is an infinite set of fractions corresponding to the single point labeled $\frac{1}{2}$. In general, if a is any counting number and b is any positive integer, there is an infinite set of fractions corresponding to the point labeled $\frac{a}{b}$.

What point is labeled $\frac{^-11}{6}$? We divide each unit segment to the *left* of 0 into 6 segments of equal length and count the first 11 of these smaller segments to the *left* of 0. The *left-end* point of the 11th segment is the point labeled $\frac{^-11}{6}$ as shown in Figure 7.4.

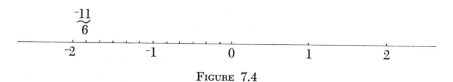

FIGURE 7.4

It is easy to see that $\frac{^-22}{12}$, $\frac{^-33}{18}$, et cetera, also correspond to the point labeled $\frac{^-11}{6}$. Again, there is an infinite set of fractions corresponding to the point labeled by $\frac{^-11}{6}$. Since each point may be labeled by any one of many fractions, we would like to have a method of determining whether two fractions are labels for the same point. By observing, for example, that $\frac{2}{4}$ and $\frac{3}{6}$ are both labels for the same point, that $2 \cdot 6 = 4 \cdot 3$, that $\frac{3}{7}$ and $\frac{9}{21}$ are both labels for the same point, and that $3 \cdot 21 = 7 \cdot 9$, we are motivated to make the following definition.

DEFINITION 2. The fractions $\frac{a}{b}$ and $\frac{c}{d}$ are said to be *equivalent* if and only if $ad = bc$.

Whenever $\frac{a}{b}$ and $\frac{c}{d}$ are equivalent, we may say that $\frac{a}{b}$ is equivalent to $\frac{c}{d}$ and write $\frac{a}{b} \approx \frac{c}{d}$. Notice that equivalence of the two fractions $\frac{a}{b}$ and $\frac{c}{d}$ is defined in terms of equality of the two integers ad and bc.

It follows immediately from Definition 2 that $\frac{^-3}{^-5} \approx \frac{3}{5}$, $\frac{3}{^-5} \approx \frac{^-3}{5}$, and in general, $\frac{^-a}{^-b} \approx \frac{a}{b}$. If this result did not follow from Definition 2, our motivation would lead us astray. Apparently, equivalent fractions may be used to label the same point on the number line. We prove this fact by proving the following theorem, which asserts that equivalence of fractions is actually an equivalence relation.

THEOREM 1. The relation $\approx$ on the set of fractions is an equivalence relation.

Proof.

(Reflexive) Since $ab = ba$, we see from Definition 2 that $\frac{a}{b} \approx \frac{a}{b}$.
Thus $\approx$ is reflexive.

(Symmetric) Let $\frac{a}{b} \approx \frac{c}{d}$.
Then by Definition 2, $ad = bc$.
Since $=$ is an equivalence relation on the set of integers, we see that $bc = ad$ and hence $cb = da$.
By Definition 2, $\frac{c}{d} \approx \frac{a}{b}$.
Thus $\approx$ is symmetric.

(Transitive) Let $\frac{a}{b} \approx \frac{c}{d}$ and $\frac{c}{d} \approx \frac{e}{f}$.
Then by Definition 2, $ad = bc$ and $cf = de$.
Hence $adf = bcf$ and $bcf = bde$.
Since $=$ is an equivalence relation on the set of integers we see that $adf = bde$.
But $d \neq 0$.
By the cancellation property for multiplication of integers, $af = be$.
Hence by Definition 2, $\frac{a}{b} \approx \frac{e}{f}$.
Thus $\approx$ is transitive.
Consequently the relation $\approx$ is an equivalence relation on the set of fractions.//

As an illustration of the transitive property, we observe that $\frac{2}{3} \approx \frac{6}{9}$ and $\frac{6}{9} \approx \frac{8}{12}$ and hence that $\frac{2}{3} \approx \frac{8}{12}$.

As we learned in Chapter 2, an equivalence relation on a set separates the elements of the set into mutually exclusive equivalence classes. Thus the equivalence relation $\approx$ separates the fractions into mutually exclusive equivalence classes of fractions. Any two fractions in the same class are equivalent, and any two fractions in two different classes are *not* equivalent. For example, $\frac{2}{3}, \frac{-4}{-6}, \frac{18}{27}$ are in the same equivalence class, but $\frac{2}{3}$ and $\frac{4}{5}$ are in different equivalence classes. We could say, for example, that any two fractions of the equivalence class $\{\frac{1}{2}, \frac{-1}{-2}, \frac{2}{4}, \frac{-2}{-4}, \frac{3}{6}, \frac{-3}{-6}, \ldots\}$ are two different names for the same point labeled by $\frac{1}{2}$ on the number line and hence are equal. Although we could have employed this less sophisticated approach and *agreed*, for example, that $\frac{1}{2} = \frac{2}{4}$, we chose the equivalence class approach because Chapters 1 and 2 have provided us with the background necessary for the more sophisticated approach, and, in addition, this approach will eliminate some of the common misconceptions about fractions. The set of numbers we desire to invent is the set of *equivalence classes* of fractions rather than the set of fractions; a serious disadvantage of the fractions is that too many unequal fractions are labels for each point of the number line. Since each equivalence class represents one and only one point on the number line, the set of equivalence classes does not have this disadvantage. The set of fractions merely provided the first step in the development.

In the next section we define the operations of addition, subtraction, multiplication, and division between equivalence classes of fractions. The following theorem is needed in the development.

THEOREM 2.   If $\frac{a}{b}$ is any fraction and k is any nonzero integer, then $\frac{ka}{kb} \approx \frac{a}{b}$.

Proof.   Let $\frac{a}{b}$ be a fraction and $k \neq 0$.

Then $kb \neq 0$.

Moreover, $kab = kba$.

Hence by Definition 2, $\frac{ka}{kb} \approx \frac{a}{b}$. //

For example, $\frac{(6 \cdot 3)}{(6 \cdot 4)} \approx \frac{3}{4}$ and $\frac{(-7 \cdot -5)}{(-7 \cdot 8)} \approx \frac{-5}{8}$.

Exercise 7.1

I. Determine whether $\frac{a}{b} \approx \frac{c}{d}$ in each of the following.

(1) $\frac{a}{b} = \frac{2}{3}, \frac{c}{d} = \frac{-4}{-6}$.

(2) $\frac{a}{b} = \frac{5}{10}, \frac{c}{d} = \frac{-1}{-2}$.

(3) $\frac{a}{b} = \frac{-5}{8}, \frac{c}{d} = \frac{5}{-8}$.

(4) $\frac{a}{b} = \frac{17}{-15}, \frac{c}{d} = \frac{-34}{30}$.

(5) $\frac{a}{b} = \frac{13}{10}, \frac{c}{d} = \frac{-13}{-10}$.

(6) $\frac{a}{b} = \frac{-10}{7}, \frac{c}{d} = \frac{10}{7}$.

(7) $\frac{a}{b} = \frac{-1}{3}, \frac{c}{d} = \frac{2}{-6}$.

(8) $\frac{a}{b} = \frac{1}{-3}, \frac{c}{d} = \frac{-2}{6}$.

(9) $\frac{a}{b} = \frac{-5}{9}, \frac{c}{d} = \frac{-8}{16}$.

(10) $\frac{a}{b} = \frac{9}{10}, \frac{c}{d} = \frac{10}{9}$.

(11) $\frac{a}{b} = \frac{0}{5}, \frac{c}{d} = \frac{0}{3}$.

(12) $\frac{a}{b} = \frac{10}{2}, \frac{c}{d} = \frac{5}{1}$.

(13) $\frac{a}{b} = \frac{18}{3}, \frac{c}{d} = \frac{6}{1}$.

(14) $\frac{a}{b} = \frac{0}{-6}, \frac{c}{d} = \frac{0}{13}$.

II. Separate each of the following sets of fractions into equivalence classes of fractions.

(1) $\{\frac{4}{5}, \frac{3}{5}, \frac{-6}{10}, \frac{3}{-5}, \frac{15}{25}, \frac{-8}{-10}, \frac{-80}{100}, \frac{0}{2}, \frac{13}{1}\}$.

(2) $\{\frac{2}{3}, \frac{6}{5}, \frac{-12}{-10}, \frac{6}{-5}, \frac{30}{25}, \frac{-30}{-25}, \frac{75}{100}, \frac{15}{-20}, \frac{0}{-21}, \frac{15}{1}\}$.

(3) $\{\frac{4}{5}, \frac{5}{5}, \frac{6}{5}, \frac{-3}{5}, \frac{-4}{5}, \frac{0}{3}, \frac{15}{3}\}$.

(4) $\{\frac{-4}{6}, \frac{6}{6}, \frac{7}{6}, \frac{4}{6}, \frac{-3}{6}, \frac{0}{6}, \frac{24}{6}\}$.

(5) $\{\frac{0}{3}, \frac{0}{-2}, \frac{0}{99}, \frac{0}{27}, \frac{0}{-1}\}$.

(6) $\{\frac{10}{-3}, \frac{0}{2}, \frac{10}{-99}, \frac{0}{-19}, \frac{0}{1}\}$.

(7) $\{\frac{2}{1}, \frac{4}{2}, \frac{6}{3}, \frac{-8}{-4}, \frac{-10}{-5}, \frac{11}{6}\}$.

(8) $\{\frac{3}{1}, \frac{6}{2}, \frac{9}{3}, \frac{-12}{-4}, \frac{-15}{-5}, \frac{19}{6}\}$.

III. Prove each of the following.

(1) If $\frac{a}{b} \approx \frac{c}{d}$ and $\frac{c}{d} \not\approx \frac{e}{f}$, then $\frac{a}{b} \not\approx \frac{e}{f}$.

(2) If $k \neq 1$ and $\frac{a}{b}$ is any fraction such that $a \neq 0$, then $\frac{ka}{b} \not\approx \frac{a}{b}$.

(3) If the numerator of some fraction in·some equivalence class is 0, then the numerator of every fraction in that equivalence class is 0.

(4) If $\frac{a}{b}$ is any fraction, then $\frac{a}{b} \approx \frac{-a}{-b}$ and $\frac{-a}{b} \approx \frac{a}{-b}$.

7.2 Rational Numbers

As we mentioned in the preceding section, we are going to define the operation of addition, subtraction, multiplication, and division between equivalence classes of fractions rather than between fractions. Before defining the operations, we shall name the equivalence classes.

DEFINITION 3. An equivalence class of fractions is called a *rational number*.

We employ the symbol $\frac{a}{b}$ or a/b to symbolize the equivalence class which contains the fraction $\frac{a}{b}$. Although a/b is merely a symbol for the rational number, we shall write and say "the rational number a/b" when we actually mean "the rational number symbolized by the numeral a/b." As in the case of a fraction $\frac{a}{b}$, we say that the *numerator* of the rational number a/b is a and the *denominator* is b. Since the fraction $\frac{a}{b}$ is not defined if $b = 0$, the symbol a/b does not represent a rational number if $b = 0$. For example, 2/0 is not defined and, therefore, is meaningless. Henceforth, when we write a/b to represent a rational number, we assume that $b \neq 0$. The word *rational* is sometimes used as an abbreviation for *rational number*. The following examples illustrate the concept of a rational number.

Example 1. $2/3 = \{\frac{2}{3}, \frac{-2}{-3}, \frac{4}{6}, \frac{-4}{-6}, \ldots\}$

Example 2. $-1/2 = \{\frac{-2}{4}, \frac{2}{-4}, \frac{-4}{8}, \frac{4}{-8}, \ldots\}$

Example 3. $-2/4 = \{\frac{-2}{4}, \frac{2}{-4}, \frac{-4}{8}, \frac{4}{-8}, \ldots\}$

Example 4. $0/3 = \{\frac{0}{1}, \frac{0}{-1}, \frac{0}{2}, \frac{0}{-2}, \ldots\}$

Since the fraction $\frac{-1}{2}$ belongs to exactly one equivalence class, we see that the symbol -1/2 represents a unique rational number. Similarly, since the fraction $\frac{-2}{4}$ belongs to exactly one equivalence class, we see that the symbol $^-2/4$ represents a unique rational number. However, since the equivalence class containing $\frac{-1}{2}$ is equal to the equivalence class containing $\frac{-2}{4}$, as shown in Examples 2 and 3, we see that $^-1/2 = {}^-2/4$. The following theorems give us criteria for equality of two rational numbers.

THEOREM 3. The rational number a/b is equal to the rational c/d if and only if $\frac{a}{b} \approx \frac{c}{d}$.

Proof. $a/b = c/d \rightleftarrows a/b$ is the same equivalence class as c/d. $\qquad (p \rightleftarrows q)$

a/b is the same equivalence class as $c/d \rightleftarrows$ $\frac{a}{b}$ is in the same equivalence class as $\frac{c}{d}$. $\qquad (q \rightleftarrows r)$

$\frac{a}{b}$ is in the same equivalence class as $\frac{c}{d} \rightleftarrows$ $\frac{a}{b} \approx \frac{c}{d}$. $\qquad (r \rightleftarrows s)$

Hence $a/b = c/d \rightleftarrows \frac{a}{b} \approx \frac{c}{d}.\!/\!/$ $\qquad \overline{(p \rightleftarrows s)}$

THEOREM 4. The rational number a/b is equal to the rational number c/d if and only if $ad = bc$.

Proof. $a/b = c/d \rightleftarrows \frac{a}{b} \approx \frac{c}{d}$ (By Theorem 3). $\qquad (p \rightleftarrows s)$

$\frac{a}{b} \approx \frac{c}{d} \rightleftarrows ad = bc$ (By Definition 2). $\qquad (s \rightleftarrows t)$

Hence $a/b = c/d \rightleftarrows ad = bc.\!/\!/$ $\qquad \overline{(p \rightleftarrows t)}$

These theorems enable us to write, and say, $1/2 = 2/4$, $4/5 = 12/15$, $3/5 = {}^-6/^-10$, $^-2/3 = 8/^-12$, and so forth. Now we have resolved the difficulty concerning the fractions. Each point on the number line previously labeled by an infinite number of fractions may now be labeled by *exactly one rational number.*

A more informal, but less precise, approach to the study of rational numbers begins at precisely this point in our development. A rational number is defined as we defined a fraction, and two rational numbers a/b and c/d are said to be equal if and only if $ad = bc$. That is, in this more informal approach, *equivalent* fractions are actually considered as *equal* fractions, and no distinction is made between a fraction and a rational number. Thus neither fraction nor rational number is defined precisely, and, moreover, the concept of equality is not clear; that is, equality actually has a double meaning. We do not intend to imply that all students should study rational numbers from the point of view presented in this text. However, every elementary and high school teacher could benefit from this approach even though he probably would not employ this approach in his classroom.

The second question to be resolved concerned the integers. Is the set of integers a subset of the set of rational numbers? Since every rational number is an equivalence class of fractions, we see that no integer is a rational number; that is, the set of integers is *not* a subset of the set of rationals. However, there is a one-to-one correspondence between the set of integers and a proper subset of the set of rationals, as shown in Figure 7.5.

$$
\begin{aligned}
-3 &\leftrightarrow \frac{-3}{1} = \left\{ \frac{-3}{1}, \frac{3}{-1}, \frac{-6}{2}, \frac{6}{-2}, \cdots \right\} \\
-2 &\leftrightarrow \frac{-2}{1} = \left\{ \frac{-2}{1}, \frac{2}{-1}, \frac{-4}{2}, \frac{4}{-2}, \cdots \right\} \\
-1 &\leftrightarrow \frac{-1}{1} = \left\{ \frac{-1}{1}, \frac{1}{-1}, \frac{-2}{2}, \frac{2}{-2}, \cdots \right\} \\
0 &\leftrightarrow \frac{0}{1} = \left\{ \frac{0}{1}, \frac{0}{-1}, \frac{0}{2}, \frac{0}{-2}, \cdots \right\} \\
1 &\leftrightarrow \frac{1}{1} = \left\{ \frac{1}{1}, \frac{-1}{-1}, \frac{2}{2}, \frac{-2}{-2}, \cdots \right\} \\
2 &\leftrightarrow \frac{2}{1} = \left\{ \frac{2}{1}, \frac{-2}{-1}, \frac{4}{2}, \frac{-4}{-2}, \cdots \right\} \\
3 &\leftrightarrow \frac{3}{1} = \left\{ \frac{3}{1}, \frac{-3}{-1}, \frac{6}{2}, \frac{-6}{-2}, \cdots \right\}
\end{aligned}
$$

FIGURE 7.5

Although the set $\{\ldots, {}^{-}4/1, {}^{-}3/1, {}^{-}2/1, {}^{-}1/1, 0/1, 1/1, 2/1, 3/1, 4/1, \ldots\}$, which is a proper subset of the set of rationals, is not the same set as the set of integers, we would like to treat the members of this set as integers, for the rational number $a/1$ and the integer a are both labels for the same point on the number line. For this reason we shall define the operations of addition, subtraction, multiplication, and division between any two rational numbers in such a manner that the above set will behave precisely as the set of integers. After we have accomplished this objective, in succeeding sections, we shall be able to identify this set with the set of integers. Subsequently in any problem involving any members of this set, we shall replace these members by their corresponding integers. For example, we shall be able to replace $^{-}3/1$ by $^{-}3$, $0/1$ by 0, and $5/1$ by 5. In the meantime, however, we must be careful not to write $a/1 = a$. As the development proceeds, these ideas will become clearer. We discuss these ideas here so that the reader will better appreciate the motivation for the definitions.

Returning to Theorem 4, we see that each rational number may be represented by infinitely many symbols. For example, the rational number $1/2$ may be represented by $1/2$, $^-1/^-2$, $2/4$, $^-2/^-4$, $3/6$, $^-3/^-6$, ... When we write $3/6 = 1/2$, we mean that the equivalence class determined by the fraction $\frac{3}{6}$ is the same class as the equivalence class determined by the fraction $\frac{1}{2}$. It is usually convenient to represent a rational number in the form a/b, in which a is an integer, b is a nonzero integer, and a and b are relatively prime. As illustrations, the rational number $\{\frac{-3}{2}, \frac{3}{-2},$ $\frac{-6}{4}, \frac{6}{-4}, \frac{-9}{6}, \frac{9}{-6}, \ldots\}$ is usually represented by $^-3/2$; the rational number $\{\frac{5}{6}, \frac{-5}{-6}, \frac{10}{12}, \frac{-10}{-12}, \frac{15}{18}, \frac{-15}{-18}, \ldots\}$ is usually represented by $5/6$. If we were to restrict the representation of a rational number to be of the form a/b, in which $(a, b) = 1$ and $b \in I^+$, then this representation would be unique. This result is stated in the following theorem. The proof is based on the unique prime factorization theorem.

THEOREM 5.   Every rational number has a unique representation of the form a/b, in which a is an integer, b is a positive integer, and $(a, b) = 1$.

Proof.   Let c/d be any rational number.

Case 1. $(c, d) = 1$ and $d \in I^+$.
c/d is of the required form.

Case 2. $(c, d) = 1$ and $d \in I^-$.
Then $c/d = {}^-1c/{}^-1d = {}^-c/{}^-d$, and $^-d \in I^+$.
Letting $a = {}^-c$ and $b = {}^-d$, we see that $c/d = a/b$, where $(a, b) = 1$ and $b \in I^+$.

Case 3. $(c, d) = k \neq 1$ and $d \in I^+$.
Then $k \mid c$ and $k \mid d$.
Thus there exist integers a and b such that $c = ak$, $d = bk$ and $b \in I^+$.
Hence $c/d = ak/bk = a/b$, and $b \in I^+$ and $(a, b) = 1$.

Case 4. $(c, d) = k \neq 1$ and $d \in I^-$.
Then $c/d = {}^-1c/{}^-1d = {}^-c/{}^-d$, and $^-d \in I^+$.

The remainder of the proof is similar to Case 3. //

DEFINITION 4.   A representation of a rational number is said to be in *lowest terms* if and only if the representation is the unique representation of Theorem 5.

The following theorem and its proof are similar to Theorem 2.

THEOREM 6.   If a/b is any rational number and k is any nonzero integer, then $ka/kb = a/b$.

The following examples illustrate Theorem 6.

Example 5. $28/20 = 4 \cdot 7/4 \cdot 5 = 7/5$.

Example 6. $6/^-15 = 3 \cdot 2/^-3 \cdot 5 = ^-3 \cdot ^-2/^-3 \cdot 5 = ^-2/5$.

Example 7. $^-4/^-9 = (^-1)(4)/(^-1)(9) = 4/9$.

Example 8. $^-a/^-b = (^-1)(a)/(^-1)(b) = a/b$.

Example 9. $3/^-8 = (^-1)(^-3)/(^-1)(8) = ^-3/8$.

Example 10. $a/^-b = (^-1)(^-a)/(^-1)(b) = ^-a/b$.

Although we usually employ Theorem 6 to reduce a rational number ka/kb to the form a/b, we frequently find it convenient to employ Theorem 6 to change the representation a/b to the form ka/kb. As we shall see in the next section, this procedure will simplify the computation involved in the addition of two rational numbers.

Exercise 7.2

I. Compute the truth value of each of the following sentences.

(1) $2/3 = 10/15$
(2) $^-5/10 = 15/^-30$
(3) $28/^-12 = ^-14/6$
(4) $16/6 = ^-8/^-3$
(5) $^-21/12 = 7/4$

(6) $^-12/21 = 4/7$
(7) $1/5 = 4/15$
(8) $6/5 = 25/20$
(9) $13/1 = 39/3$
(10) $15/1 = 60/4$

II. Convert each of the following open sentences to a true sentence by replacement of the variable by an integer.

(1) $x/3 = ^-2/6$
(2) $x/6 = ^-3/6$
(3) $x/^-2 = 3/6$
(4) $y/^-7 = 3/21$
(5) $^-3/^-5 = 6/y$

(6) $1/2 = 2/y$
(7) $15/^-25 = 6/v$
(8) $4/5 = 4/v$
(9) $^-9x/15 = 3/5$
(10) $6/^-9 = 3x/18$

III. Compute the truth value of each of the following sentences.

(1) For some integer x, $x/6 = 2/3$.
(2) For some integer y, $y/7 = 3/9$.
(3) For no integer v, $2/v = 3/v$.
(4) For no integer w, $6/w = w/6$.
(5) For all integers x, $2x/7 = {}^-6x/{}^-21$.
(6) For all integers x, $3/{}^-x = {}^-36/12x$.
(7) For all integers x, $(x+2)/3 = (6x+12)/18$.
(8) For all integers x, $10/x = x/10$.
(9) For some integer t, $5/(t-1) = (t+1)/5$.
(10) For no integer t, $t/1 = 2t/6$.

IV. Reduce to lowest terms.

(1) $16/6$
(2) $18/4$
(3) $^-27/12$
(4) $27/^-15$
(5) $39/^-13$

(6) $13/^-39$
(7) $^-102/^-63$
(8) $^-99/^-66$
(9) $2000/200$
(10) $6000/1000$

V. Prove each of the following.

(1) If $(a, b) = 1$ and $a/b = c/d$, then there exists an integer $k \neq 0$ such that $c = ka$ and $d = kb$.
(2) Theorem 5.
(3) Theorem 6.

7.3 Addition of Rational Numbers

In the preceding section we invented the rational numbers to resolve the difficulty concerning fractions; for example, $\frac{1}{2} \neq \frac{2}{4}$ but $1/2 = 2/4$. Although we know what rational numbers are, we still have not defined addition of two rational numbers. If a baker sells one-half of a chocolate cake to one customer and one-third of the cake to a second customer, how does he calculate the total amount of the cake sold? The *one-half* cake and *one-third* cake are *fractions* of the cake. When the baker writes $1/2 + 1/3$ to compute the total amount of cake sold, he has made a mathematical model of the physical problem and is now adding *rational numbers*.

The definition of addition of any two rational numbers is motivated by our desire of a mathematical system which can serve as a mathematical model of physical problems such as the above. The advantage of such a mathematical system is that one mathematical model will serve for many different physical problems. After all, if one-half inch of rain falls in the morning and one-third inch in the afternoon, the total

amount of rainfall for the day may be computed from the model
1/2 + 1/3. Although the two physical problems (half cake + one-third
cake and half-inch rain + one-third inch rain) are different, the mathematical model is the same for both. Consequently, after we have learned
to compute with rational numbers, we do not need to learn different
rules for adding fractions of cake, fractions of an inch of rainfall,
et cetera. *One* set of rules for adding rational numbers serves the purpose of adding fractions of any physical object.

Before we formulate a definition for the addition of any two rational
numbers, we consider several special cases. First we consider the case
in which both denominators are 1; for example, $5/1 \oplus 3/1$. The symbol
$\oplus$ is used to emphasize that it is really not the same as + previously
defined between integers. As we mentioned earlier, we want any rational
number of the form $a/1$, for any integer a, to behave like the integer a.
Since $5 + 3 = 8$, we should *define* $\oplus$ so that $5/1 \oplus 3/1 = (5 + 3)/1$
$= 8/1$. Similarly, $3/1 \oplus {}^-5/1 = (3 + {}^-5)/1 = {}^-2/1$. In general, we should
define $\oplus$ so that $a/1 \oplus b/1 = (a + b)/1$.

Now we consider the case in which both denominators are equal,
but not necessarily 1. Since $2/5 \oplus 1/5$ may be interpreted as a mathematical model for the sum of two-fifths of a cake and one-fifth of a cake,
we should *define* $2/5 \oplus 1/5 = (2 + 1)/5 = 3/5$. In general, we should
define $a/c \oplus b/c = (a + b)/c$.

Lastly, we consider the case in which the denominators are unequal.
Now $1/2 \oplus 1/3$ may be interpreted as a mathematical model for the
sum of one-half of a cake and one-third of a cake. As one-half of a cake
is equivalent to three-sixths of a cake and one-third of a cake is equivalent to two-sixths of a cake, we see that the total amount of cake is
equivalent to five-sixths of a cake. Thus we should define $1/2 \oplus 1/3$
$= 5/6$. In order to avoid the routine of leaving the mathematical model
(1/2 + 1/3), going to the physical problem (the cake), and then
returning to the mathematical model, we can actually employ the second
case (in which the denominators are equal) to define the sum $1/2$
$\oplus 1/3$. To add these two rational numbers by the second case, we must
first express them with equal denominators. By Theorem 6, we know
that $1/2 = (1 \cdot 3)/(2 \cdot 3)$ and $1/3 = (1 \cdot 2)/(3 \cdot 2)$. Hence $1/2 \oplus 1/3$
$= (1 \cdot 3)/(2 \cdot 3) \oplus (1 \cdot 2)/(3 \cdot 2) = 3/6 \oplus 2/6 = (3 + 2)/6 = 5/6$.
In general, $a/b \oplus c/d = (ad)/(bd) \oplus (bc)/(bd) = (ad + bc)/bd$.

Because of the above considerations, we define the binary operator
$\oplus$ and the *sum* of any two rational numbers as follows.

DEFINITION 5. The *sum* of any two rational numbers a/b and c/d is the
rational number $(ad + bc)/bd$; that is, $a/b \oplus c/d = (ad + bc)/bd$.

Notice that the sum of two rational numbers is defined in terms of the sum and product of integers. If $a_1/b_1 = a_2/b_2$ and $c_1/d_1 = c_2/d_2$, can we be certain that $a_1/b_1 \oplus c_1/d_1 = a_2/b_2 \oplus c_2/d_2$ and hence that $(a_1d_1 + b_1c_1)/b_1d_1 = (a_2d_2 + b_2c_2)/b_2d_2$? If not, then the rational numbers would be as troublesome as the fractions, because the sum in Definition 5 would not be *well-defined*. The following theorem establishes the fact that the sum in Definition 5 *is* well-defined; that is, the sum does *not* depend on the particular symbols used to represent the rational numbers.

THEOREM 7. If $a_1/b_1 = a_2/b_2$ and $c_1/d_1 = c_2/d_2$, then $a_1/b_1 \oplus c_1/d_1 = a_2/b_2 \oplus c_2/d_2$.

Proof. Letting $a_1/b_1 = a_2/b_2$ and $c_1/d_1 = c_2/d_2$, we wish to prove that $a_1/b_1 \oplus c_1/d_1 = a_2/b_2 \oplus c_2/d_2$. That is, we wish to prove that $(a_1d_1 + b_1c_1)/b_1d_1 = (a_2d_2 + b_2c_2)/b_2d_2$.

By Theorem 4, $(a_1d_1 + b_1c_1)/b_1d_1 = (a_2d_2 + b_2c_2)/b_2d_2$ if and only if $b_2d_2(a_1d_1 + b_1c_1) = b_1d_1(a_2d_2 + b_2c_2)$. Hence we shall prove that $b_2d_2(a_1d_1 + b_1c_1) = b_1d_1(a_2d_2 + b_2c_2)$.

Since $a_1/b_1 = a_2/b_2$ and $c_1/d_1 = c_2/d_2$, it follows from Theorem 4 that $a_1b_2 = a_2b_1$ and $c_1d_2 = c_2d_1$.

Thus $d_1d_2(a_1b_2) = d_1d_2(a_2b_1)$ and $b_1b_2(c_1d_2) = b_1b_2(c_2d_1)$.

Hence $d_1d_2a_1b_2 + b_1b_2c_1d_2 = d_1d_2a_2b_1 + b_1b_2c_2d_1$.

Thus $b_2d_2(a_1d_1) + b_2d_2(b_1c_1) = b_1d_1(a_2d_2) + b_1d_1(b_2c_2)$.

Hence $b_2d_2(a_1d_1 + b_1c_1) = b_1d_1(a_2d_2 + b_2c_2)$.

Hence $(a_1d_1 + b_1c_1)/b_1d_1 = (a_2d_2 + b_2c_2)/b_2d_2$.

Therefore $a_1/b_1 \oplus c_1/d_1 = a_2/b_2 \oplus c_2/d_2$.//

Although you may believe that the above theorem is obvious and the proof is unnecessary, you should realize that a_1/b_1 may be equal to a_2/b_2 even though $a_1 \neq a_2$ and $b_1 \neq b_2$. For example, $5/8 = 20/32$ but $5 \neq 20$ and $8 \neq 32$.

By Definition 5, the sum of any two rational numbers is a rational number; by Theorem 7, this sum is well-defined. Thus the sum is unique. This property of the rational numbers is called the *closure property for addition of rational numbers*. In fact, the following properties of the rational numbers follow from the corresponding properties of the integers.

CLOSURE PROPERTY FOR ADDITION

If a/b and c/d are any rational numbers, then $a/b \oplus c/d$ is a unique rational number.

COMMUTATIVE PROPERTY FOR ADDITION

If a/b and c/d are any rational numbers, then $a/b \oplus c/d = c/d \oplus a/b$.

ASSOCIATIVE PROPERTY FOR ADDITION

If a/b, c/d, and e/f are any rational numbers, then $(a/b \oplus c/d) \oplus e/f = a/b \oplus (c/d \oplus e/f)$.

CANCELLATION PROPERTY FOR ADDITION

If a/b, c/d, and e/f are any rational numbers and $a/b \oplus c/d = a/b \oplus e/f$, then $c/d = e/f$.

IDENTITY PROPERTY FOR ADDITION

The rational number $0/1$ has the property that $a/b \oplus 0/1 = a/b$ for any rational number a/b. Moreover, if $a/b \oplus z/1 = a/b$ for some rational number $z/1$, then $z/1 = 0/1$.

To prove the commutative property for addition of rational numbers, we employ Definition 5 and the commutative property for addition and multiplication of integers.

$$
\begin{aligned}
\text{Thus } a/b \oplus c/d &= (ad + bc)/bd \\
&= (bc + ad)/bd \\
&= (cb + da)/db \\
&= c/d \oplus a/b.
\end{aligned}
$$

In the exercises you will be asked to supply the proofs of the associative property for addition, the cancellation property for addition, and the identity property for addition. Although $\oplus$ is really a different operator from $+$, henceforth we shall use the $+$ for both operators. From the context we can always tell which operator is intended.

Although Definition 5 enables us to add any two rational numbers, the following theorem simplifies the addition when the two denominators are equal.

THEOREM 8.   If a/b and c/b are two rational numbers, then $a/b + c/b = (a + c)/b$.

Proof.

$$
\begin{aligned}
a/b + c/b &= (ab + bc)/bb \\
&= (ab + cb)/bb \\
&= (a + c)b/(b)b \\
&= (a + c)/b \quad \text{(By Theorem 6).}\,/\!/
\end{aligned}
$$

Even if the denominators of two rational numbers are not equal, the application of Definition 5 may be tedious. In computing the sum of two rational numbers, the concept of least common multiple is helpful. The following examples illustrate the procedure usually employed.

Example 1.   Compute $5/9 + 1/12$.

$$5/9 + 1/12 = 5/3^2 + 1/2^2 \cdot 3$$
$$= 5 \cdot 2^2/3^2 \cdot 2^2 + 1 \cdot 3/(2^2 \cdot 3) \cdot 3$$
$$= 5 \cdot 2^2/3^2 \cdot 2^2 + 1 \cdot 3/2^2 \cdot 3^2$$
$$= 20/2^2 \cdot 3^2 + 3/2^2 \cdot 3^2$$
$$= (20 + 3)/2^2 \cdot 3^2$$
$$= 23/36.$$

In the second step we employed Theorem 6 to rewrite the rational numbers so that their denominators would be equal. In this form we could add them by Theorem 8. The reason we chose the denominator $2^2 \cdot 3^2$ is that the least common multiple of 9 and 12 is $2^2 \cdot 3^2$; that is, $[9, 12] = 2^2 \cdot 3^2$ by Theorem 11 of Chapter 6.

Example 2.   Compute $7/12 + 5/144$.

$$7/12 + 5/144 = (7 \cdot 12)/(12 \cdot 12) + 5/144$$
$$= 84/144 + 5/144$$
$$= 89/144.$$

Example 3.   Compute $1/12 + 1/15$.

$$1/12 + 1/15 = 1/2^2 \cdot 3 + 1/3 \cdot 5$$
$$= 1 \cdot 5/(2^2 \cdot 3)5 + 2^2 \cdot 1/2^2(3 \cdot 5)$$
$$= 5/2^2 \cdot 3 \cdot 5 + 4/2^2 \cdot 3 \cdot 5$$
$$= 9/2^2 \cdot 3 \cdot 5$$
$$= 3 \cdot 3/(2^2 \cdot 5) \cdot 3$$
$$= 3/2^2 \cdot 5$$
$$= 3/20.$$

The above examples illustrate that the procedure is to compute the least common multiple $[b, d]$ of the denominators b and d and rewrite the two rational numbers with $[b, d]$ as their common denominators.

DEFINITION 6.   The *least common denominator* of two rational numbers a/b and c/d is the least common multiple $[b, d]$ of their denominators.

Although the least common denominator method is usually the simpler method for computing the sum of two rational numbers, it is sometimes simpler to employ Definition 5 than to compute the least common denominator.

Exercise 7.3

I. Compute each of the following sums by use of Definition 5, and reduce to lowest terms.

(1) $3/5 + 4/7$
(2) $3/15 + 4/12$
(3) $12/25 + 15/16$
(4) $10/9 + 15/8$
(5) $11/18 + 23/21$
(6) $6/25 + 18/25$
(7) $1/7 + 7/1$
(8) $1/24 + 1/16$
(9) $8/19 + 11/19$
(10) $2/21 + 3/28$

II. By use of the least common denominator and Theorem 8, compute each sum in Exercise I.

III. Convert each of the following open sentences to a true sentence by replacement of the variable.

(1) $x/3 + 4/3 = 12/3$
(2) $x/7 + 6/7 = 21/7$
(3) $x/3 + 4/3 = 4/1$
(4) $x/7 + 6/7 = 3/1$
(5) $x/6 + x/3 = 5/1$
(6) $x/5 + x/10 = 6/2$
(7) $3/x + 2/3 = 5/3$
(8) $7/3 + 5/x = 8/2$
(9) $2x/x + 3/x = 3/1$
(10) $5/x + 3x/x = 11/2$

IV. (1) Prove the associative property for addition of rational numbers.
(2) Prove the identity property for addition of rational numbers.
(3) Prove the cancellation property for addition of rational numbers.

V. Construct a mathematical model to solve each of the following physical problems.

(1) Pete has half a tank of gasoline and adds one seventh of a tank. What part of the tank is filled?
(2) One-third liter of HCl is added to one-fourth liter of H_2O. What is the total amount of solution?
(3) One and a half loads of top soil is added to a pile of top soil containing two-thirds of a load of top soil. How many loads of top soil are there altogether?
(4) Beverly bought a coat for a fifth of her husband's monthly salary and bought a dress for one-tenth of her husband's monthly salary. What part of her husband's monthly salary did Beverly spend?

(5) Vernon mowed 1/4 of his lawn on Friday and 3/5 on Satur-
    day. What part of his lawn did he mow altogether?
(6) John painted 2/5 of the house and Lane painted 1/2 of the
    house. How much of the house did they paint?
(7) Maggie typed 2/7 of a thesis, Vee typed 2/5 of the thesis,
    and Shirleen typed the rest. How much of the thesis did
    Maggie and Vee type?
(8) Aline typed 4/15 of a report and Joyce typed 7/12 of the
    report. How much of the report did Aline and Joyce type?
(9) Herbert prepared 5/16 of a report, Robert prepared 5/18 of
    the report, and James prepared the balance. How much of
    the report did Herbert and Robert prepare?
(10) Helen, Lewis, and William collaborated on a textbook. Helen
    wrote 5/16 of the text, Lewis wrote 5/13 of the text, and
    William wrote the rest. What part of the text did Helen and
    Lewis write?

VI. (1) Distinguish between rational number and fraction.
    (2) Sketch the development of the rational numbers from the
        fractions.
    (3) Briefly describe the abstract nature of mathematics and its
        relation to physical problems.

7.4 Subtraction of Rational Numbers and Additive Inverses

Now that we know how to add any two rational numbers, we would
like to consider the problem of subtraction, which we have not yet
defined, between rational numbers. The definition of subtraction of
rational numbers, which we shall formulate, will be motivated by our
desire for an operation which is an extension of the operation of subtraction of integers defined in Section 5.2. Before formulating the definition, we consider the following physical problem. Paul has a can
containing four-fifths of a gallon of gasoline and fills the lawn mower
gas tank, whose capacity is one quart. How much is left in the can? We
may answer this question by determining what fraction of a gallon must
be added to one-fourth of a gallon to yield four-fifths of a gallon. A
mathematical model of the latter problem is $a/b + 1/4 = 4/5$. However,
we desire a mathematical model of the problem (as originally stated),
which involves the concept of "take away"; namely, $4/5 - 1/4 = a/b$.
Thus we should define $4/5 - 1/4$ to be that rational number a/b such
that $a/b + 1/4 = 4/5$. This example and numerous similar examples
lead us to make the following definition of the binary operator $-$, the
operation *subtraction*, and the *difference* of two rational numbers.

DEFINITION 7. The *difference* in the subtraction of the rational number c/d from the rational number a/b (written $a/b - c/d$) is the rational number e/f if and only if $a/b = c/d + e/f$. (That is, $a/b - c/d = e/f$ if and only if $a/b = c/d + e/f$.)

As in the case of the addition $a/b \oplus c/d$, the subtraction in Definition 7 should be written $a/b \ominus c/d$. However, there will be no ambiguity if the conventional symbol for subtraction is employed. Notice that $a/b - c/d$ is defined in terms of *addition*. It follows easily from the cancellation property for addition that the difference $a/b - c/d$ in Definition 7 is *well-defined*. Because of Definition 7, subtraction is frequently called the *inverse* operation of addition. The concept of *additive inverse* is useful.

DEFINITION 8. The rational number c/d is said to be an *additive inverse* of the rational number a/b if and only if $a/b + c/d = 0/1$.

Definition 8 does not guarantee that each rational number has an additive inverse. However, the following theorem guarantees that every rational number has *exactly one* additive inverse and actually exhibits that inverse.

THEOREM 9. (a) If a/b is any rational number, then $^-a/b$ is an additive inverse of a/b.

(b) If c_1/d_1 is an additive inverse of a/b and if c_2/d_2 is an additive inverse of a/b, then $c_1/d_1 = c_2/d_2$; that is, no rational number has two additive inverses.

Proof. (a) $a/b + {}^-a/b = (a + {}^-a)/b$ (By Theorem 8)
$$= 0/b$$
$$= 0/1.$$

Hence $^-a/b$ is an additive inverse of a/b (by Definition 8).

(b) Let c_1/d_1 be an additive inverse of a/b and c_2/d_2 be an additive inverse of a/b.

Then $a/b + c_1/d_1 = 0/1$ and $a/b + c_2/d_2 = 0/1$.

Thus $a/b + c_1/d_1 = a/b + c_2/d_2$.

Hence $c_1/d_1 = c_2/d_2$ (by the cancellation property for addition).//

According to Theorem 9, each rational number has exactly *one* additive inverse. Hence we speak of *the* additive inverse of a/b and denote it by $^-(a/b)$. Thus $a/b + {}^-(a/b) = 0/1$. It follows from Theorem 9(a) that $^-a/b = {}^-(a/b)$.

For example, the additive inverse of $6/7$ is $^-6/7$, and the additive inverse of $6/^-7$ is $^-6/^-7$; that is, $^-(6/^-7) = {}^-6/^-7 = 6/7$.

The following theorem states that the set of rational numbers is closed under the operation of subtraction and also yields a procedure for computing the difference.

THEOREM 10.   If a/b and c/d are any rational numbers, then $a/b - c/d$
= $a/b + {}^-c/d$.

Proof.   Similar to Theorem 4, Chapter 5.//

The following examples illustrate the applications of Theorem 10. The four sets of blocks in Example 1 show a physical illustration of subtraction.

Example 1. $4/5 - 1/4 = 4/5 + {}^-1/4$
                        $= 16/20 + {}^-5/20$
                        $= (16 + {}^-5)/20$
                        $= 11/20.$

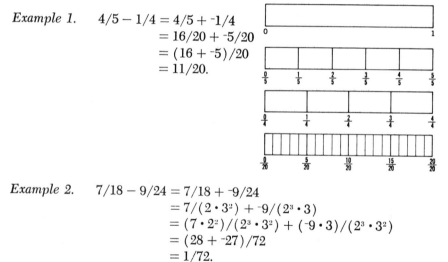

Example 2. $7/18 - 9/24 = 7/18 + {}^-9/24$
                        $= 7/(2 \cdot 3^2) + {}^-9/(2^3 \cdot 3)$
                        $= (7 \cdot 2^2)/(2^3 \cdot 3^2) + ({}^-9 \cdot 3)/(2^3 \cdot 3^2)$
                        $= (28 + {}^-27)/72$
                        $= 1/72.$

Example 3. $1/^-7 - {}^-1/4 = 1/^-7 + {}^-({}^-1)/4$
                        $= {}^-1/7 + 1/4$
                        $= ({}^-4 + 7)/28$
                        $= 3/28.$

As Theorem 10 expresses the difference in terms of a sum of two rational numbers, and as the set of rationals is closed under addition, it follows from the cancellation property for addition of rational numbers that the set of rationals is closed under the operation of subtraction.

CLOSURE PROPERTY FOR SUBTRACTION

If a/b and c/d are any two rational numbers, then $a/b - c/d$ is a unique rational number.

As in the subtraction of integers, there is no commutative property for the subtraction of rational numbers and no associative property.

The following properties of rational numbers may be proved as the analogous properties of the integers, which were proved in Theorems 2 and 3 of Chapter 5.

DOUBLE NEGATIVE PROPERTY

If a/b is any rational number, then $^-(^-a/b) = a/b$.

SIGN PROPERTY FOR ADDITION

If a/b and c/d are any rational numbers, then $^-(a/b + c/d) = ^-(a/b) + ^-(c/d) = ^-a/b + ^-c/d$.

According to the sign property for addition, the additive inverse of the sum of any two rational numbers is equal to the sum of the additive inverses of the rational numbers.

Example 4. $^-[^-(3/5)] = 3/5$.

Example 5. $^-[^-(3/^-5)] = 3/^-5$.

Example 6. $^-(3/^-5) = ^-(^-3/5) = 3/5$.

Example 7. $^-(5/7 + 2/3) = ^-5/7 + ^-2/3$.

Example 8. $^-(^-7/8 + 3/5) = ^-(^-7/8) + ^-3/5 = 7/8 + ^-3/5$.

Exercise 7.4

I. Compute each of the following by means of Definition 7.

(1) $3/5 - 4/3$ (6) $7/12 - 8/9$

(2) $4/3 - 3/5$ (7) $^-4/7 - 3/7$

(3) $4/5 - 6/7$ (8) $4/7 - ^-3/7$

(4) $4/7 - 6/5$ (9) $^-5/8 - ^-3/8$

(5) $5/9 - 5/8$ (10) $^-5/8 - 3/8$

II. Compute each difference in Exercise I by means of Theorem 10.

III. Express, in lowest terms, the additive inverse of each of the following rational numbers.

(1) $6/12$ (3) $^-5/15$

(2) $15/9$ (4) $6/^-15$

(5) 2/-20   (8) -5/1
(6) -6/-3   (9) 0/1
(7) 5/-1   (10) 1/1

IV. Employ the sign property to express each of the following as a sum of rational numbers.

(1) -(4/5 + 7/8)   (6) -(-7/10 + -6/7)
(2) -(9/10 + 11/12)   (7) -(8/9 - 2/5)
(3) -(9/-10 + 10/11)   (8) -(7/15 - 3/4)
(4) -(6/7 + 7/-8)   (9) -(6/-5 - 5/6)
(5) -(6/5 + -8/9)   (10) -(8/-9 - 9/8)

V. Construct a mathematical model and solve each of the following physical problems.

(1) Mary did 2/5 of the work organizing and planning a party, Adele did 1/4 of the work, and Robert did the rest. What part of the work did Robert do?

(2) Joseph organized a program for civic improvement and assigned the details to Thomas, Howard, and Francis. If Thomas did 1/4 of the over-all work, Howard did 2/10 of the over-all work, and Francis did 11/50 of the over-all work, what part of the over-all work was contributed to organization?

(3) Claude's gasoline tank reads 1/4 full. He adds 3/5 of a tank. How much more must he add to fill the tank?

(4) Luis drove 3/8 of a trip, Irving drove 2/9 of the trip, Alex drove 1/7 of the trip, and Jude drove the rest of the way. What part of the trip did Jude drive?

(5) Nelson painted 3/11 of a house, Leonard painted 4/15 of the house, Phil painted 3/16 of the house, and Walter painted the rest. How much of the house did Walter paint?

(6) Bertrand, Bernard, Claudius, and Lawrence remodeled their house. If Bertrand did 4/21 of the work, Bernard did 4/17 of the work, Claudius did 4/15 of the work, and Lawrence did the rest, how much of the work did Lawrence do?

VI. As in Example 1, illustrate each subtraction in Exercise V by means of blocks.

VII. Convert each of the following open sentences to a true sentence by replacement of the variable by an integer.

(1) 2/5 + x/5 = 0/1   (4) 9/10 + 18/x = 0/1
(2) 7/11 + x/11 = 0/1   (5) x/9 + -4/9 = 0/1
(3) 6/7 + 12/x = 0/1   (6) x/17 + -15/17 = 0/1

    (7) $1/1 + 3/x = 0/1$ (11) $x/3 - x/5 = 2x/15$
    (8) $5/5 + 3/x = 0/1$ (12) $x/5 - x/7 = 2x/35$
    (9) $x/3 - x/5 = {}^-4/15$ (13) $x/3 + x/3 = 0/1$
   (10) $x/5 - x/7 = {}^-4/35$ (14) $x/10 - x/10 = 0/1$

VIII. (1) Prove Theorem 10.
     (2) Prove the double negative property.
     (3) Prove the sign property.

  IX. Give a physical example which motivates a probable definition of multiplication of rational numbers.

7.5 Multiplication of Rational Numbers

Now that we know how to add any two rational numbers and subtract any rational number from any rational number, we would like to be able to multiply any two rational numbers. The definition of multiplication, which we shall formulate shortly, will be motivated partly by our desire for an operation which combines the rational numbers $a/1$ and $b/1$ in the same manner that the operation of multiplication between integers combines the integers a and b. Accordingly, we should define the product of $a/1$ and $b/1$ to be the rational number $ab/1$; that is, we should define *product* so that $(a/1) \cdot (b/1) = ab/1$. Before formulating the definition, we consider the following physical problem. Marcia has four-fifths of a cake and decides to give one-third of it to her neighbor. We would like to construct a mathematical model of this physical problem so that $(1/3) \cdot (4/5)$ is the rational number which may be interpreted as the amount of cake Marcia gave to her neighbor. The physical problem is to compute one-third *of* four-fifths of a cake. Physically, Marcia divides the four-fifths cake into three pieces of equal size and gives one of these pieces to her neighbor. Since four-fifths of a cake is equivalent to twelve-fifteenths of a cake, and $12/15 = 4/15 + 4/15 + 4/15$, we see that the answer to the problem is $4/15$. Consequently, we should define multiplication so that $(1/3) \cdot (4/5) = (1 \cdot 4)/(3 \cdot 5)$. With such a definition, the operator $\cdot$ of the mathematical model portrays the *of* of the physical problem. Similarly, since two-thirds *of* four-fifths of a cake is eight-fifteenths of a cake, we should define multiplication so that $(2/3) \cdot (4/5) = 8/15$. These considerations motivate us to make the following definition of the binary operator $\cdot$ (or $\times$), the operation *multiplication*, and the *product* of two rational numbers.

DEFINITION 9. The *product* of any two rational numbers a/b and c/d [written $(a/b) \cdot (c/d)$ or simply $a/b \cdot c/d$] is the rational number ac/bd. That is, $a/b \cdot c/d = ac/bd$.

Notice that the product of two rational numbers is defined in terms of the products of two pairs of integers (ac and bd). As in the case of addition and subtraction of rational numbers, the multiplication should really be written $a/b \odot c/d$ rather than $a/b \cdot c/d$. However, there will be no confusion if the conventional symbol $\cdot$ is employed. In fact, when the rational numbers are written in the form $\frac{a}{b}$, we frequently indicate the product by $\frac{a}{b}\frac{c}{d}$, without the dot. Moreover, since each rational number may be represented by many symbols, you may wonder whether the product of two rational numbers depends on the particular symbols employed. The product of Definition 9 is well-defined if and only if it depends *not* on the particular symbols but only on the rational numbers. The following theorem establishes the fact that the *product* of Definition 9 *is* well-defined; that is, the product does not depend on the particular symbols which represent the rational numbers. The proof is assigned as an exercise.

THEOREM 11.   If $a_1/b_1 = a_2/b_2$ and $c_1/d_1 = c_2/d_2$, then
$a_1/b_1 \cdot c_1/d_1 = a_2/b_2 \cdot c_2/d_2$.

By Definition 9, the product of any two rational numbers is a rational number; by Theorem 11, this product is well-defined. Thus the product is unique. This property of the rational numbers is called the *closure property for multiplication of rational numbers*. The following properties of the rational numbers follow from the corresponding properties of the integers.

CLOSURE PROPERTY FOR MULTIPLICATION
If a/b and c/d are any rational numbers, then $a/b \cdot c/d$ is a unique rational number.

COMMUTATIVE PROPERTY FOR MULTIPLICATION
If a/b and c/d are any rational numbers, then $a/b \cdot c/d = c/d \cdot a/b$.

MULTIPLICATION PROPERTY FOR ZERO
If a/b and c/d are any rational numbers, then $a/b \cdot c/d = 0/1$ if and only if $a/b = 0/1$ or $c/d = 0/1$.

CANCELLATION PROPERTY FOR MULTIPLICATION
If a/b, c/d, and e/f are any rational numbers, $a/b \neq 0/1$, and $a/b \cdot c/d = a/b \cdot e/f$, then $c/d = e/f$.

ASSOCIATIVE PROPERTY FOR MULTIPLICATION
If a/b, c/d, and e/f are any rational numbers, then $(a/b \cdot c/d)\, e/f = a/b\, (c/d \cdot e/f)$.

IDENTITY PROPERTY FOR MULTIPLICATION

If a/b is any rational number, then $a/b \cdot 1/1 = a/b$. Moreover, if $a/b \cdot u/1 = a/b$, for some rational number $a/b \neq 0/1$, then $u/1 = 1/1$.

DISTRIBUTIVE PROPERTY

If a/b, c/d, and e/f are any rational numbers, then $a/b \, (c/d + e/f) = a/b \cdot c/d + a/b \cdot e/f$.

The manner in which we defined the operator $\cdot$ in Definition 9 set the stage so that the above properties, proved previously in Chapter 5 for the set of integers, would be properties of the set of rational numbers.

To prove the associative property for multiplication of rational numbers, we employ Definition 9 and the associative property for multiplication of integers.

Thus $(a/b \cdot c/d) \, e/f = (ac/bd)(e/f)$ (by Definition 9)

$\qquad = (ac)e/(bd)f$ (by Definition 9)

$\qquad = a(ce)/b(df)$ (by associative property
                                for multiplication of integers)

$\qquad = (a/b) \, (ce/df)$ (by Definition 9)

$\qquad = (a/b)(c/d \cdot e/f)$ (by Definition 9).

To prove the distributive property for rational numbers, we employ Definition 5 and several properties of the integers.

Thus $(a/b)(c/d + e/f) = (a/b)[(cf + de)/df]$ (by Definition 5)

$\qquad = a(cf + de)/b(df)$ (by Definition 9)

$\qquad = [a(cf) + a(de)]/b(df)$ (by distributive property for integers)

$\qquad = [(ac)f + (ad)e]/(bd)f$ (by associative property for multiplication of integers)

$\qquad = (ac)f/(bd)f + (ad)e/(bd)f$ (by Theorem 8)

$\qquad = (ac)f/(bd)f + (ae)d/(bf)d$ (by commutative and associative property for multiplication of integers)

$\qquad = ac/bd + ae/bf$ (by Theorem 6).

Example 1. $3/5 \cdot {}^-7/8 = (3 \cdot {}^-7)/(5 \cdot 8) = {}^-21/40$.

Example 2. $17/9 \cdot 0/1 = (17 \cdot 0)/(9 \cdot 1) = 0/9 = 0/1$.

Example 3. $6/7 \cdot {}^-5/9 = (3 \cdot 2)/7 \cdot {}^-5/(3 \cdot 3) = [3 \cdot (2 \cdot {}^-5)]/[3 \cdot (3 \cdot 7)] = (2 \cdot {}^-5)/(3 \cdot 7) = {}^-10/21.$

Example 4. $6/13({}^-7/9 + 8/{}^-7) = 6/13 \cdot {}^-7/9 + 6/13 \cdot 8/{}^-7$
$= 6 \cdot {}^-7/13 \cdot 9 + {}^-6 \cdot 8/13 \cdot 7$
$= 3 \cdot 2 \cdot {}^-7/3 \cdot 3 \cdot 13 + {}^-6 \cdot 8/13 \cdot 7$
$= 2 \cdot {}^-7/3 \cdot 13 + {}^-6 \cdot 8/13 \cdot 7$
$= {}^-14/39 + {}^-48/91.$

Example 5.   If there exists a such that $3/19 \cdot a/5 = 6/38 \cdot 7/5$, then there exists a such that $3/19 \cdot a/5 = 3/19 \cdot 7/5$. If there exists a such that $3/19 \cdot a/5 = 3/19 \cdot 7/5$, then there exists a such that $a/5 = 7/5$. If there exists a such that $a/5 = 7/5$, then there exists a such that $5a = 5(7)$. If there exists a such that $5a = 5(7)$, then there exists a such that $a = 7$.

Exercise 7.5

I. Formulate a mathematical model necessary for the solution of each of the following physical problems.

(1) Susan has 2/3 of a pie and gives 1/3 of it to Leslie. What amount of pie does Susan give Leslie?

(2) Ralph has 4/5 of a quart of milk and drinks 3/4 of it. What amount of milk does Ralph drink?

(3) Carol has 7/8 package of typing paper and uses 3/4 of it on a report. What amount of paper does Carol use?

(4) Toby has 5/6 bushel of crawfish and cooks 2/3 of a bushel. What amount of crawfish does Toby cook?

(5) Merlin gives 2/5 of his 5/6 pound of tea to Lane. What amount of tea does Merlin have left?

(6) Craig has 9/10 kilogram of KCl and spills 1/4 of it. What amount of KCl does Craig have left?

(7) Catherine has 5/6 of a box of mimeograph stencils and uses 1/2 of a box. What part of a box does Catherine have left? If there are 24 stencils in a full box, how many stencils does Catherine have left?

(8) On a vacation trip, Alcide drove 2/5 of the distance and Marty drove 1/3 of the distance. If Roy drove 2/3 of the remainder of the distance, and Wayne drove the rest of the way, what fraction of the distance did Roy drive?

(9) Judy has $2\frac{2}{3}$ bushel of rice and gives 2/5 of it to Jo. How much rice does Judy have left?

(10) Edith makes $3\frac{4}{5}$ gallons of ice cream. She puts 3/5 of it in the freezer, eats 1/50 of it, and gives the rest to her friends. How much ice cream does Edith give to her friends?

II. Illustrate each multiplication in Exercise I by means of blocks.

III. Write each of the following in the form a/b, in which a and b are integers.

(1) $2/3(^-6/7 + 3/5)$

(2) $^-3/5 \, (7/9 + \,^-4/3)$

(3) $2/3 \cdot \,^- 6/7 + 3/5$

(4) $^-3/5 \cdot 7/9 + \,^-4/3$

(5) $6/7 \cdot 1/1 - 6/7 \cdot 2/1$

(6) $7/9 \cdot 1/1 - 7/9 \cdot 3/1$

(7) $^-3/10 \cdot 2/^-15 - \,^-3/25$

(8) $^-5/12 \cdot 3/^-25 - \,^-7/20$

(9) $5/17 \cdot 0/1 - 5/13 \cdot 1/1$

(10) $7/19 \cdot 0/1 - 5/13 \cdot 1/1$

(11) $3/7 \cdot 7/3$

(12) $8/15 \cdot 15/8$

(13) $^-10/17 \cdot \,^-17/10$

(14) $^-9/16 \cdot 16/^-9$

(15) $11/^-8 \cdot \,^-8/11$

(16) $^-13/5 \cdot \,^-5/13$

(17) $^-105/23 \cdot 23/105$

(18) $^-210/29 \cdot 29/210$

(19) $(14/3 \cdot 6/5) \cdot 10/7$

(20) $14/3 \cdot (6/5 \cdot 10/7)$

IV. (1) Prove Theorem 11.

(2) Prove the commutative property for multiplication of rational numbers.

(3) Prove the multiplication property of zero.

(4) Prove the cancellation property for multiplication of rational numbers.

(5) Prove the identity property for multiplication of rational numbers.

V. Prove each of the following.

(1) If a/b and c/d are any rational numbers, then $^-(a/b) \cdot \,^-(c/d) = a/b \cdot c/d$.

(2) If a/b and c/d are any rational numbers, then $(a/b) \cdot \,^-(c/d) = \,^-(a/b \cdot c/d)$.

(3) If a/b and c/d are any rational numbers, then $(a/b) \cdot (^-c/d) = \,^-(a/b \cdot c/d)$.

7.6 Division of Rational Numbers and Multiplicative Inverses

Recall that division between integers was defined only for certain pairs of integers. This serious defect of the integers was one of the reasons that motivated the invention of the rational numbers. If the set of rational numbers is to serve the purpose for which it was invented, we should be able to define division of any rational number a/b by any rational number $c/d \neq 0/1$ in such a manner that $a/1 \div b/1 = c/1$ if and only if $a \div b = c$. Thus, for example, under an appropriate definition of division, $10/1 \div 2/1 = 5/1$; that is, $10/1 \div 2/1 = 10/1 \cdot 1/2$. Since $30/3 = 10/1$ and $8/4 = 2/1$, we should have $30/3 \div 8/4 = 5/1$. However, $30/3 \cdot 4/8 = 5/1$. Hence, under the appropriate definition, $30/3 \div 8/4 = 30/3 \cdot 4/8$.

These considerations motivate us to make the following definition of the binary operator $\div$, the operation of *division*, and the *quotient* of two rational numbers.

DEFINITION 10. The *quotient* in the division of the rational number a/b by the rational number $c/d \neq 0/1$ (written $a/b \div c/d$) is the rational number e/f if and only if $a/b = c/d \cdot e/f$. (That is, $a/b \div c/d = e/f$ if and only if $a/b = c/d \cdot e/f$.)

The use of the conventional $\div$ in the division of rational numbers, instead of a new symbol such as $\oslash$, should cause no confusion. Notice that division is defined in terms of multiplication. It follows easily from the cancellation property for multiplication of rational numbers that division of rational numbers, as defined in Definition 10, is well-defined; that is, if $a/b \div c/d = e_1/f_1$ and $a/b \div c/d = e_2/f_2$, then $e_1/f_1 = e_2/f_2$. Because of this definition, division is sometimes called the *inverse* operation of multiplication. An alternate way of writing $a/b \div c/d$ is $\frac{a/b}{c/d}$. The concept of *multiplicative inverse* is useful.

DEFINITION 11. The rational number c/d is said to be a *multiplicative inverse* (or *reciprocal*) of the rational number $a/b \neq 0/1$ if and only if $a/b \cdot c/d = 1/1$.

Definition 11 does not guarantee that each rational number $a/b \neq 0/1$ has a multiplicative inverse. However, the following theorem guarantees that every rational number except $0/1$ has *exactly* one multiplicative inverse and actually exhibits that inverse.

THEOREM 12.   (a) If a/b is any rational number except $0/1$, then b/a is a multiplicative inverse of a/b.
(b) If c_1/d_1 is a multiplicative inverse of a/b and if c_2/d_2 is a multiplicative inverse of a/b, then $c_1/d_1 = c_2/d_2$; that is, no rational number has two multiplicative inverses.

Proof.   (a) $a/b \cdot b/a = ab/ba$
$$= ab/ab$$
$$= 1/1$$

Hence b/a is a multiplicative inverse of a/b.

(b) Let c_1/d_1 be a multiplicative inverse of a/b and c_2/d_2 be a multiplicative inverse of a/b.

Then $a/b \cdot c_1/d_1 = 1/1$ and $a/b \cdot c_2/d_2 = 1/1$.

Thus $a/b \cdot c_1/d_1 = a/b \cdot c_2/d_2$.

Hence $c_1/d_1 = c_2/d_2$ (by the cancellation property for multiplication of rational numbers).//

According to Theorem 12, every rational number a/b except $0/1$ has a unique multiplicative inverse b/a. Hence we speak of *the* multiplicative inverse of a/b and denote it by $\frac{1}{a/b}$. Thus $\frac{a}{b} \cdot \frac{1}{a/b} = \frac{1}{1}$. It follows from Theorem 12(a) that $\frac{1}{a/b} = b/a$.

For example, the multiplicative inverse of $6/7$ is $7/6$, and the multiplicative inverse of $^-8/1$ is $^-1/8$; that is, $\frac{1}{6/7} = 7/6$ and $\frac{1}{-8/1} = ^-1/8$. However, $0/1$ has no multiplicative inverse.

The following theorem asserts that the set of rational numbers is closed under the operation of division, except for $a/b \div 0/1$, and also yields the procedure for computing the quotient. The reason that $a/b \div c/d$ is not defined if $c/d = 0/1$ is that, by Definition 10, $a/b \div 0/1 = e/f$ if and only if $a/b = 0/1 \cdot e/f$. However, since $0/1 \cdot e/f = 0/1$ for every rational number e/f, this would mean that a/b would have to be equal to $0/1$. Consequently, division would be defined only if $a/b = 0/1$. If $a/b = 0/1$ and $c/d = 0/1$, then e/f could be any rational number. Since we desire a unique answer to any division problem, we require that $c/d \neq 0/1$ in Definition 10.

THEOREM 13.   If a/b is any rational number and c/d is any rational number except $0/1$, then $a/b \div c/d = a/b \cdot d/c$.

Proof.   Let $a/b \div c/d = e/f$.

Then $a/b = c/d \cdot e/f$ (by Definition 10).

Thus $a/b = e/f \cdot c/d$.

Hence $a/b \cdot d/c = (e/f \cdot c/d) \cdot d/c$
$$= e/f \cdot (c/d \cdot d/c)$$
$$= e/f \cdot 1/1$$
$$= e/f.$$

But $a/b \div c/d = e/f$.

Hence $a/b \div c/d = a/b \cdot d/c$.//

The following examples illustrate Theorem 13.

Example 1. $4/5 \div 3/4 = 4/5 \cdot 4/3 = (4 \cdot 4)/(5 \cdot 3) = 16/15.$

Example 2. $^-7/9 \div 7/9 = ^-7/9 \cdot 9/7 = ^-1(7 \cdot 9)(7 \cdot 9) = ^-1/1.$

Example 3. $18/5 \div ^-3/1 = 18/5 \cdot 1/^-3 = ^-6/5.$

Example 4. $0/25 \div 6/5 = 0/25 \cdot 5/6 = 0/1.$

Example 5.   Beverly has five-thirds yards of ribbon and cuts it into smaller pieces each one-third yard in length to make hair ribbons. How many ribbons does she obtain from the longer ribbon?

The mathematical model for the physical problem is $5/3 \div 1/3 = 5/3 \cdot 3/1 = 5/1.$

The ribbons below illustrate the mathematical concept of division.

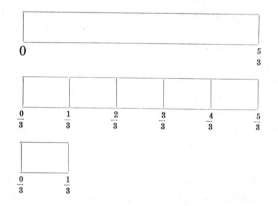

As Theorem 13 expresses the quotient of two rational numbers in terms of a product of two rational numbers and as the set of rationals is closed under multiplication, it follows from the cancellation property for multiplication that the set of rationals is closed under the operation of division, provided that division by 0/1 is excluded.

CLOSURE PROPERTY FOR DIVISION
If a/b is any rational number and c/d is any rational number except $0/1$, then $a/b \div c/d$ is a unique rational number.

As in the subtraction of rational numbers, there is no commutative property for the division of rational numbers, and there is no associative property. Obviously $a/b \div 1/1 = a/b$ for every rational.

Recall that the set $\{\ldots, \, {}^-3/1, \, {}^-2/1, \, {}^-1/1, \, 0/1, \, 1/1, \, 2/1, \, 3/1, \, \ldots\}$ of rational numbers is in one-to-one correspondence with the set $\{\ldots, \, {}^-3, \, {}^-2, \, {}^-1, \, 0, \, 1, \, 2, \, 3, \ldots\}$ of integers as shown in Figure 7.6.

$$\{\ldots \, {}^-3/1, \, {}^-2/1, \, {}^-1/1, \, 0/1, \, 1/1, \, 2/1, \, 3/1, \, \ldots\}$$
$$\ldots \quad \updownarrow \quad \updownarrow \quad \updownarrow \quad \updownarrow \quad \updownarrow \quad \updownarrow \quad \updownarrow \quad \ldots$$
$$\{\ldots \quad {}^-3, \quad {}^-2, \quad {}^-1, \quad 0, \quad 1, \quad 2, \quad 3, \quad \ldots\}$$

FIGURE 7.6

The four binary operations between rational numbers were defined so that the set $\{\ldots, \, {}^-3/1, \, {}^-2/1, \, {}^-1/1, \, 0/1, \, 1/1, \, 2/1, \, 3/1, \, \ldots\}$ would behave in a manner similar to the set of integers under the appropriate operations, as illustrated in Figure 7.7. The circles around the symbols $+, -, \cdot,$ and $\div$ are employed in Figure 7.7 for emphasis.

Rational Numbers		*Integers*
$a/1 \oplus b/1 = (a + b)/1$	$\leftrightarrow$	$a + b$
$a/1 \ominus b/1 = (a - b)/1$	$\leftrightarrow$	$a - b$
$a/1 \odot b/1 = a \cdot b/1$	$\leftrightarrow$	$a \cdot b$
$a/1 \oslash b/1 = a/b$	$\leftrightarrow$	$a \div b$ (whenever $b \mid a$)

FIGURE 7.7

Since these two sets of *different* elements are *abstractly alike* we treat them as if they were identical and, in actual practice, we replace the symbol $a/1$ for a rational number by the symbol a for the corresponding integer. *Thus we consider the set of integers to be a proper subset of the set of rational numbers.*

Since $a/1 \div b/1$ is a unique *rational* number a/b for any integer a and any nonzero integer b, it follows that division is now defined *in the set of rational numbers* between any integer a and any nonzero integer b. In particular, since $a/1 \div b/1 = a/b = a \div b$, we sometimes refer to the rational number a/b as $a \div b$. Similarly, $a/b \div c/d$ may be written $\frac{a/b}{c/d}$.

Example 6. $10/5 + 16/4 = 2/1 + 4/1 = 2 + 4 = 6.$

Example 7. ${}^-6/1 + 15/{}^-3 = {}^-6/1 + {}^-5/1 = {}^-6 + {}^-5 = {}^-11.$

Example 8. $8 \cdot (3/4) = 8/1 \cdot 3/4 = 6/1 = 6.$

The Rational Numbers

Example 9. $a \cdot (c/d) = a/1 \cdot c/d = ac/d.$

Example 10. $a \cdot (1/a) = a/1 \cdot 1/a = a/a = 1/1 = 1.$

Example 11. $6/7 \div 2/7 = 6/7 \cdot 7/2 = 6/2 = 3/1 = 3.$

Example 12. $8/13 \div 4/13 = 8/13 \cdot 13/4 = 8/4 = 2/1 = 2.$

Example 13. $3 \div 5 = 3/1 \div 5/1 = 3/1 \cdot 1/5 = 3/5.$

Example 14. $17 \div 3 = 17/1 \div 3/1 = 17/1 \cdot 1/3 = 17/3.$

Observe that Example 10 actually exhibits two important properties of rational numbers with which you are very familiar; namely, if $a \neq 0$, then $a \cdot (1/a) = 1$, and $a/a = 1$.

Exercise 7.6

I. Compute each of the following quotients.

    (1) $4/3 \div 3/2$ (6) $6/5 \div 5/3$
    (2) $3/3 \div 2/5$ (7) $7/8 \div 3/3$
    (3) $0/6 \div 3/3$ (8) $6/11 \div 11/11$
    (4) $0/5 \div 1/1$ (9) $12/11 \div 22/15$
    (5) $7/8 \div 3/4$ (10) $15/13 \div 26/25$

II. Compute each of the following quotients *without* replacing any rational number of the form $a/1$ by the corresponding integer a.

    (1) $15/1 \div 5/1$ (6) $51/1 \div 3/1$
    (2) $35/1 \div 5/1$ (7) $^{-}98/1 \div 49/1$
    (3) $15/1 \div 3/1$ (8) $^{-}98/1 \div 2/1$
    (4) $35/1 \div 7/1$ (9) $56/1 \div {}^{-}8/1$
    (5) $51/1 \div 17/1$ (10) $56/1 \div {}^{-}7/1$

III. In Exercise II replace each rational number of the form $a/1$ by the corresponding integer a, and then compute each quotient.

IV. Express, in lowest terms, the multiplicative inverse of each of the following rational numbers, if the multiplicative inverse exists.

    (1) $2/5$ (6) $^{-}5/1$
    (2) $5/2$ (7) $^{-}18/15$
    (3) $^{-}3/8$ (8) $^{-}21/18$
    (4) $^{-}7/10$ (9) $0/^{-}7$
    (5) $4/^{-}1$ (10) $^{-}0/8$

V. Compute each of the following sums, products, differences, and quotients. Reduce answers to lowest terms. The integers a and b are such that no denominator of any rational number in (17) through (20) is equal to 0.

(1) $(3/2 + 2/5) \div 1/3$

(2) $(5/2 + 2/3) \div 1/5$

(3) $^-4/3 \div (3/5 - 1/4)$

(4) $7/^-3 \div (4/5 - 3/4)$

(5) $(^-4/3 \div 3/5) - 1/4$

(6) $(7/^-3 \div 4/5) - 3/4$

(7) $19/7 \cdot {}^-14/15 + 13/15$

(8) $23/8 \cdot {}^- 24/17 + 15/17$

(9) $19/7 \cdot (^-14/15 + 13/15)$

(10) $23/8 \cdot (^-24/17 + 15/17)$

(11) $(2/5 \div 7/8) \div (3/8 \div 9/4)$

(12) $(7/8 \div 2/5) \div (9/4 \div 3/8)$

(13) $\dfrac{2/5 \div 7/8}{3/8 \div 9/4}$

(14) $\dfrac{7/8 \div 2/5}{9/4 \div 3/8}$

(15) $\dfrac{2/5 - 4/3}{^-7/15 + 2/3}$

(16) $\dfrac{4/5 - 5/7}{^-8/35 + 4/7}$

(17) $\dfrac{1/a - 1/b}{1/b - 1/a}$

(18) $\dfrac{2/a - 3/b}{2b/5 - 3a/5}$

(19) $\dfrac{\frac{a/b - 2/3}{3a - 2b}}{3}$

(20) $\dfrac{\frac{5/7 - a/b}{5b - 7a}}{b}$

VI. Observe that there was a quantifier implied in (17), (18), (19), and (20) of Problem V. State which quantifier was implied. Rework these four parts of Problem V and express the quantifier at each step.

VII. Construct a mathematical model and solve each of the following physical problems.

(1) Sondra has 2/3 gallon of punch. She drinks 1/6 of it and divides the rest equally among Laura, Mona, and Polly. How much punch does she give each girl?

(2) Ethelyn has 6¾ gallons of punch and serves 3/32 gallon to each child at a party. How many children are at the party?

(3) Norma and Jeanette distribute 140 cookies at a party by giving each child 2½ cookies. How many children are at the party?

(4) At a picnic Anita, Henri, and Inez divide 189 candy bars by giving each child 3½ bars. How many children are at the party?

(5) Shirley and Sue spent 23⅕ hours in conferences. If each conference lasted 2/5 hour, how many conferences did Shirley and Sue attend?

(6) Helen read a certain book at the rate of 2⅕ pages per minute. Lois read another book at the rate of 2¾ pages per

minute. How long did it take Helen to read $71\frac{1}{2}$ pages? How long did it take Lois to read $71\frac{1}{2}$ pages?

(7) Lucille read a certain book at the rate of $2\frac{7}{8}$ pages per minute. Rita read another book at the rate of $2\frac{5}{6}$ pages per minute. How long did it take Lucille to read $83\frac{1}{2}$ pages? How long did it take Rita to read $83\frac{1}{2}$ pages?

(8) Dorothy divides $67\frac{1}{2}$ ounces of a chemical in $6\frac{3}{4}$ ounce containers. Sabra divides $73\frac{1}{2}$ ounces of a chemical in $6\frac{3}{4}$ ounce containers. How many containers do they fill altogether?

(9) Blanche and Gene divided $45\frac{2}{5}$ lb of candy among a group of children at a picnic by giving each one $\frac{3}{5}$ lb of candy. What is the largest number of children receiving candy? How much candy was left over after the largest possible number of children received their candy?

(10) Dorris and René served two kinds of punch at a party. There were $46\frac{2}{5}$ pints of red punch and $38\frac{2}{3}$ pints of yellow punch. If each child at the party received exactly $4/5$ pint of red punch, how many children were at the party? How much yellow punch does each child receive if the yellow punch is divided equally among the children?

VIII. Illustrate each division in Exercise VII by means of blocks.

IX. Prove the following.

(1) If a/b is any nonzero rational number, then b/a is $\frac{1}{a/b}$.

(2) If a/b is any nonzero rational number, then the multiplicative inverse of a/b is $\frac{1}{a/b}$.

(3) If c is any nonzero integer and a/b is any rational number, then $\frac{a/b}{c} = a/bc$.

(4) If a is any integer and b/c is any nonzero rational number, then $\frac{a}{b/c} = ac/b$.

(5) Division of rational numbers is well-defined.

7.7 Order Properties of the Rational Numbers

As there is an order relation ($<$) on the set of integers, it is natural to extend the concept of order to the set of rational numbers. Since $4 < 5$ and $4/1 = 4$ and $5/1 = 5$, for example, the extension of the definition of order to the set of rationals should be consistent with the definition of order on I; that is, from the definition we shall make of $a/b < c/d$, we must be able to conclude that $4/1 < 5/1$ and hence that

$4 < 5$. Before we define the order relation on the set of rationals, we shall first define *positive rational number* and *negative rational number*.

DEFINITION 12 (a) The rational number a/b is said to be a *positive rational* if and only if $a < 0$ and $b < 0$, or $0 < a$ and $0 < b$.

(b) The rational number a/b is said to be a *negative rational* if and only if $a < 0$ and $0 < b$, or $0 < a$ and $b < 0$.

For example, $^-3/^-5$ and $4/5$ are positive rationals, whereas $^-3/5$ and $4/^-5$ are negative rationals.

Recalling the definition of order on the integers, we define order on the rationals as follows:

DEFINITION 13. The rational number a/b is said to be *less than* the rational number c/d if and only if there exists a positive rational number e/f such that $a/b + e/f = c/d$. (That is, $a/b < c/d$ if and only if $a/b + e/f = c/d$ for some positive rational number e/f.)

Since $a/b < c/d$ is defined in terms of addition of two rational numbers, and addition of rational numbers is well-defined, we see that the definition of order does not depend on the symbols representing the rational numbers.

Example 1. $3/5 < 4/5$ because $3/5 + 1/5 = 4/5$.

Example 2. $^-3/^-5 < 4/5$ because $^-3/^-5 + 1/5 = 4/5$.

Example 3. $5/7 < 5/6$ because $5/7 + 5/42 = 5/6$.

Example 4. $^-6/7 < 0$ because $^-6/7 + 6/7 = 0$.

Example 5. $0 < 2/3$ because $0 + 2/3 = 2/3$.

Example 6. $^-5/6 < ^-5/7$ because $^-5/6 + 5/42 = ^-5/7$.

The following theorem, which follows from Definition 13, gives us another method for determining whether a given rational is less than another rational.

THEOREM 14.   If a/b and c/d are rational numbers with positive denominators b and d, then $a/b < c/d$ if and only if $ad < bc$.

Proof.

$(\rightarrow)$ Let $a/b < c/d$.

Then there exists $e \in I^+, f \in I^+$ such that $a/b + e/f = c/d$
                                                   (by Definition 12).

Thus $(af + be)/bf = c/d$ (by Definition 5).

Hence $(af + be)d = bfc$ (by Theorem 4).

Thus $adf + bde = bcf$ (by distributive property for integers).

Hence $(adf + bde)/f = bcf/f$ (by closure property for division of rationals).

Therefore, $adf/f + bde/f = bcf/f$ (by Theorem 8).

Thus $ad + bde/f = bc$ (by Theorem 6).

But ad and bc are integers   (by closure property for multiplication of integers).

Hence bde/f is an integer   (by closure property for subtraction of integers).

Moreover, bde/f is positive.

Thus $ad < bc$ (by Definition 9 of Chapter 5).

$(\leftarrow)$ Let $ad < bc$.

Then there exist $k \in I^+$ such that $ad + k = bc$ (by Definition 9 of Chapter 5).

Hence $(ad + k)/bd = bc/bd$ (by closure property for division of rationals).

Thus $ad/bd + k/bd = bc/bd$ (by Theorem 8).

Hence $a/b + k/bd = c/d$ (by Theorem 6).

Moreover, k/bd is positive.

Thus $a/b < c/d$ (by Definition 12).$/\!/$

By Theorem 5, any rational number can be written with a positive denominator. Hence Theorem 14 is sufficient for comparing *any* two rational numbers. Thus to compare $2/^-5$ and $^-1/5$, we would rewrite $2/^-5$ as $^-2/5$. By Theorem 14, $^-2/5 < ^-1/5$ because $(^-2)(5) < 5(^-1)$.

Since Theorem 14 provides an alternate method of determining the order relation between any two rational numbers a/b and c/d with positive denominators b and d, we may now determine the order relation between the rational numbers a/b and c/d by determining the order relation between the integers ad and bc. By the trichotomy property for order of the integers, one and only one of the following is true:

(1) $ad = bc$,
(2) $ad < bc$,
(3) $bc < ad$.

If $ad = bc$, then $a/b = c/d$; if $ad < bc$, then $a/b < c/d$; and if $bc < ad$, then $c/d < a/b$. Hence we may state the *trichotomy property* of the rationals.

TRICHOTOMY PROPERTY
If a/b and c/d are any rational numbers, then one and only one of the following is true:
(1) $a/b = c/d$,
(2) $a/b < c/d$,
(3) $c/d < a/b$.

The following theorems and their proofs are similar to the corresponding theorems of Section 5.4. In the exercises you will be requested to supply the proofs.

THEOREM 15.   If a/b and c/d are any positive rationals, then $a/b < c/d$ if and only if $^-(c/d) < {}^-(a/b)$.

THEOREM 16.   If a/b, c/d, and e/f are any rationals such that $a/b < c/d$, then $a/b + e/f < c/d + e/f$.

THEOREM 17.   (a) If a/b and c/d are any rationals such that $a/b < c/d$, and if e/f is any positive rational, then $a/b \cdot e/f < c/d \cdot e/f$.

(b) If a/b and c/d are any rationals such that $a/b < c/d$, and if e/f is any negative rational, then $c/d \cdot e/f < a/b \cdot e/f$.

THEOREM 18.   If a/b, c/d, and e/f are any rationals such that $a/b < c/d$ and $c/d < e/f$, then $a/b < e/f$ (transitive property for $<$).

Recall that, although there is a well-ordering property for the set of counting numbers, there is no well-ordering property for the set of integers. The set I^- does not contain a least element. Similarly, as the set of negative rationals does not contain a least element, we see that there is no well-ordering property for the set of rationals. However, if we are guided by the well-ordering property for the set C_0, we are tempted to conclude that there is a corresponding well-ordering property for the set of nonnegative rationals. While this may seem feasible at first, we shall prove that there is no well-ordering property for the set of nonnegative rationals; that is, we shall prove that *not* every nonempty subset of the set of nonnegative rationals has a least element. The following theorem will enable us to construct a subset of the nonnegative rationals which does not have a least element.

THEOREM 19.   If a/b and e/f are any rational numbers such that $a/b < e/f$, then there exists a rational c/d such that $a/b < c/d$ and $c/d < e/f$; that is, $a/b < c/d < e/f$.

Proof.   It is probably obvious to you that the arithmetic mean (average), $(1/2)(a/b + e/f)$, is one rational number which lies between a/b and e/f. Thus we want to prove that $a/b < 1/2\ (a/b + e/f)$ and $1/2\ (a/b + e/f) < e/f$. First we shall prove that $a/b < 1/2\ (a/b + e/f)$.

$a/b < 1/2\ (a/b + e/f) \rightleftarrows a/b < 1/2 \cdot a/b$
$\quad + 1/2 \cdot e/f$ (by distributive property), $(p \rightleftarrows q)$
$a/b < 1/2 \cdot a/b + 1/2 \cdot e/f \rightleftarrows a/b + {}^-1/2$
$\quad \cdot a/b < 1/2 \cdot e/f$ (by Theorem 16), $(q \rightleftarrows r)$
$a/b + {}^-1/2 \cdot a/b < 1/2\ e/f \rightleftarrows a/2b < 1/2$
$\quad \cdot e/f$ (by Theorem 6 and Theorem 8), $(r \rightleftarrows s)$
$a/2b < 1/2 \cdot e/f \rightleftarrows a/b < e/f$ (by The-
$\qquad\qquad\qquad\qquad\qquad$orem 17). $(s \rightleftarrows t)$
Thus $a/b < 1/2\ (a/b + e/f) \rightleftarrows a/b < e/f$. $(p \rightleftarrows t)$
But $a/b < e/f$. t
Hence $a/b < 1/2\ (a/b + e/f)$. $\overline{\qquad\qquad}$
                                                  $\therefore\ p$
The proof that $1/2\ (a/b + e/f) < e/f$ is similar.//

It should be clear that Theorem 19 really establishes the existence of infinitely many rational numbers between any two different rational numbers.

Example 7.   Compute a rational number which lies between 7/9 and 4/5. By Theorem 19, one rational number between 7/9

and 4/5 is $(1/2)(4/5 + 7/9) = (1/2)[(36 + 35)/45]$
$= (1/2)(71/45) = 71/90$. Thus $70/90 = 7/9 < 71/90$
$< 4/5 = 72/90$.

Example 8.   Compute a rational number which lies between 7/9 and
71/90. One rational number is $1/2 (7/9 + 71/90) = 1/2$
$(70 + 71)/90 = 1/2 (141/90) = 1/2 (47/30) = 47/60$.
Thus $7/9 < 47/60 < 71/90$.

The following theorem establishes the existence of a nonempty subset of the nonnegative rationals which does not contain a least element.

THEOREM 20.   The set of nonnegative rationals is not well-ordered.

Proof.   Consider the set $A = \{a/b\colon 1 < a/b < 2\}$.
         Assume that A contains a least element
         a_0/b_0. $(p$ assumed$)$
         Then $1 < a_0/b_0$.
         Thus there exists a rational number c/d
         such that $1 < c/d < a_0/b_0$ (Theorem
         19). r
         But $a_0/b_0 \leq c/d$ (since a_0/b_0 is the
         least element of A). $\sim r$
         Hence $c/d < a_0/b_0 \wedge c/d \nless a_0/b_0$. $\dfrac{(r \wedge \sim r)}{\therefore \sim p}$
         Thus A does not contain a least element.
         Hence the set of nonnegative rationals is
         not well-ordered. //

We have already seen that each rational number corresponds to one
and only one point on the number line. It follows from Definition 13 that
$a/b < c/d$ if and only if the point labeled a/b is to the left of the point
labeled c/d on the number line, as illustrated in Figure 7.8.

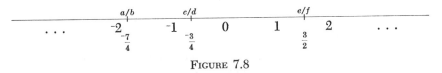

FIGURE 7.8

Thus every negative rational is less than 0 and less than every positive rational, and 0 is less than every positive rational.

Exercise 7.7

I. In each of the following, employ Definition 13 and Theorem 4 to determine whether $a/b < c/d$, $a/b = c/d$, or $c/d < a/b$.

(1) $a/b = 7/3, c/d = 0$ (7) $a/b = 8/^-9, c/d = ^-9/8$
(2) $a/b = ^-7/3, c/d = 0$ (8) $a/b = 7/^-8, c/d = ^-8/7$
(3) $a/b = ^-4/5, c/d = 4/5$ (9) $a/b = 0/3, c/d = 1/3$
(4) $a/b = 3/^-4, c/d = 3/4$ (10) $a/b = 5/5, c/d = 0/5$
(5) $a/b = 6/^-7, c/d = ^-6/7$ (11) $a/b = ^-7/^-9, c/d = 7/9$
(6) $a/b = ^-10/9, c/d = 10/^-9$ (12) $a/b = 15/8, c/d = ^-15/^-8$

II. Employ Theorem 4 and Theorem 14 to solve Exercise I.

III. Employ Theorems 15, 16, 17, 18 to determine whether each sentence q follows from the sentence p.

(1) p: $2/4 < 3/7$; q: $^-3/7 < ^-2/4$.
(2) p: $3/7 < 4/7$; q: $^-3/7 < ^-4/7$.
(3) p: $4/9 < 5/9$; q: $4/9 + 4/7 < 5/9 + 4/7$.
(4) p: $3/4 < 5/4$; q: $3/4 + 2/3 < 5/4 + 2/3$.
(5) p: $2/3 < 9/10$; q: $2/3 \cdot 8/5 < 9/10 \cdot 8/5$.
(6) p: $4/7 < 8/9$; q: $4/7 \cdot 2/3 < 8/9 \cdot 2/3$.
(7) p: $2/5 < 3/5$; q: $2/5 \cdot ^-7/11 < 3/5 \cdot ^-7/11$.
(8) p: $4/9 < 5/9$; q: $4/9 \cdot ^-8/13 < 5/9 \cdot ^-8/13$.
(9) p: $^-2/5 < 0$ and $0 < 3/7$; q: $^-2/5 < 3/7$.
(10) p: $^-14/7 < 0$ and $0 < 81/83$; q: $^-14/7 < 81/83$.

IV. Compute two rational numbers between the rational numbers a/b and c/d in each of the following.

(1) $a/b = 4/5; c/d = 5/6$ (5) $a/b = ^-8/3; c/d = 8/9$
(2) $a/b = 3/4; c/d = 4/5$ (6) $a/b = ^-6/5; c/d = 9/8$
(3) $a/b = 0/1; c/d = 2/3$ (7) $a/b = ^-15; c/d = ^-4$
(4) $a/b = 0/1; c/d = 1/2$ (8) $a/b = ^-7; c/d = ^-1$

V. Illustrate Exercise IV on the number line.

VI. (1) Prove Theorem 15.
(2) Prove Theorem 16.
(3) Prove Theorem 17.
(4) Prove Theorem 18.
(5) Prove Theorem 19(b).
(6) Prove $a/b < (a + c)/(b + d) < c/d$ for all integers a and c and all positive integers b and d such that $a/b < c/d$.

VII. Without using the number line, prove each of the following.

(1) Every negative rational number is less than 0.
(2) Zero is less than every positive rational number.

(3) Any negative rational number is less than any positive rational number.

(4) If a subset of the rational numbers has a least element, then the least element is unique.

7.8 Mixed Numbers and Absolute Value

In the preceding section we studied the order properties of the rational numbers. By Definition 13 and Theorem 14 we can determine which rational number of any two different rational numbers is smaller. Moreover, after one has studied rationals thoroughly, one has enough experience to compare many pairs of rationals between $^-1$ and 1 without the use of Definition 13 and Theorem 14. Also, comparison of any two integers is a simple procedure. Since any positive rational larger than 1 is the sum of a positive integer and a nonnegative rational less than 1, one may compare two positive rationals larger than 1 by comparing the two integers and the two nonnegative rationals less than 1. For example, to compare 52/5 and 61/6, one may write $52/5 = (50 + 2)/5 = 10 + 2/5$ and $61/6 = (60 + 1)/6 = 10 + 1/6$ and conclude that $61/6 < 52/5$. This conclusion is based on the fact that $1/6 < 2/5$ and thus $10 + 1/6 < 10 + 2/5$ by Theorem 16. The fact that any positive rational larger than 1 may be expressed as the sum of a positive integer and a nonnegative rational less than 1 is an immediate consequence of the division algorithm. For example, $52 = 5(10) + 2$ and hence $52/5 = 10 + 2/5$. In general, if a/b is larger than 1, then $b < a$, and by the division algorithm it follows that $a = bq + r$, in which $1 \leq q$ and $0 \leq r < b$. Consequently $a/b = (bq + r)/b = bq/b + r/b = q + r/b$. The following examples further illustrate the procedure.

Example 1. Determine the order relation between 235/31 and 289/37. By the division algorithm, $235 = 31(7) + 18$ and $289 = 37(7) + 30$. Thus $235/31 = 7 + 18/31$ and $289/37 = 7 + 30/37$.
Now $18/31 < 30/37$.
Thus $235/31 < 289/37$ (by Theorem 16).

Example 2. Determine the order relation between 457/11 and 632/15. Now $457/11 = 41 + 6/11$ and $632/15 = 42 + 2/15$.
Since $41 < 42$, it is unnecessary to compare $6/11$ and $2/15$.
Hence $457/11 < 632/15$.

Another reason for expressing any positive rational number larger than 1 as the sum of a positive integer and a nonnegative rational less than 1 is that it is easier to locate the point on the number line corresponding to the rational number. For example, since $61/16 = 3 + 13/16$, the corresponding point on the number line is located $13/16$ unit to the right of the point labeled 3. A third reason derives from physical considerations. For example, it is easier to visualize $5 + 1/4$ cakes than $21/4$ cakes. Moreover, $21/4$ may be the answer in a mathematical model of a physical problem which asks for the total weight of two bags of rice. In the physical problem, we usually say that the total weight is five and one-quarter pounds rather than $21/4$ pounds. In the mathematical model, we write five *and* one-fourth as $5 + 1/4$. The *and* of the physical problem is translated to the binary operator $+$ (*plus*) in the mathematical model. In actual practice, we usually write the so-called *mixed number* $5\frac{1}{4}$ to mean $5 + 1/4$ and read the mixed number $5\frac{1}{4}$ as 5 *and* 1/4. Even if we write $5\frac{1}{4}$ in the mathematical model, we should think of $5\frac{1}{4}$ as an abbreviation, or *nicksymbol*, for $5 + 1/4$. Under no circumstances should $5\frac{1}{4}$ (for the sum $5 + 1/4$) be confused with the product $5 \cdot \frac{1}{4}$ or $5(1/4)$.

Whenever two rational numbers are combined by means of $+$, $-$, $\cdot$, or $\div$, it is important that the proper symbols, rather than the nicksymbols, of the rational numbers be employed. The following examples illustrate the procedure.

Example 3. $5\frac{1}{4} + 3\frac{13}{16} = (5 + 1/4) + (3 + 13/16) = (20/4 + 1/4)$
$+ (48/16 + 13/16) = (20 + 1)/4 + (48 + 13)/16$
$= 21/4 + 61/16 = 84/16 + 61/16 = (84 + 61)/16$
$= 145/16.$

Example 4. $4\frac{2}{3} - 4\frac{4}{5} = (4 + 2/3) - (4 + 4/5) = 14/3 - 24/5$
$= 70/15 + {}^{-}72/15 = {}^{-}2/15.$

Example 5. $1\frac{2}{5} \cdot 5\frac{3}{8} = (1 + 2/5)(5 + 3/8) = 7/5 \cdot 43/8 = 301/40.$

Example 6. $3\frac{1}{5} \div 2\frac{2}{15} = (3 + 1/5) \div (2 + 2/15) = 16/5 \div 32/15$
$= 16/5 \cdot 15/32 = 3/2.$

The following examples illustrate the procedure for comparing negative rationals less than ${}^{-}1$.

Example 7.   Determine the order relation between ${}^{-}235/31$ and ${}^{-}289/37$.
Now ${}^{-}235/31 = {}^{-}(235/31) = {}^{-}(7 + 18/31)$, and ${}^{-}289/37$
$= {}^{-}(289/37) = {}^{-}(7 + 30/37).$
Since $18/31 < 30/37$, it follows from Theorem 16 that
$7 + 18/31 < 7 + 30/37.$
Hence by Theorem 15, ${}^{-}(7 + 30/37) < {}^{-}(7 + 18/31).$
Thus ${}^{-}289/37 < {}^{-}235/31.$

Example 8.   Determine the order relation between $^-17/3$ and $^-19/5$.
       Now $^-17/3 = {}^-(17/3) = {}^-(5 + 2/3)$ and $^-19/5 = {}^-(19/5)$
       $^-(3 + 4/5)$.
       Now $3 + 4/5 < 5 + 2/3$.
       Hence by Theorem 15, $^-(5 + 2/3) < {}^-(3 + 4/5)$.
       Thus $^-17/3 < {}^-19/5$.

Observe that we may compare two different negative rationals by comparing their additive inverses and then applying Theorem 15: if $(a/b) < (c/d)$, then $^-(c/d) < {}^-(a/b)$.

Since $^-17/3 = {}^-(17/3) = {}^-(5 + 2/3) = {}^-(5\tfrac{2}{3})$, we see that we could use the nicksymbol $^-(5\tfrac{2}{3})$ as an abbreviation for the rational number $^-17/3$. Notice that $^-(5\tfrac{2}{3})$ is an abbreviation for $^-5 + {}^-2/3$ and *not* for $^-5 + 2/3$. The abbreviation for $^-5 + 2/3$ is the nicksymbol $^-(4\tfrac{1}{3})$.

Although $^-17/3 \neq 17/3$ and, in general, $^-a/b \neq a/b$, there is a relationship between $^-17/3$ and $17/3$ and, in general, between $^-a/b$ and a/b. The point $^-17/3$ lies to the left of 0 on the number line, and the point $17/3$ lies to the right of 0 on the number line. In fact, they are the *same distance* from 0 but in *opposite directions*. In general, $^-a/b$ is the same distance from 0 as a/b but in the opposite direction. Physically, if an ant walked from 0 to $^-17/3$, he would walk a distance of $17/3$ units; if he walked from 0 to $17/3$, he would still walk a distance of $17/3$ units. Although his terminal position in the first case is to the left of his terminal position in the second case, the actual *distance* walked is the same in both cases. Mathematically, we may say that two distances from 0 are equal by saying that the numbers which label the two terminal positions have the same (or equal) *absolute value*. Thus the absolute value of a/b means the distance from the point 0 to the point a/b.

DEFINITION 14. The *absolute value* of the rational number a/b (written $|a/b|$) is the rational number
       (a) $^-a/b$ if a/b is negative,
       (b) 0 if and only if $a/b = 0$,
       (c) a/b if a/b is positive.

The following examples illustrate the concept of absolute value.

Example 9.   The absolute value of $^-29$ is 29. Symbolically, $|^-29|$
       $= {}^-(^-29) = 29$.

Example 10.   The absolute value of 0 is 0. Symbolically, $|0| = 0$.

Example 11.   The absolute value of 5 is 5. Symbolically, $|5| = 5$.

Example 12.   The absolute value of $^-17/3$ is $17/3$. Symbolically, $|^-17/3|$ $= {}^-({}^-17/3) = 17/3$.

Example 13. $|16/3 - 18/3| = |^-2/3| = {}^-({}^-2/3) = 2/3$.

Example 14. $|16/19 - 32/38| = |16/19 - 16/19| = |0| = 0$.

Example 15. $|^-3 - 2\%| = |^-15/5 - 12/5| = |^-27/5| = 27/5$.

Observe that $|a/b|$ is always positive or 0. Moreover, Example 15 illustrates that $|a/b - c/d|$ is not, in general, equal to $|a/b| - |c/d|$, because $|^-3| - |2\%| = 3 - 2\% = 3/5 \neq 27/5$.

Exercise 7.8

I. Determine the order relation between a/b and c/d.

(1) $a/b = 2/3, c/d = 4/5$
(2) $a/b = 4/5, c/d = 5/6$
(3) $a/b = {}^-89/10, c/d = {}^-98/11$
(4) $a/b = 79/9, c/d = {}^-77/10$
(5) $a/b = 115/{}^-19, c/d = 117/{}^-21$
(6) $a/b = 218/{}^-23, c/d = 219/{}^-24$
(7) $a/b = 538/169, c/d = 653/277$
(8) $a/b = 746/253, c/d = 847/357$
(9) $a/b = {}^-100/17, c/d = {}^-100/16$
(10) $a/b = {}^-160/23, c/d = {}^-160/21$

II. Write the proper symbol for the rational number symbolized by each of the following nicksymbols.

(1) 4%
(2) $5\frac{3}{4}$
(3) $^-10\%$
(4) $^-9\frac{8}{11}$
(5) 7%
(6) $9\frac{8}{11}$
(7) 10%
(8) 11%
(9) $^-12\frac{15}{16}$
(10) $^-14\frac{16}{17}$

III. By use of the number line determine the order relation among the ten rational numbers symbolized in Exercise II.

IV. (1) Compute the absolute value of each rational number in Exercise II.

(2) By use of the number line determine the order relation among the ten rational numbers of (1).

V. Compute each of the following sums, products, differences, and quotients. Be certain to replace the nicksymbols by the proper symbols for the rational numbers.

(1) $5\% + 3\frac{2}{5}$
(2) $3\frac{4}{7} + 5\frac{4}{5}$
(3) $10\frac{8}{15} - 9\frac{2}{25}$
(4) $8^{11}\!/_{15} - 4\frac{5}{9}$
(5) $2\frac{3}{4} \,(7\frac{1}{8} - 6\frac{5}{12})$

(6) $(3\frac{1}{4})\,(6\frac{5}{6} - 5^{11}\!/_{12})$
(7) $5\frac{2}{15} \div 6\frac{4}{9}$
(8) $7\frac{5}{9} \div 3\frac{7}{15}$
(9) $(2\frac{1}{3} - 6\frac{2}{5}) \div (7\frac{1}{8} + 6\frac{2}{3})$
(10) $(1\frac{1}{5} - 8\frac{3}{4}) \div (6\frac{5}{9} + 3\frac{1}{2})$

VI. Compute the absolute value of each of the following.

(1) $2/3 - 3/5$
(2) $4/5 - 5/7$
(3) $9/4 - 9/2$
(4) $11/4 - 11/2$
(5) $15/2 - 19/2$

(6) $17/2 - 19/2$
(7) $2\,(3/5) - 1/5\,(6)$
(8) $8\,(11/12) - 22/5\,(5/3)$
(9) $4/5 \div {}^{-}3/4$
(10) ${}^{-}3/4 \div 4/5$

VII. Compute each of the following.

(1) $|\,4\,|$
(2) $|\,{}^{-}5\,|$
(3) $|\,2 + {}^{-}5\,|$
(4) $|\,{}^{-}3\,(7 + {}^{-}7)\,|$
(5) $|\,{}^{-}3\,|\,(7 + {}^{-}1)$

(6) $|\,{}^{-}3 + 4 + |\,{}^{-}5\,|\,|$
(7) $|\,{}^{-}7 + |\,{}^{-}8 + 2\,|\,|$
(8) $|\,{}^{-}7 + {}^{-}8 + 2\,|$
(9) $|\,12 + {}^{-}3\,| + |\,{}^{-}5\,| + 1$
(10) $|\,a + b\,|$

VIII. State the truth-value of each of the following sentences. (Some quantifiers are implied.)

(1) The absolute value of any negative rational number is negative.
(2) The absolute value of zero is zero.
(3) The absolute value of any rational number cannot be negative.
(4) If the absolute value of a/b is positive, then a/b is positive.
(5) The absolute value of $a + b$ is the absolute value of a plus the absolute value of b.
(6) If $a/b < c/d$, then $|\,a/b\,| < |\,c/d\,|$.
(7) If a/b and c/d are any rational numbers, then $|\,a/b\,| - |\,c/d\,| < |\,a/b - c/d\,|$.
(8) If $|\,a/b\,| < |\,c/d\,|$, then $a/b < c/d$.
(9) If a/b is any rational number, then $|\,a/b\,| = |\,a\,|/|\,b\,|$.
(10) If a/b and c/d are any rational numbers, then $|\,a/b\,|\,|\,c/d\,| = |\,a/b \cdot c/d\,|$.

7.9 The System of Rational Numbers

In the preceding sections we developed the set of rational numbers, defined the operations of addition, subtraction, multiplication, and division between any two rational numbers (except for division by 0), de-

fined an order relation between any two rational numbers, and proved
the following properties of the set of rational numbers with respect to
the operations of addition and multiplication. In the following properties, rational numbers are symbolized by the letters $a, b, c, \ldots$ rather
than by the symbols $a/b, c/d, e/f, \ldots$.

1. If a and b are any rational numbers, then $a + b$ is a unique rational
   number (closure property for addition).

2. If a, b, and c are any rational numbers, then $(a + b) + c = a
   + (b + c)$ (associative property for addition).

3. There exists a unique rational number 0 such that $a + 0 = 0 + a
   = a$ for any rational number a (identity property for addition).

4. If a is any rational number, then there exists a unique rational number ^-a such that $a + {}^-a = {}^-a + a = 0$ (inverse property for addition).

5. If a and b are any rational numbers, then $a + b = b + a$ (commutative property for addition).

6. If a and b are any rational numbers, then $a \cdot b$ is a unique rational
   number (closure property for multiplication).

7. If a, b, and c are any rational numbers, then $(a \cdot b) \cdot c = a \cdot (b \cdot c)$
   (associative property for multiplication).

8. There exists a unique rational number 1 such that $a \cdot 1 = 1 \cdot a = a$
   for any rational number a (identity property for multiplication).

9. If a is any nonzero rational number, then there exists a unique
   rational number $1/a$ such that $a \cdot 1/a = 1/a \cdot a = 1$ (inverse property for multiplication).

10. If a and b are any rational numbers, then $a \cdot b = b \cdot a$ (commutative
    property for multiplication).

11. If a, b, and c are any rational numbers, then $a(b + c) = ab + ac$
    (distributive property).

Although the above-listed 11 properties are not the only properties
of the set of rational numbers with respect to addition and multiplication

which were proved in this chapter, all of the remaining additive and multiplicative properties may be proved from the above properties. Moreover, as subtraction is defined as the inverse of addition and division is defined as the inverse of multiplication, the subtraction and division properties may be proved from the 11 properties above. Thus all properties of the rationals, except the order properties, may be proved from the above 11 properties.

When we say that the set of rational numbers has the above 11 properties, we really mean that the *system* of rational numbers has these 11 properties; that is, we mean that the set of rationals, with the two binary operations of addition and multiplication defined between any two elements of the set, has these properties. By a *system* we mean any non-null set with one or more binary operations defined between any two elements of the set. In Chapter 3 when we spoke of the properties of the set of counting numbers, we were really referring to the properties of the *system* $(C_0, +, \cdot)$. Similarly, in Chapter 5 when we spoke of the properties of the set of integers, we were referring to the properties of the *system* $(I, +, \cdot)$. Letting R_a be the set of all rational numbers, we speak of the properties of the rational number *system* $(R_a, +, \cdot)$.

Since there are systems other than $(R_a, +, \cdot)$ which possess the 11 properties above, it is advantageous to study an *abstract* system which has these 11 properties. Such a system, called a *field*, is defined in Definition 15.

DEFINITION 15. A mathematical system $(F, +, \cdot)$ consisting of a nonempty set F and two binary operators $+$ and $\cdot$ is said to be a *field* if and only if the system possesses the properties F1 through F11.

F1.   If a and b are any elements of F, then $a + b$ is a unique element of F (closure property for addition).

F2.   If a, b, and c are any elements of F, then $(a + b) + c = a + (b + c)$ (associative property for addition).

F3.   There exists a unique element 0 of F such that $a + 0 = a$ for any element of F (identity property for addition).

F4.   If a is any element of F, then there exists a unique element ^-a of F such that $a + {}^-a = 0$ (inverse property for addition).

F5.   If a and b are any elements of F, then $a + b = b + a$ (commutative property for addition).

F6. If a and b are any elements of F, then $a \cdot b$ is a unique element of F (closure property for multiplication).

F7. If a, b, and c are any elements of F, then $(a \cdot b) \cdot c = a \cdot (b \cdot c)$ (associative property for multiplication).

F8. There exists a unique element 1 of F such that $a \cdot 1 = a$ for any element of F (identity property for multiplication).

F9. If a is any nonzero element of F, then there exists a unique element $1/a$ of F such that $a \cdot 1/a = 1$ (inverse property for multiplication).

F10. If a and b are any elements of F, then $a \cdot b = b \cdot a$ (commutative property for multiplication).

F11. If a, b, and c are any elements of F, then $a(b + c) = ab + ac$ (distributive property).

An immediate example of a field is the set of rational numbers together with the operators $+$ and $\cdot$. As the set of integers with the operators $+$ and $\cdot$ do not constitute a field, the rational number system is the only example of a field which we have studied so far.

There are several advantages to studying such an abstract system as a field. First, there are many other systems which are fields and hence have the same properties ($F1$ through $F11$) as the rational number system. As any theorem we prove, or problem we solve, based on properties $F1$ through $F11$, will be true in *any* field, we achieve a large degree of efficiency. Much of advanced abstract mathematics is devoted to proving theorems from the eleven field properties ($F1$ through $F11$), without regard to any other properties of the rational number system. In fact, volumes have been written on studies of mathematical systems whose only assumed properties are $F1$ through $F4$. Second, when we study a system abstractly, we are less likely to be influenced by certain special facts which are of no significance in the study of the properties of a field. Third, when the number of postulates is small, it is easy to test the set of postulates for inconsistencies, without checking each particular number system. Fourth, there are many physical problems whose mathematical models may be formulated in terms of all or some of the properties of a field. In a subsequent chapter, abstract mathematical systems will be studied in more detail. Since the rational number system, which we have studied in this chapter, is a field, it is appropriate to discuss briefly the field properties and their applications in this chapter.

Observe that the 11 field properties do not specify anything about positive or negative numbers. In fact, it is impossible to define an order relation between elements of any field so that order properties similar to those of the rational number system may be deduced from the order relation and the field properties *F1* through *F11*. The following order properties which were proved for the rational number system reveal that the rational number system possesses more properties than are deducible from the 11 field properties.

1. If a and b are any rational numbers, then exactly one of the following sentences is true:

   (a) $a < b$,
   (b) $a = b$,
   (c) $b < a$.

2. If a, b, and c are any rational numbers and $a < b$, then $a + c < b + c$.

3. If a and b are any rational numbers, c is any positive rational number, and $a < b$, then $ac < bc$.

4. If a and b are any rational numbers, c is any negative rational number, and $a < b$, then $bc < ac$.

5. If a, b, and c are any rational numbers, $a < b$, and $b < c$, then $a < c$.

All other order properties of the rational number system may be proved from the 5 above-listed order properties. Since the rational number system possesses the properties of order, which are not deducible from properties *F1* through *F11*, we see that the rational number system is a special kind of field, which we call an *ordered field*.

DEFINITION 16. A mathematical system $(F, +, \cdot, <)$ consisting of a non-null set F, two binary operators $+$ and $\cdot$, and an order relation $<$ is said to be an *ordered field* if and only if $(F, +, \cdot)$ is a field and $(F, +, \cdot, <)$ possesses the properties $O1$ through $O5$.

$O1$. If a and b are any elements of F, then exactly one of the following sentences is true:

   (a) $a < b$,
   (b) $a = b$,
   (c) $b < a$.

O2. If a, b, and c are any elements of F and $a < b$, then $a + c < b + c$.

O3. If a, b, and c are any elements of F, $0 < c$, and $a < b$, then $ac < bc$.

O4. If a, b, and c are any elements of F, $c < 0$, and $a < b$, then $bc < ac$.

O5. If a, b, and c are any elements of F, $a < b$, and $b < c$, then $a < c$.

As properties *F*1 through *F*11 and *O*1 through *O*5 are true for the rational number system, we see that the rational number system is an ordered field. All properties of the rational number system may be proved from the above 16 properties (*F*1 through *F*11 and *O*1 through *O*5). In fact, we could have studied the rational numbers by defining the rational number system as one which possesses the properties *F*1 through *F*11 and *O*1 through *O*5. If we had done this, all of the properties and definitions of the rational number system would have unfolded. However, such an abstract approach would have denied us the insight and motivation of the development and thus would have been inconsistent with our approach to the study of the structure of the various number systems. Recall that the entire approach has been motivational in character, based on elementary logic, elementary set theory, the assumption that one knows how to count, the well-ordering property, and the Archimedean property. At each step in the development, we were motivated by the desire to create a mathematical system which would provide mathematical models for various physical problems.

However, in the motivational approach we have sacrificed some economies of abstraction. By repeated application of the commutative property, the associative property, and the distributive property one may justify the generalized commutative and associative property and the generalized distributive property in any field; and, in particular, in the system of rational numbers. This fact illustrates the economy of studying abstract systems. After one has justified the generalized properties in any field, it is unnecessary for him to justify these properties in particular number systems which are fields. For example, in the next chapter we shall study a number system known as the *real number system* and shall learn that the real number system is itself a field. Hence it will not be necessary to justify the generalized commutative and associative property and the generalized distributive property in the real number system. An actual proof of each of these properties depends on the postulate of finite induction.

For future reference, we state the generalized commutative and associative property and the generalized distributive property for any field with elements a, a_1, a_2, ...

GENERALIZED COMMUTATIVE AND ASSOCIATIVE PROPERTY FOR ADDITION

If $a_1, a_2, \ldots, a_k$ are any elements of a field, then all arrangements and punctuations of $a_1 + a_2 + \ldots + a_k$ yield the same element of the field.

GENERALIZED COMMUTATIVE AND ASSOCIATIVE PROPERTY

FOR MULTIPLICATION

If $a_1, a_2, \ldots, a_k$ are any elements of a field, then all arrangements and punctuations of $a_1 a_2 \ldots a_k$ yield the same element of the field.

GENERALIZED DISTRIBUTIVE PROPERTY

If $a, a_1, a_2, \ldots, a_k$ are any elements of a field, then $a(a_1 + a_2 + \ldots + a_k) = aa_1 + aa_2 + \ldots + aa_k$.

Example 1. In any field, $a + b + c + d = a + c + b + d$
$$= a + c + d + b$$
$$= a + d + c + b$$
$$= d + a + c + b$$
$$= d + c + a + b$$
$$= d + c + b + a, \text{ et cetera.}$$

Example 2. In any field, $a(b + c + d + e) = ab + ac + ad + ae$.

Example 3. In the rational number system,
$$(1/3)(4a + {}^-6b + {}^-a + 5) = (1/3)(4a + {}^-a + {}^-6b + 5)$$
$$= (1/3)(3a + {}^-6b + 5)$$
$$= a + {}^-2b + 5/3.$$

Before concluding this section, we make the following remarks concerning Definitions 15 and 16. We could have stated F3, F4, F8, and F9 of Definition 15 without the word *unique*. Then we could have *proved* the uniqueness from this modified definition. Similarly, in Definition 16 we could have omitted order property O4 and then *proved* this property from the properties F1–F11 of Definition 15 and the remaining properties O1, O2, O3, and O5 of Definition 16.

Exercise 7.9

I. State the truth-value of each of the following sentences.

(1) The set of positive integers is a subset of the set of counting numbers.

(2) The set of positive integers is a subset of the set of integers.

(3) The set of integers is a subset of the set of counting numbers.

(4) The set of integers is a subset of the set of rational numbers.

(5) The set of integers is a subset of the set of positive integers.

(6) The set of integers is a subset of the set of nonnegative rational numbers.

(7) The set of positive rational numbers is a subset of the set of rational numbers.

(8) The set of rational numbers is a subset of the set of rational numbers.

(9) The set of negative rational numbers is a subset of the set of rational numbers.

(10) The set of counting numbers is a subset of the set of integers.

(11) The set of counting numbers is a subset of the set of positive integers.

(12) The set of counting numbers is a subset of the set of positive rational numbers.

(13) The set of counting numbers is a subset of the set of rational numbers.

(14) The set of negative rational numbers is a subset of the set of positive rational numbers.

(15) The set $\{0\}$ is a subset of the set of counting numbers.

(16) The set $\{0\}$ is a subset of the set of positive integers.

(17) The set $\{0\}$ is a subset of the set of even counting numbers.

(18) The set $\{1, 5, 9, 13, \ldots\}$ is a subset of the set of counting numbers.

(19) The set of even integers is a subset of the set of counting numbers.

(20) The set of odd integers is a subset of the set of counting numbers.

II. (1) Does $(I, +, \cdot)$ possess $F1$ through $F11$?

(2)' Does $(I, +, \cdot)$ possess $F1$ through $F8$?

(3) Does $(I, +, \cdot)$ possess $F1$ through $F9$?

(4) Does $(I, +, \cdot)$ possess $F1$ through $F8$, $F10$, and $F11$?

(5) Is $(I, +, \cdot)$ a field?

(6) Is $(\{0\}, +, \cdot)$ a field? If so, what is the multiplicative identity?

(7) Does $(I, +, \cdot)$ possess the order properties $O1$ through $O5$?

(8) Is $(I, +, \cdot)$ an ordered field?

(9) Does $(C_0, +, \cdot)$ possess properties $F1$ through $F5$?

(10) Does $(C_0, +, \cdot)$ possess properties $F1$, $F2$, $F3$, $F5$, $F6$, $F7$, $F8$, $F10$, and $F11$?

III. Apply the generalized distributive property to prove that each of the following sentences is true.

(1) $(7/5)(5/3 + {}^-10/21 + 5/7) = 5/3 + 1.$

(2) $(a/b)(2/a + b/3 + b/a) = 2/b + a/3 + 1.$

(3) $({}^-7/b)(3/7 + b/14 + {}^-3b/7 + 2/3) = {}^-3/b + {}^-1/2 + 3 - 14/3b.$

(4) $(a/3c)(c + {}^-3c/2a + c/3a - 3c/a) = a/3 - 1/2 + 1/9 - 1.$

IV. (1) Write the 24 ways in which the product of a, b, c, and d may be written by the generalized commutative and associative property for multiplication.

(2) How many ways can the product of a, b, c, d, and e be written?

V. Let $(\{1\}, +, \cdot)$ be a number system in which $1 + 1 = 1$ and $1 \cdot 1 = 1$. Prove that $(\{1\}, +, \cdot)$ is a field.

Chapter 8

DECIMALS AND THE REAL NUMBER SYSTEM

8.1 Decimal Numeration System

In Chapter 4 we learned that any counting number may be expressed in terms of powers of 10. For example, $2372 = 2(10^3) + 3(10^2) + 7(10) + 2(1)$. In general, the place value of any digit (except the units digit) is 10 times the place value of the digit immediately to the right. In this section we extend the decimal numeration system so that any rational number may be expressed in terms of powers of 10. Once we have expressed any positive rational number in terms of powers of 10, it is a simple matter to express any negative rational in terms of powers of 10. All that is necessary is the prefixing of the negative sign. For this reason, we confine our attention to positive rationals. The rational number 0 is obviously expressible in terms of powers of 10. To accomplish this objective, we introduce the well-known *decimal point* (.). For example, it is natural to express the rational number $2(100) + 3(10) + 7(1) + 5(1/10) + 9(1/100)$ in the form 23759; however, according to the convention of the Hindu-Arabic numeration system, the right-end digit 9 represents 9 units. Since the units digit of the given rational number is 7, we indicate this fact by writing a decimal point after the 7 and before the 5. Then the decimal representation of $2(100) + 3(10) + 7(1) + 5(1/10) + 9(1/100)$ is written 237.59 and is read "two hundred thirty-seven *and* fifty-nine one-hundredths," or, alternatively, "two three seven *point* five nine."

Now we have extended the decimal system so that any rational number of the form $a_k 10^k + a_{k-1} 10^{k-1} + \ldots + a_0(1) + b_1(1/10) + b_2(1/10)^2 + b_3(1/10)^3 + \ldots + b_{j-1}(1/10)^{j-1} + b_j(1/10)^j$ may be expressed in the form $a_k a_{k-1} \ldots a_1 a_0 . b_1 b_2 \ldots b_j$, in which $a_i \in \{0, 1, 2,$

..., 9} and $b_i \in \{0, 1, 2, \ldots, 9\}$. In this representation, the place value of any digit (except the right-end digit) is 10 times the place value of the digit immediately to the right. The only difference is that the units' digit is the first digit to the left of the decimal point.

In the elementary schools, rules are taught for adding, subtracting, multiplying, and dividing any two decimals. For example, the sum of 852.6 and 27.23 is computed as follows:

$$
\begin{array}{r}
852.6 \\
+\ 27.23 \\
\hline
879.83
\end{array}
$$

According to the rule, the decimal points are lined up in a column, the digits are added as if the decimals were counting numbers, and a decimal point is placed in this sum in the same column as the other decimal points. Let us analyze and justify this rule or algorithm.

Recall that $852.6 = 8(100) + 5(10) + 2(1) + 6(1/10)$ and $27.23 = 2(10) + 7(1) + 2(1/10) + 3(1/100)$.

Thus $852.6 + 27.23 = [8(100) + 5(10) + 2(1) + 6(1/10)] + [2(10)$
$$+ 7(1) + 2(1/10) + 3(1/100)]$$
$$= 8(100) + [5(10) + 2(10)] + [2(1) + 7(1)]$$
$$+ [6(1/10) + 2(1/10)] + 3(1/100)$$
$$= 8(100) + 7(10) + 9(1) + 8(1/10) + 3(1/100)$$
$$= 879.83, \text{ the sum computed by the algorithm.}$$

An alternative procedure is to convert both decimals to integers by multiplying each by the appropriate power of 10, computing the sum of the resulting integers, and dividing this sum by the same power of 10 to obtain the required sum. In this example, we employ the second power of 10; that is, 10^2. The details of the computation are as follows:

$$
\begin{aligned}
852.6 + 27.23 &= (100/100)(852.6 + 27.23) \\
&= 100(852.6 + 27.23)/100 \\
&= [100(852.6) + 100(27.23)]/100 \\
&= (85{,}260 + 2{,}723)/100 \\
&= 87{,}983/100 \\
&= 879.83.
\end{aligned}
$$

The latter computation illustrates that when we line up the decimal points, we are really thinking of the addition as follows.

$$
\begin{array}{r}
852.60 \\
+\ 27.23 \\
\hline
879.83
\end{array}
$$

The justification of the algorithm for subtracting a decimal from a decimal is similar.

According to the rule for multiplication of decimals, the product is computed as if the decimals were counting numbers, the total number j of digits to the right of the decimal point in the multiplicand and also the multiplier are counted, and the decimal point is placed in the product so that the number of digits to the right of the decimal point is equal to j. For example, the product of 94.3 and 6.78 is usually computed as follows.

$$
\begin{array}{ll}
\quad 94.3 & (\text{1 digit to the right of the decimal point}) \\
\underline{\times\ 6.78} & (\text{2 digits to the right of the decimal point}) \\
\quad 7544 & \\
\quad 6601 & (j = 1 + 2 = 3) \\
\underline{\quad 5658} & \\
639.354 & (\text{3 digits to the right of the decimal point})
\end{array}
$$

The analysis and justification of this algorithm are shown below.

$$
\begin{aligned}
(94.3)(6.78) &= (10/10)(94.3) \cdot (100/100)(6.78) \\
&= (943/10)(678/100) \\
&= (943)(678)/(10)(100) \\
&= (943)(678)/1000 \\
&= 639{,}354/1000 \\
&= 639.354.
\end{aligned}
$$

The justification for computing the product of 943 and 678 was given in Chapter 4.

So far we have extended the Hindu-Arabic numeration system, studied in Chapter 4, to include decimals in which there are only a finite number of digits to the right of the decimal point. Any decimal which has only a finite number of digits to the right of the decimal point, and hence terminates, is called a *terminating decimal*. Every terminating decimal is a rational number. We have observed that the sum of two terminating decimals is a terminating decimal, the difference between two terminating decimals is a terminating decimal, and the product of two terminating decimals is a terminating decimal. However, we have not shown that the quotient of two terminating decimals is a terminating decimal. We close this section with the following questions, which are answered in the next section.

(1) Is the quotient of two terminating decimals a terminating decimal?

(2) Can every rational number be expressed as a terminating decimal?

Exercise 8.1

I. Justify the rule for multiplying a decimal by a power of 10 in each of the following. (Rule: To *multiply* by 10^k, shift the decimal point k places to the *right*.)

(1) 28.23×10^2
(2) 67.89×10^2
(3) 4.672×10^3
(4) 5.267×10^3
(5) 107.3×10

(6) 701.3×10
(7) 26.3×10^3
(8) 88.5×10^3
(9) 1093.12×10^5
(10) 9301.27×10^5

II. Justify the algorithm for computing the sum of two decimals in each of the following.

(1) $23.82 + 6.125$
(2) $37.17 + 8.623$
(3) $0.4 + 6.00251$

(4) $0.3 + 5.01062$
(5) $2.03 + 1.4$
(6) $7.05 + 3.2$

III. Justify the rule for dividing a number by a power of 10 in each of the following. (Rule: To *divide* by 10^k, shift the decimal point k places to the *left*.)

(1) $653 \div 10$
(2) $256 \div 10$
(3) $887 \div 10^2$
(4) $786 \div 10^2$
(5) $6.25 \div 10^3$

(6) $2.25 \div 10^3$
(7) $0.512 \div 10^2$
(8) $0.432 \div 10^2$
(9) $0.0512 \div 10$
(10) $0.0432 \div 10$

IV. Justify the algorithm for subtracting a decimal from a decimal in each of the following.

(1) $263.72 - 48.64$
(2) $298.27 - 53.79$
(3) $823.5 - 4.831$

(4) $961.4 - 8.625$
(5) $69.72 - 9.703$
(6) $83.67 - 3.603$

V. Justify the algorithm for computing the product of two decimals in each of the following.

(1) $7.05(3.2)$
(2) $2.03(1.4)$
(3) $0.3(5.01062)$

(4) $0.4(6.00251)$
(5) $20.63(70.81)$
(6) $30.51(60.93)$

VI. Write a rational number which expresses the amount of money in each of the following physical problems.

(1) Susan spent $3.25.
(2) Tommy spent $7.75.
(3) Lisa spent $4.63.
(4) Craig spent $3.57.

(5) Helen gave Jessie 72 cents.
(6) Marcia gave Toby 17 cents.
(7) Leslie gave Carol 89 cents.
(8) Charles gave Trev 83 cents.
(9) Carolyn paid Lane $1.27 for the bat.
(10) Dave paid Maurice $2.23 for the book.

8.2 Decimal Representation of Rational Numbers

We have already learned that any rational number of the form $a_k 10^k + a_{k-1} 10^{k-1} + \ldots + a_0(1) + b_1(1/10) + \ldots + b_{j-1}(1/10)^{j-1} + b_j(1/10)^j$ may be represented by the terminating decimal $a_k a_{k-1} \ldots a_0.b_1 \ldots b_{j-1} b_j$, in which the a_i and the b_i are elements of $\{0, 1, 2, \ldots, 9\}$. Can every rational number, whether of the above form or not, be represented by a terminating decimal? For example, can the rational number $1/3$ be represented by a terminating decimal? Before answering this question, we consider the following examples.

Example 1.   Consider the computational device for division of 3 by 8.

$$\begin{array}{r} .375 \\ 8\overline{)3.000} \\ 24 \\ \hline 60 \\ 56 \\ \hline 40 \\ 40 \\ \hline \end{array}$$

Let us analyze and justify this algorithm.

$3/8 = (1000/1000)(3/8) = (1/1000)(3000/8) = (1/1000)(375) = 0.375.$

The justification for computing the quotient $3000/8$ was given in Chapter 6.

Example 2.   Now we consider the computational device for dividing 27.2 by 3.2.

$$\begin{array}{r} 8.\,5 \\ 3.2\overline{)27.2\ 0} \\ 25.6 \\ \hline 1\ 6\ 0 \\ 1\ 6\ 0 \\ \hline \end{array}$$

Let us analyze and justify this algorithm.

$$27.2/3.2 = [100/(10)(10)] \ (27.2/3.2) = 100(27.2)/10(10)(3.2)$$
$$= 2720/10(32) = (1/10)(85) = 8.5.$$

Example 3.   Next we consider the computational device which yields
$$1 = 7(0.142) + 0.006.$$

```
      .142
  7)1.000
    7
    ─
    30
    28
    ──
     20
     14
     ──
      6
```

To justify the procedure we write

$$1 = 1000/1000 = [7(142) + 6]/1000 = 7(142)/1000 + 6/1000$$
$$= 7(0.142) + 0.006.$$

The above examples illustrate the process of long division involving decimals. Example 1 justifies pointing off the decimal point in the quotient when the divisor is a positive integer. Example 2 justifies shifting the decimal point in the divisor and dividend. Example 3 shows the remainder is not the positive integer 6 but the rational number 0.006.

We now return to the problem of the representation of the rational 1/3 as a terminating decimal. As in the above examples, we exhibit the work as follows.

```
   .3          .33           .333
3)1.0       3)1.00        3)1.000
  9            9             9
  ─            ──            ──
  1            10            10
               9             9
               ─             ──
               1             10      . . .
                             9
                             ─
                             1
```

$$1 = 3(0.3) + 0.1, \quad 1 = 3(0.33) + 0.01, \quad 1 = 3(0.333) + 0.001, \quad \ldots$$

It is intuitively clear that the above process will not terminate; that is, 1/3 cannot be represented by a terminating decimal. The following argument is a proof that 1/3 cannot be represented by a terminating decimal.

Assume $1/3 = 0.b_1b_2 \ldots b_k$.

Then $1/3 = (10^k/10^k)(0.b_1b_2 \ldots b_k) = b_1b_2 \ldots b_k/10^k$.

Thus there is a counting number a such that $1/3 = a/10^k$.

Hence $10^k = 3a$.

Thus $3 \mid 10^k$ (by Definition 1 of Chapter 6).

Hence $3 \mid 10$ (by Theorem 9 of Chapter 6).

But $3 \nmid 10$.

Thus $3 \mid 10$ and $3 \nmid 10. /\!/$

This contradiction assures us that the assumption that $1/3$ can be represented by a terminating decimal is a false assumption. Hence $1/3$ *cannot* be represented by a terminating decimal; that is, the decimal representation of $1/3$ contains infinitely many digits to the right of the decimal point.

Although $1/3$ cannot be written as a terminating decimal, it can be *approximated* by a terminating decimal. Since $1 = 3(0.3) + 0.1$, $1 = 3(0.33) + 0.01$, $1 = 3(0.333) + 0.001$, . . . , we see that $1/3$ may be approximated by 0.3, 0.33, 0.333, ... The errors in the approximations are, respectively, *less than* 0.1, 0.01, 0.001, ... Thus $1/3$ may be approximated by a terminating decimal to any desired degree of accuracy. For example, if we wish an approximation of $1/3$ with an error of less than 0.000001, we employ the approximation 0.333333. The important fact to realize is that the accuracy of the approximation increases as the number of decimal places in the approximation increases. That is, the sequence of decimals 0.3, 0.33, 0.333, 0.3333, 0.33333, 0.333333, 0.3333333, . . . approaches closer and closer the rational number $1/3$ without ever becoming equal to $1/3$. For this reason, we extend the decimal numeration system to include nonterminating decimals. Now we may represent $1/3$ by the infinite decimal 0.3333 . . . , in which the three dots indicate that the 3 repeats indefinitely. Under this convention, $1/3 = 0.3333 \ldots$. This example answers the question posed at the beginning of this section: *not every rational number can be written as a terminating decimal.*

It is important that you understand the meaning of a nonterminating decimal. The nonterminating decimal $0.b_1b_2b_3$ . . . is that number which the sequence of rational numbers $0.b_1$, $0.b_1b_2$, $0.b_1b_2b_3$, $0.b_1b_2b_3b_4$, . . . approaches.

However, now that we have included nonterminating decimals in the decimal numeration system, two more questions arise. (1) Can any rational number be represented by a decimal? (2) Is every nonterminating decimal a rational number; that is, does there exist a sequence $0.b_1$, $0.b_1b_2$, $0.b_1b_2b_3$, . . . of rational numbers which does not approach a rational number? In the next section we shall answer the first of these questions. In Section 8.4 we answer the second question.

Exercise 8.2

I. Complete the details in each of the following, and justify the algorithm.

(1) $8 \overline{)\ 5.000}$ $.625$

(6) $4.2 \overline{)\ 40.32}$

(2) $8 \overline{)\ 7.000}$ $.875$

(7) $0.32 \overline{)\ 2.720}$

(3) $4 \overline{)\ 3.00}$ $.75$

(8) $0.32 \overline{)\ 272.0}$

(4) $4 \overline{)\ 1.00}$ $.25$

(9) $6 \overline{)\ 5.000}$

(5) $4.2 \overline{)\ 36.12}$

(10) $6 \overline{)\ 1.000}$

II. By the method of Example 3, determine whether each of the following rational numbers can be written as a terminating decimal.

(1) 3/50   (6) 6/75
(2) 7/50   (7) 3/75
(3) 1/30   (8) 6/35
(4) 7/30   (9) 2/15
(5) 4/75   (10) 1/15

III. Write the first eight terms of the sequence 0.4, 0.45, 0.454, ... of rational numbers which approaches the nonterminating decimal 0.454545 . . . .

8.3 Decimal Representation of Rational Numbers (continued)

Recall the first question posed in the last section: Can any rational number be represented by a decimal? In order to gain sufficient insight to answer this question, we consider the following examples.

Example 1. Represent the rational number 5/11 as a decimal.

$$11 \overline{)\ 5.0} \quad .4$$
$$4\,4$$
$$\overline{6}$$

$$11 \overline{)\ 5.00} \quad .45$$
$$4\,4$$
$$\overline{60}$$
$$55$$
$$\overline{5}$$

$$11 \overline{)\ 5.000} \quad .454$$
$$4\,4$$
$$\overline{60}$$
$$55$$
$$\overline{50}$$
$$44$$
$$\overline{6}$$

$$5 = 11(0.4) + 0.6$$

$$5 = 11(0.45) + 0.05$$

$$5 = 11(0.454) + 0.006$$

```
      .4545                    .45454                    .454545
11 ) 5.0000              11 ) 5.00000             11 ) 5.000000
     4 4                      4 4                       4 4
     ───                      ───                       ───
      60                       60                        60
      55                       55                        55
      ──                       ──                        ──
       50                       50                        50
       44                       44                        44
       ──                       ──                        ──
        60                       60                        60
        55                       55                        55
        ──                       ──                        ──
         5                        50                        50
                                  44                        44
                                  ──                        ──
                                   6                         60
                                                             55
                                                             ──
                                                              5
```

$$5 = 11(0.4545) \qquad 5 = 11(0.45454) \qquad 5 = 11(0.454545)$$
$$+ \ 0.0005 \qquad\qquad + \ 0.00006 \qquad\qquad + \ 0.000005$$

The above application of the division algorithm illustrates that the sequence 0.4, 0.45, 0.454, 0.4545, 0.45454, 0.454545, . . . approaches the rational number 5/11.

Example 2. Represent the rational number 1/7 as a decimal.

```
     .142857
7 ) 1.000000
    7
    ─
    30
    28
    ──
     20
     14
     ──
      60
      56
      ──
       40
       35
       ──
        50
        49
        ──
         1
```

$$1 = 7(0.142857) + 0.000001$$

Repeated application of the division algorithm yields
$1 = 7(0.142857142857) + 0.000000000001$, et cetera.

Thus we see that the sequence 0.1, 0.14, 0.142, 0.1428, 0.14285, 0.142857, 0.1428571, 0.14285714, ... approaches rational number 1/7.

At any step in the application of the division algorithm in Example 2, the "remainder" must be less than 7; that is, $0 \le r_i < 7$. Since the only possible "remainders" are 0, 1, 2, 3, 4, 5, and 6, either the "remainder" is 0 or eventually repeats. If $r_i = 0$, then the decimal representation is a *terminating* decimal. If the "remainder" repeats, then the decimal representation is a *repeating* decimal. Since the "remainder" eventually repeats in this example, we see that 1/7 can be represented by a repeating decimal; that is, $1/7 = 0.142857142857 \ldots$, in which the three dots indicate that the digits 142857 repeat. In general, the three dots indicate that a pattern has been established and is continued. We may indicate that the repeating digits are 142857 by placing a bar (——) over the 142857. Then we may write $1/7 = 0.\overline{142857}$. It is important to realize that the repeating decimal $0.\overline{142857}$ is not equal to 0.142857 but is the rational number which the sequence in Example 2 approaches. Similarly, we may write $5/11 = 0.\overline{45}$ (or 0.4545...) and $1/3 = 0.\overline{3}$ (or 0.33...). In the former, $0.\overline{45}$ is the rational number which the sequence 0.4, 0.45, 0.454, 0.4545, ... approaches. More generally, $0.b_1 b_2 \overline{b_3 b_4 b_5 b_6}$ is the rational number which the sequence $0.b_1$, $0.b_1 b_2$, $0.b_1 b_2 b_3$, $0.b_1 b_2 b_3 b_4$, $0.b_1 b_2 b_3 b_4 b_5$, $0.b_1 b_2 b_3 b_4 b_5 b_6$, $0.b_1 b_2 b_3 b_4 b_5 b_6 b_3$, $0.b_1 b_2 b_3 b_4 b_5 b_6 b_3 b_4$, ... approaches.

If we generalize the above argument, we may prove the following theorem, which answers the first question in the affirmative.

THEOREM 1.   If a/b is any rational number, then a/b can be written as a terminating decimal or a repeating decimal.

Proof.   Apply the division algorithm to obtain $a = bq + r$, $0 \le r < b$.

If $r = 0$, then $a/b = q$.

If $r \ne 0$, apply the division algorithm again.

If the "remainder" is 0 at some step in the division, then the decimal terminates.

If the "remainder" is never 0, then one of the "remainders" must repeat before b divisions (because the only possibe remainders are $0, 1, 2, \ldots, b$).

At this step, the decimal begins to repeat. //

By Theorem 1, we know that any rational number a/b can be written as a terminating decimal or a repeating decimal. The following examples illustrate the fact that the decimal terminates if the only prime factors of b are 2 and 5.

Example 3. $3/20 = 15/100 = 0.15$.

Example 4. $7/50 = 14/100 = 0.14$.

Example 5. $27/8 = (1000/1000)(27/8) = (1/1000)(27000/8)$
              $= (1/1000)(3375) = 3.375$.

The following theorem guarantees that our conclusion is correct.

THEOREM 2.   If a/b is a rational number whose denominator b has no prime factors other than 2 and 5, then a/b can be expressed as a terminating decimal.

Proof. $a/b = a/2^j5^k = 2^k5^j/2^k5^j \cdot a/2^j5^k = 2^k5^ja/2^{j+k}5^{j+k}$
          $= 2^k5^ja/(2 \cdot 5)^{j+k} = 2^k5^ja/10^{j+k}$ $(0 \le j, 0 \le k)$.
          Since 2^k5^ja is a counting number c, and $j + k$ is a counting number m, we may write $a/b = c/10^m$.
          Since $c/10^m$ can be represented by a terminating decimal, we see that a/b may be represented by a terminating decimal.//

If the denominator b of the rational number a/b contains a prime factor other than 2 or 5, can we conclude that a/b can *not* be expressed as a terminating decimal? The following theorem, the inverse of Theorem 2, answers this question.

THEOREM 3.   If a/b is a rational number (in lowest terms) whose denominator b has a prime factor other than 2 or 5, then a/b can not be expressed as a terminating decimal.

Proof.   Assume a/b may be expressed as a terminating decimal.
          By the hypothesis there exists a prime p other than 2 or 5 such that $p \mid b$.
          Hence there exists $q \in I$ such that $b = pq$.
          Thus $a/b = a/pq$.

However, by assumption $a/b = a_k a_{k-1} \ldots a_0 . b_1 \ldots b_j$
$$= (10^j / 10^j)(a_k a_{k-1} \ldots a_0 . b_1 \ldots b_j)$$
$$= a_k a_{k-1} \ldots a_0 b_1 \ldots b_j / 10^j = c/10^j.$$

But $a/b = a/pq$.

Hence $a/pq = c/10^j$.

Thus $10^j a = p(qc)$.

Hence $p \mid 10^j a$.

But $p \nmid 10^j$ (since p is a prime factor other than 2 or 5).

Hence $p \mid a$ (by Theorem 8 of Chapter 6).

But $(p,a) = 1$.

Thus $p \nmid a$.

Hence $p \mid a$ and $p \nmid a$.

This contradiction proves that the assumption is false.

Hence a/b can not be expressed as a terminating decimal. //

Observe that the denominator 14 of the rational number $7/14$ has the prime factor 7 (which is neither 2 nor 5). Although you may be tempted to conclude from Theorem 3 that $7/14$ can not be expressed as a terminating decimal, you should realize that $7/14 = 1/2 = 0.5$. The reason that Theorem 3 does not apply in this case is that $7/14$ is *not* in lowest terms, as required by the hypotheses of Theorem 3.

Exercise 8.3

I. Illustrate Theorem 1 in each of the following.

(1) 2/5   (6) 4/7
(2) 6/10   (7) 3/8
(3) 2/3   (8) 5/8
(4) 2/11   (9) 17/15
(5) 3/7   (10) 13/12

II. Illustrate Theorem 2 in each of the following.

(1) 3/10   (6) 57/200
(2) 7/10   (7) 31/500
(3) 7/20   (8) 37/500
(4) 3/20   (9) 31/625
(5) 77/200   (10) 37/625

III. Illustrate Theorem 3 in each of the following or explain why Theorem 3 is not applicable.

(1) 2/15   (11) 3/21
(2) 7/15   (12) 7/21
(3) 6/35   (13) 3/15
(4) 3/14   (14) 7/35
(5) 3/7   (15) 12/15
(6) 4/7   (16) 7/15
(7) 11/22   (17) 17/68
(8) 14/28   (18) 41/164
(9) 4/33   (19) 7/60
(10) 4/21   (20) 3/140

IV. Write each of the following repeating decimals so that the repeating digits are written three times followed by three dots.

(1) $0.3\overline{456}$ (6) $0.5\overline{732}$
(2) $0.5\overline{732}$ (7) $0.\overline{3456}$
(3) $0.\overline{3456}$ (8) $0.\overline{5732}$
(4) $0.573\overline{2}$ (9) $16.\overline{3}$
(5) $0.345\overline{6}$ (10) $17.\overline{7}$

V. Write each of the following repeating decimals by use of the horizontal bar.

(1) 5.7565656...   (6) 16.171717...
(2) 7.3424242...   (7) 17.161161161...
(3) 0.050414141...   (8) 16.171171171...
(4) 0.505636363...   (9) 3.333...
(5) 11.121212...   (10) 5.555...

VI. Convert each of the following terminating decimals to the form a/b, in which a and b are integers.

(1) 0.4563   (6) 12.345
(2) 0.6343   (7) 256.7
(3) 0.8910   (8) 625.9
(4) 0.9180   (9) 27.00
(5) 21.235   (10) 98.000

8.4 Real Numbers

We have already proved that every rational number can be written as a terminating decimal or a repeating decimal. Now we prove that any repeating decimal is a rational number. The following examples illustrate the method of proof.

Example 1.   Let $a = 0.\overline{123}$; that is, $a = 0.123123123...$.
              Then $1000a = 123.123123...$.

Hence $1000a - a = 123.123123\ldots - 0.123123\ldots$.
Thus $999a = 123$.
Hence $999a/999 = 123/999$.
Thus $a = 123/999 = 41/333$.
Hence a is a rational number.

Example 2.   Let $a = 0.1\overline{23}$; that is, $a = 0.1232323\ldots$.
Then $1000a = 123.2323\ldots$.
Also $10a = 1.2323\ldots$.
Thus $990a = 122$.
Hence $990a/990 = 122/990$.
Thus $a = 122/990 = 61/495$.
Hence a is a rational number.

Example 3.   Let $a = 35.67\overline{2}$; that is, $a = 35.67222\ldots$.
Then $1000a = 35672.222\ldots$.
Also $100a = 3567.222\ldots$.
Thus $900a = 32,105$.
Hence $a = 32,105/900$.
Thus $a = 6421/180$.
Hence a is a rational number.

Example 4.   Let $a = 0.\overline{142857}$; that is, $a = 0.142857142857\ldots$.
Then $1,000,000a = 142857.142857142857\ldots$.
Moreover, $a = 0.142857142857\ldots$.
Thus $999,999a = 142857$.
Hence $a = 142,857/999,999$.
Thus $a = 1/7$.
Hence a is a rational number.

Example 5.   Let $a = 0.1\overline{9}$; that is, $a = 0.1999\ldots$.
Then $100a = 19.999\ldots$.
Also $10a = 1.999\ldots$.
Thus $90a = 18$.
Hence $a = 18/90$.
Thus $a = 1/5$.
Hence a is a rational number.

Example 6.   Let $a = 0.2\overline{0}$; that is, $a = 0.2000\ldots$.
Thus $a = 2/10$.
Thus $a = 1/5$.
Hence a is a rational number.

THEOREM 4.   Any repeating decimal is a rational number.

Proof.   Similar to the above examples. //

   In Example 5 we saw that $0.1\overline{9} = 1/5$; in Example 6 we saw that $0.2\overline{0} = 1/5$. Although any repeating decimal is a rational number and, conversely, any rational number can be represented by a repeating decimal, we see that the representation is not unique. The fact that $0.999 \ldots = 1$ should not bother you because we have agreed that 0.999 . . . represents that number which the sequence 0.9, 0.99, 0.999, 0.9999, . . . approaches; we see that this sequence approaches the rational number 1. It should be clear that only a number which can be expressed as a *terminating* decimal will have two different decimal representations; *one of these representations will have repeating 0's, the other will have repeating 9's.* We agree to choose that representation with repeating 0's. Under this agreement, the decimal representation of any rational number is unique.

   Let us consider the second question of Section 8.2; namely, does every nonterminating decimal represent a rational number? The following argument answers this question. The nonterminating decimal 0.101001000100001 . . . is also nonrepeating. If this decimal represented a rational number a, then a would have two different decimal representations—this decimal representation and a repeating decimal representation. However, we have concluded that a has exactly *one* decimal representation. Hence this decimal cannot represent a rational number and, thus, the answer to the above question is *no.*

   Since we have exhibited a nonterminating nonrepeating decimal which does not represent a rational number, we see that there are two courses of action open:

   1. We could go back to the point at which we extended the decimal numeration system and require that all nonterminating decimals be repeating decimals. Under this condition, every decimal would represent a rational number and the nonrepeating "decimal" would really be a meaningless symbol and *not* a decimal at all.

   2. We could extend the number system to include new numbers which are *not* rational.

   If we had no need for the new numbers, we would choose the first course of action. However, the following example illustrates the need for new numbers.

Example 7.   Compute the length of the segment from 0 to r indicated in the accompanying figure.

By the Pythagorean Theorem, $r^2 = 1^2 + 1^2 = 2$.
Thus the length of the hypotenuse is that number which converts the open sentence $r^2 = 2$ to a true sentence.
If this number is not a rational number, then we see a need for extending the numeration system to include numbers which are not rational. We now prove that no rational number exists which converts the open sentence $r^2 = 2$ to a true sentence and thus that it is impossible to express the length of the segment by a rational number. The method of proof is contradiction.

THEOREM 5.   The open sentence $r^2 = 2$ cannot be converted to a true sentence by replacement of the variable r by a rational number.

Proof.   Assume there exists a rational number a/b such that $(a/b)^2 = 2$.

Then $(a/b)(a/b) = 2$.

Thus $aa = 2bb$.

By the unique prime factorization theorem, a and b may be factored uniquely into prime factors.

Thus $a = p_1p_2 \ldots p_k$ and $b = q_1q_2 \ldots q_m$.

Hence $(p_1p_2 \ldots p_k)(p_1p_2 \ldots p_k) = 2(q_1q_2 \ldots q_m)$
$(q_1q_2 \ldots q_m)$.

The factor 2 appears an even number of times in aa and an odd number of times in $2bb$.

Thus the unique prime factorization of aa is different from the unique prime factorization of $2bb$.

But $aa = 2bb$.

This is a contradiction to the unique prime factorization theorem.

Hence the assumption is false.

Thus there is no rational number a/b such that $(a/b)^2 = 2$.//

By Theorem 5 it is impossible to convert the open sentence $r^2 = 2$ to a true sentence by replacement of the variable r by a rational number; that is, there is no terminating or repeating decimal whose square is equal to 2. However, Figure 8.1 presents convincing evidence that the second course of action is more appropriate than the first.

a/b	$(a/b)^2$
1.4	1.96
1.41	1.9881
1.414	1.999396
1.4142	1.99996164

FIGURE 8.1

In the following section we extend the rational number system to the real number system which includes new numbers called irrational numbers. It will be possible, in the expanded number system, to convert the open sentence $r^2 = 2$ to a true sentence by replacement of the variable r by an *irrational number*.

Exercise 8.4

I. Express each of the following rational numbers in the form a/b.

(1) 5.7565656 ...   (6) 16.171717 ...
(2) 7.3424242 ...   (7) 17.161161161 ...
(3) 0.050414141 ...   (8) 16.171171171 ...
(4) 0.505636363 ...   (9) 3.333 ...
(5) 11.121212 ...   (10) 5.555 ...

II. Write each of the following repeating decimals as terminating decimals.

(1) 0.65$\bar{0}$ (4) 60.5$\bar{0}$
(2) 0.72$\bar{0}$ (5) 20.3000 ...
(3) 20.3$\bar{0}$ (6) 60.5000 ...

III. (1) Prove that the open sentence $r^2 = 3$ cannot be converted to a true sentence by replacement of the variable by a rational number.

(2) Prove that the open sentence $r^2 = 4$ *can* be converted to a true sentence by replacement of the variable by a rational number. If, as in (1), you try to prove that the open sentence $r^2 = 4$ cannot be converted to a true sentence by

replacement of the variable by a rational number, where does the proof fail?

(3) Prove that the open sentence $r^2 = 6$ cannot be converted to a true sentence by replacement of the variable by a rational number.

IV. Compute the truth-value of each of the following sentences.

(1) $0.2\overline{5} < 0.25\overline{4}$

(2) $0.2\overline{5} = 0.25$

(3) $0.2\overline{54} < 0.25\overline{4}$

(4) $0.254 < 0.25\overline{4}$

(5) $5.62\overline{3} < 5.623\overline{9}$

(6) $5.62\overline{3} < 5.623$

(7) $4.00\overline{3} < 4.00\overline{3}$

(8) $4.00\overline{3} < 4.00\overline{3}$

(9) $0.9\overline{8} < 0.9\overline{8}$

(10) $0.8\overline{9} < 0.89$

V. In Figure 8.1 write the largest 6-digit number whose square is less than 2.

8.5 The Real Number System

In Example 7 and Theorem 5 of Section 8.4 we saw that there is a point on the number line which does not correspond to a rational number. This fact is equivalent to the fact that the open sentence $r^2 = 2$ cannot be converted to a true sentence by replacement of the variable by a rational number. Of course, there are many other points of the number line which do not correspond to rational numbers and, equivalently, many other open sentences which cannot be converted to true sentences by replacement of the variables by rational numbers. Moreover, in Figure 8.1, we saw that there are terminating decimals whose squares are very close to 2; that is, there are terminating decimals whose squares *approximate* 2 to any desired number of decimal places. These considerations lead us to extend the rational number system to a more inclusive number system so that each point on the number line will correspond to exactly *one* number and each number will correspond to exactly *one* point. Then it will be possible to convert many open sentences, and, in particular, any open sentence of the form $r^2 = k$, where k is any counting number, to a true sentence by replacement of the variable r by some number from the more inclusive number system. The numbers of the more inclusive number system, called *real numbers,* are defined below.

DEFINITION 1. A number is said to be a *real number* if and only if it can be expressed as an infinite decimal in one of the following forms:

(a) $^-a_k a_{k-1} \ldots a_0.b_1 b_2 b_3 \ldots$ $\left\{\begin{array}{l} k \text{ is a counting number} \\ a_k, \ldots, a_0, b_1, b_2, \ldots \in \\ \{0, 1, 2, 3, 4, 5, 6, 7, 8, 9\} \end{array}\right.$

(b) $a_k a_{k-1} \ldots a_0.b_1 b_2 b_3 \ldots$ There is no positive integer j such that $b_i = 9$ for all $j \le i$.

In Definition 1, the a's and b's are members of the set $\{0, 1, 2, 3, 4, 5, 6, 7, 8, 9\}$. The reason for the restriction concerning $b_i = 9$ is that we do not allow infinitely repeating 9's. For example, we do not allow an infinite decimal of the form 13.4052999 . . . but instead, we employ the notation 13.4053000 . . . or simply 13.4053.

The *set* of all real numbers will be denoted by R. The following examples of real numbers illustrate Definition 1.

Example 1. $^-634.72900\ldots$

$k = 2$	$b_1 = 7$
$a_2 = 6$	$b_2 = 2$
$a_1 = 3$	$b_3 = 9$
$a_0 = 4$	$b_4 = 0$
	$b_5 = 0$
	$b_6 = 0$
	. . .

Note that this repeating decimal with 0's repeating can be expressed as the terminating decimal $^-634.729$.

Example 2.   0

$k = 0$	$b_1 = 0$
$a_0 = 0$	$b_2 = 0$
	. . .

Note that $0 = 0.000\ldots$

Example 3.   67342.503222 . . .

$k = 4$	$b_1 = 5$
$a_4 = 6$	$b_2 = 0$
$a_3 = 7$	$b_3 = 3$
$a_2 = 3$	$b_4 = 2$
$a_1 = 4$	$b_5 = 2$
$a_0 = 2$	$b_6 = 2$
	. . .

Note that this repeating decimal can be expressed as $67342.50\overline{32}$.

Example 4. 0.202002000200002 ...

$$k = 0 \qquad b_1 = 2$$
$$a_0 = 0 \qquad b_2 = 0$$
$$b_3 = 2$$
$$b_4 = 0$$
$$b_5 = 0$$
$$b_6 = 2$$

. . .

Note that this decimal does not terminate and does not repeat. However, it is a well-defined number; that is, for any counting number m, it is possible to determine the first m digits of the number.

DEFINITION 2. (a) Any real number not equal to 0 is said to be a *negative real number* if and only if it can be expressed in form (a) of Definition 1.

(b) Any real number not equal to 0 is said to be a *positive real number* if and only if it can be expressed in form (b) of Definition 1.

The set of all negative real numbers will be denoted by R^- and the set of all positive real numbers will be denoted by R^+. The definition of *absolute value* of a real number is analogous to the definition of absolute value of a rational number as given in Definition 14 of Chapter 7.

Recall that every rational number may be expressed as a terminating decimal or a repeating decimal. Since every terminating decimal may be expressed as a repeating decimal with 0's repeating, we see that every rational number may be written as an infinite repeating decimal. Hence every rational number is a real number. Moreover, since every integer is a rational number, we see that every integer is a real number. However, we have proved that there are real numbers which are not rational numbers. The following definition gives a name to any real number which is not rational.

DEFINITION 3. A real number is said to be an *irrational number* if and only if it is not a rational number.

Thus we see that the set of real numbers is the union of the set of rational numbers and the set of irrational numbers and that these sets are *disjoint*. Every rational number can be expressed as a repeating decimal (since every terminating decimal can be written as a repeating decimal with repeating 0's) and every repeating decimal is a rational number. That is, *the set of rational numbers is identically the set of repeating decimals. The set of irrational numbers is identically the set of nonrepeating decimals.*

Now that we have extended the set of rationals to the set of reals, we would like to define the binary operations of addition, subtraction, multiplication, and division between any two real numbers. Since every rational number is also a real number, it is important that the definitions be consistent with the definitions of Chapter 7 for the rational numbers. The following examples illustrate the method of definition.

Example 5. $(23.61232323\ldots) + (^-6.16353535\ldots)$ is that number which the following sequence approaches: $(23.6 + ^-6.1)$, $(23.61 + ^-6.16)$, $(23.612 + ^-6.163)$, $(23.6123 + ^-6.1635)$, $\ldots$.

Example 6. $(^-6.16353535\ldots) + (23.61232323\ldots)$ is that number which the following sequence approaches: $(^-6.1 + 23.6)$, $(^-6.16 + 23.61)$, $(^-6.163 + 23.612)$, $(^-6.1635 + 23.6123)$, $\ldots$.

Example 7. $(23.61232323\ldots)(36.16353535\ldots)$ is equal to that number which the following sequence approaches: $[(23.6)(36.1)]$, $[(23.61)(36.16)]$, $[(23.612)(36.163)]$, $[(23.6123)(36.1635)]$, $\ldots$.

Example 8. $(36.16353535\ldots)(23.61232323\ldots)$ is equal to that number which the following sequence approaches: $[(36.1)(23.6)]$, $[(36.16)(23.61)]$, $[(36.163)(23.612)]$, $[(36.1635)(23.6123)]$, $\ldots$.

Consideration of Examples (5) and (6) leads us to define the binary operator $+$ and the sum of any two real numbers as follows.

DEFINITION 4. The *sum* of any two real numbers $r = a_k \ldots a_0.b_1b_2b_3 \ldots$ and $s = c_j \ldots c_0.d_1d_2d_3 \ldots$ is the real number which the sequence $[(a_k \ldots a_0.b_1) + (c_j \ldots c_0.d_1)]$, $[(a_k \ldots a_0.b_1b_2) + (c_j \ldots c_0.d_1d_2)]$, $[(a_k \ldots a_0.b_1b_2b_3) + (c_j \ldots c_0.d_1d_2d_3)]$, $\ldots$ approaches.

Similarly, Examples 7 and 8 motivate the following definition of the binary operator $\cdot$ and the *product* of any two real numbers.

DEFINITION 5. The *product* of any two real numbers $r = a_k \ldots a_0.b_1b_2b_3$ $\ldots$ and $s = c_j \ldots c_0.d_1d_2d_3 \ldots$ is the real number which the sequence $[(a_k \ldots a_0.b_1)(c_j \ldots c_0.d_1)]$, $[(a_k \ldots a_0.b_1b_2)(c_j \ldots c_0.d_1d_2)]$, $[(a_k \ldots a_0.b_1b_2b_3)(c_j \ldots c_0.d_1d_2d_3)]$, $\ldots$ approaches.

From Definition 4 (and Examples 5 and 6 which motivated Definition 4), we see that $r + s = s + r$ for any real numbers r and s. Similarly from Definition 5 (and Examples 7 and 8), we see that $rs = sr$ for any real numbers r and s. Once again, we have set the stage so that all properties of the rational number system $(R_a, +, \cdot)$ would also be properties of the real number system $(R, +, \cdot)$. In fact, we defined *sum* and *product* in Definition 4 and Definition 5, respectively, so that we could prove the properties of the real number system by use of the properties of the rational number system. In particular, we can prove that $(R, +, \cdot)$ is a field. For example, to prove that $r \cdot 1 = r$ for any real number r, we note that $r \cdot 1 = (a_k \ldots a_0.b_1b_2 \ldots) \cdot (1.000 \ldots)$ and hence $r \cdot 1$ is that number which the sequence $[(a_k \ldots a_0.b_1)(1.0)]$, $[(a_k \ldots a_0.b_1b_2)(1.00)]$, $[(a_k \ldots a_0.b_1b_2b_3)(1.000)]$, $\ldots$ approaches. However, this sequence is the same sequence as $[a_k \ldots a_0.b_1]$ $[a_k \ldots a_0.b_1b_2]$, $[a_k \ldots a_0.b_1b_2b_3]$, $\ldots$, which approaches r.

We now define an order relation $<$ between real numbers so that $(R, +, \cdot, <)$ will be an ordered field.

DEFINITION 6. The real number r is said to be *less than* the real number s (written $r < s$) if and only if there exists a positive real number t such that $r + t = s$.

It follows readily that $(R, +, \cdot, <)$ is an ordered field. That is, $(R, +, \cdot, <)$ has the following properties.

F1. If a and b are any elements of R, then $a + b$ is a unique element of R (closure property for addition).

F2. If a, b, and c are any elements of R, then $(a + b) + c = a + (b + c)$ (associative property for addition).

F3. There exists a unique element 0 of R such that $a + 0 = a$ for any element a of R (identity property for addition).

F4. If a is any element of R, then there exists a unique element ^-a of R such that $a + {}^-a = 0$ (inverse property for addition).

F5.   If a and b are any elements of R, then $a + b = b + a$ (commutative property for addition).

F6.   If a and b are any elements of R, then $a \cdot b$ is a unique element of R (closure property for multiplication).

F7.   If a, b, and c are any elements of R, then $(a \cdot b) \cdot c = a \cdot (b \cdot c)$ (associative property for multiplication).

F8.   There exists a unique element 1 of R such that $a \cdot 1 = a$ for any element a of R (identity property for multiplication).

F9.   If a is any nonzero element of R, then there exists a unique element $1/a$ of R such that $a \cdot (1/a) = 1$ (inverse property for multiplication).

F10.   If a and b are any elements of R, then $a \cdot b = b \cdot a$ (commutative property for multiplication).

F11.   If a, b, and c are any elements of R, then $a(b + c) = ab + ac$ (distributive property).

O1.   If a and b are any elements of R, then exactly one of the following sentences is true:
(a) $a < b$,
(b) $a = b$,
(c) $b < a$.

O2.   If a, b, and c are any elements of R and $a < b$, then $a + c < b + c$.

O3.   If a and b are any elements of R, c is any positive element of R, and $a < b$, then $ac < bc$.

O4.   If a and b are any elements of R, c is any negative element of R, and $a < b$, then $bc < ac$.

O5.   If a, b, and c are any elements of R, $a < b$, and $b < c$, then $a < c$ (transitive property for order).

The above 16 properties completely characterize the algebraic structure of the *real number system* $(R, +, \cdot, <)$; that is, all other properties of the real number system can be proved from them, and subtraction and division are implied in F4 and F9, respectively. However, for future reference and for convenience in creating mathematical models for solving physical problems, we define subtraction and division and state those properties which are analogous to the properties of $(R_a, +, \cdot, <)$ studied in Chapter 7. The binary operator $-$, the operation *subtraction*, and the *difference* of two real numbers is given in Definition 7. The binary operator $\div$, the operation *division*, and the *quotient* of two real numbers is given in Definition 8.

DEFINITION 7. For any real numbers a and b, the *difference* in the subtraction of b from a (written $a - b$) is the real number c if and only if $a = b + c$ (that is, $a - b = c$ if and only if $a = b + c$).

DEFINITION 8. For any real number a and any nonzero real number b, the *quotient* in the division of a by b (written $a \div b$) is the real number c if and only if $a = bc$ (that is, $a \div b = c$ if and only if $a = bc$).

CLOSURE PROPERTY FOR SUBTRACTION
If a and b are any real numbers, then $a - b$ is a unique real number.

DOUBLE NEGATIVE PROPERTY
If a is any real number, then $^-(^-a) = a$.

SIGN PROPERTY FOR ADDITION
If a and b are any real numbers, then $^-(a + b) = {}^-a + {}^-b$.

MULTIPLICATION PROPERTY OF ZERO
If a and b are any real numbers, then $ab = 0$ if and only if $a = 0$ or $b = 0$.

CANCELLATION PROPERTY FOR MULTIPLICATION
If a, b, and c are any real numbers, $a \neq 0$, and $ab = ac$, then $b = c$.

CLOSURE PROPERTY FOR DIVISION
If a is any real number and b is any nonzero real number, then $a \div b$ is the unique real number $a \cdot 1/b$, denoted by a/b.

SIGN PROPERTY FOR MULTIPLICATION
If a and b are any real numbers, then $^-a \cdot {}^-b = a \cdot b$, $^-a \cdot b = {}^-(ab)$, and $a \cdot {}^-b = {}^-(ab)$.

SIGN PROPERTY FOR DIVISION

If a is any real number and b is any nonzero real number, then $^-a/^-b = a/b$, $^-a/b = ^-(a/b)$, and $a/^-b = ^-(a/b)$.

The closure property for subtraction follows from Definition 7 and the cancellation property for addition.

The closure property for division follows from Definition 8 and the cancellation property for multiplication.

In the sign property for division, observe that the real number a/b is not necessarily a rational number, since a and b are not necessarily integers but real numbers. As in the case of rational numbers, when a/b is written, it is understood that $b \neq 0$.

Although every irrational number is an infinite decimal which does not repeat (or terminate), Theorem 6 asserts that every real number (whether rational or irrational) can be *approximated* to any number of decimal places by a terminating decimal. Before stating and proving the theorem, we illustrate it with an example.

Example 9.   Give a terminating decimal approximation of the infinite decimal 257.6343434 ..., with an error of less than $1/10^9$.

Now 257.634343434 < 257.634343434 ...

< 257.634343434999 ... = 257.634343434

+ 0.000000000999 ... .

However, we have agreed not to employ repeating 9's. Hence we replace 0.000000000999 ... by 0.000000001000

... .

Thus 257.634343434999 ... = 257.634343434 + $1/10^9$.

Hence 257.634343434 < 257.634343434 ...

< 257.634343434 + $1/10^9$.

THEOREM 6.   (a) If $a_k \ldots a_0.b_1b_2b_3 \ldots$ is any positive real number, then $a_k \ldots a_0.b_1b_2b_3 \ldots b_j \leq a_k \ldots a_0.b_1b_2b_3 \ldots b_j \ldots$ $\leq (a_k \ldots a_0.b_1b_2b_3 \ldots b_j) + 1/10^j$.

(b) If $^-a_k \ldots a_0.b_1b_2b_3 \ldots b_j \ldots$ is any negative real number, then $(^-a_k \ldots a_0.b_1b_2b_3 \ldots b_j) + ^-1/10^j \leq ^-a_k \ldots$ $a_0.b_1b_2b_3b_j \ldots < ^-a_k \ldots a_0 b_1b_2b_3 \ldots b_j$.

Proof.   (a) Since $a_k \ldots a_0.b_1b_2b_3 \ldots b_j = a_k \ldots a_0.b_1b_2b_3 \ldots b_j000$ ... and $a_k \ldots a_0.b_1b_2b_3 \ldots b_j000 \ldots \leq a_k \ldots a_0.b_1b_2b_3$ $\ldots b_j \ldots$, we see that $a_k \ldots a_0.b_1b_2b_3 \ldots b_j \leq a_k \ldots$ $a_0.b_1b_2b_3 \ldots b_j \ldots$. Now $a_k \ldots a_0.b_1b_2b_3 \ldots b_j \ldots$

$\leq a_k \ldots a_0.b_1b_2b_3 \ldots b_j999\ldots = a_k \ldots a_0.b_1b_2b_3 \ldots$
$b_j + 0.00 \ldots \underbrace{0999}_{j\text{-}0\text{'s}} \ldots .$

However we have agreed not to employ repeating 9's to represent a rational number. Hence we replace $\underbrace{0.00 \ldots 0999}_{j\text{-}0\text{'s}} \ldots$ by $\underbrace{0.000 \ldots 0100}_{(j\text{-}1)\text{-}0\text{'s}} \ldots$; that is,
by $1/10^j$. Thus $a_k \ldots a_0.b_1b_2b_3 \ldots b_j \ldots \leq (a_k \ldots a_0.b_1b_2b_3 \ldots b_j) + 1/10^j$.

(b) The proof of part (b) is similar. However, one must remember that $^-3.1416$, for example, is equal to $^-3 + {}^-0.1416.$ //

Since every terminating decimal is a rational number, we see that every real number can be approximated (to any desired degree of accuracy) by a rational number. For this reason, mathematicians say that the set of rationals is *dense* in the set of reals.

Although the points on the number line corresponding to the rational numbers do not "fill up" the number line, the points corresponding to the real numbers do "fill up" the number line. The proof of this fact actually depends on an important property known as the *Dedekind property.*

THEOREM 7.   If $A \cap B = \phi$, $A \cup B = R$, $A \neq \phi$, $B \neq \phi$, and each element of A is less than every element of B, then A contains a largest element or B contains a smallest element, but not *both.*

Exercise 8.5

I. By Definition 4, compute each of the following sums.

(1) $47.\overline{24} + 2.\overline{71}$ (3) $0.5\overline{42} + 10.7\overline{36}$
(2) $63.\overline{35} + 5.\overline{43}$ (4) $0.8\overline{34} + 12.4\overline{43}$

II. Convert each repeating decimal in Exercise I to the form a/b, compute each sum in Exercise I by the method of Chapter 7, convert the sum to a repeating decimal, and check the answer in each part of I.

III. By Definition 5, compute each of the following products.

(1) $(0.\bar{3})(0.1)$ (2) $(0.\bar{5})(0.\bar{1})$

IV. Convert each of the following repeating decimals to the form a/b, compute the product by the method of Chapter 7, and check each answer of Exercise III.

(1) $(0.\bar{3})(0.1)$ (2) $(0.\bar{5})(0.\bar{1})$

V. Prove each of the following properties of the real number system.

(1) If $a \neq 0$, then there exists a' such that $a \cdot a' = 1$.
(2) For all a, b, and $c \in R$, $a(b + c) = ab + ac$.
(3) If $a - b = c_1$ and $a - b = c_2$, then $c_1 = c_2$. (*Hint.* Use Definition 7 and the cancellation property for addition.)

VI. Prove each of the following properties of the real number system.

(1) If $a < b$, then $^-b < ^-a$.   (5) $^-(^-a) = a$.
(2) $^-a \cdot ^-b = ab$.   (6) $^-(a + b) = ^-a + ^-b$.
(3) $^-a \cdot b = ^-(ab)$.   (7) $^-a \div b = ^-(a/b)$.
(4) $a \cdot ^-b = ^-(ab)$.   (8) $a \div ^-b = ^-(a/b)$.

VII. Prove that the real number system does not possess the well-ordering property.

VIII. Prove that the following sentence is false.
There exists a real number x such that $x^2 = ^-1$.

8.6 Percent

As we assume that you are already familiar with the application of *percent* (%), we give only a brief review of the fundamentals of the concept of *percent* and *percentage*. You may read in the papers that 70% of the world is covered by water, or 87% of an iceberg is submerged, or Mr. Jones is in the 92% tax bracket, or the interest rate at the local bank is 6½%. What is the meaning of the sentence "87% of an iceberg is submerged"? The word *percent* means *per hundred*. Thus this sentence means that 87/100 of an iceberg is submerged; that is, 87 parts per hundred parts is below water. When one says that 1% of his income is spent on sales tax, he means that one-hundredth of each dollar is spent on sales tax. Thus 1% of b means 1/100 of b, and, in general, $p\%$ of b means $p/100$ of b. The main reason that the term *percent* is used is that it provides a *common standard* of comparison. That is, it is easier to compare percents than fractions with different denominators; after all, 87% and 83% mean 87/100 and 83/100. The denominators are *equal*.

When we say that 87% of a 47,000 ton iceberg is submerged, we are referring to a physical problem. This is the same as the physical problem which states that 87/100 of a 47,000 ton iceberg is submerged. The mathematical model of this physical problem is 87/100 (47,000). The following examples illustrate computations involving the use of percent.

Example 1. In a class of 24 students, 25% made A on the first test. How many students made A on the first test?
(25/100)(24) = 6. Hence 6 students made A.

Example 2. The population of the United States is approximately 190,000,000 persons. Five-tenths of one percent of the population are elementary school teachers. Approximately how many elementary school teachers are there in the U. S.?
(0.5/100)(190,000,000) = (5/1000)(190,000,000) = 5 (190,000) = 950,000. Thus there are approximately 950,000 elementary school teachers in the U. S.

Example 3. A sodium chloride solution contains 100 grams of water and 25 grams of sodium chloride. What percent of the solution is sodium chloride?
25/(100 + 25) = 25/125 = 1/5 = 20/100.
Hence 20% of the solution is sodium chloride.

Example 4. A merchant sold a coat at a profit of 33⅓% of the selling price. The profit was $40. At what price did the merchant sell the coat?
(33⅓)/100 = (100/3)/100 = ⅓.
⅓ · s = 40.
3(⅓ · s) = 3 (40).
Thus s = 120.
Hence he sold the coat for $120.

Exercise 8.6

I. Formulate a mathematical model for each of the following problems and employ the model to answer each question.

(1) A realtor earns 5% commission on each house he sells. How much commission does he earn on a house which he sells for $24,000?

(2) An automobile salesman earns a salary of $100 per week plus a commission of 5% on all sales in excess of $5,000. If his sales amounted to $7,500 during Christmas week, how much did he earn for the week?

(3) A loan company borrows money at 6% and lends money at 24%. The cost of doing business is 8% of the amount of money it lends. How much money does the company earn in a year in which the company borrows $1,500,000 and lends $1,500,000 for a year?

(4) By what percent does a man's salary increase if his present· salary is $9,000 and he accepts a new job at a salary of $12,000?

(5) By what percent does a man's salary decrease if his present salary is $12,000 and he accepts a new job at $9,000?

(6) A furniture merchant earns a profit of 40% of the selling price of each item he sells. If a sofa cost him $300, at what price should he sell the sofa?

(7) If the population of a city increases from 100,000 to 120,000, what is the percent of increase?

(8) If the population of a city decreases from 120,000 to 100,000, what is the percent of decrease?

(9) The following tax items appeared on Mr. Brown's estate tax bill:

School	60
City	80
County	28
State	24
Misc.	8

What percent of the total tax was charged for each item?

(10) The enrollment at a small midwestern college was as follows:

Freshmen	500
Sophomores	350
Juniors	250
Seniors	150

What percent of the total enrollment did each class represent?

8.7 Exponents

In Chapter 4 we studied exponentials of the form a^m, in which a is a counting number and m is a positive integer. In this section we shall

extend the concept of exponential to include any real number as base
and any integer as exponent, except that we shall define 0^m only if m
is a positive integer. For example, we shall give meaning to expressions
such as $(\sqrt{5})^0$, $^-7^0$, $(^-7)^0$, $(^-5)^4$, 3^{-5}, $(2/3)^4$ $(4/11)^{-5}$, $(\sqrt{2})^3$, but we
shall not define 0^{-1}, 0^{-4}, and so on. In the following definition a meaning
is given to any exponential in which a is any real number and m is any
positive integer.

DEFINITION 9. For any real number a and any positive integer m

(a) $a^m = \underbrace{a \cdot a \cdot \ldots \cdot a}_{m\text{-factors}}.$

(b) The real number a is called the *base*.

(c) The positive integer m is called the *exponent*.

(d) The real number a^m is called an *exponential*.

Example 1. $(2/3)^4 = (2/3)(2/3)(2/3)(2/3)$
$\qquad = (2)(2)(2)(2)/(3)(3)(3)(3) = 2^4/3^4.$

Example 2. $(^-5)^4 = (^-5)(^-5)(^-5)(^-5) = 625 = 5^4.$

Example 3. $(^-5)^3 = (^-5)(^-5)(^-5) = ^-125 = ^-5^3.$

Example 4. $(2 \cdot 3)^4 = (2 \cdot 3)(2 \cdot 3)(2 \cdot 3)(2 \cdot 3)$
$\qquad = (2 \cdot 2 \cdot 2 \cdot 2)(3 \cdot 3 \cdot 3 \cdot 3) = 2^4 \cdot 3^4.$

Example 5. $(2/5)^3 \cdot (2/5)^4$
$\qquad = (2/5)(2/5)(2/5)[(2/5)(2/5)(2/5)(2/5)]$
$\qquad = (2/5)^7.$

Example 6. $(4/7)^1(4/7)^5$
$\qquad = (4/7)[(4/7)(4/7)(4/7)(4/7)(4/7)] = (4/7)^6.$

Example 7. $5^6/5^3 = (5^3 \cdot 5^3)/5^3 = (5^3/5^3) \cdot 5^3 = (5/5)^3 5^3$
$\qquad = 1^3 \cdot 5^3 = 1 \cdot 5^3 = 5^3.$

Example 8. $6^5/6^3 = (6^3 \cdot 6^2)/6^3 = (6^3/6^3) \cdot 6^2 = 1(6)^2 = 6^2.$

Example 9. $4^3/4^5 = 4^3/(4^3 \cdot 4^2) = 4^3/4^3 \cdot 1/4^2 = 1 \cdot 1/4^2 = 1/4^2.$

Example 10. $(10.1)^7/(10.1)^8 = (10.1)^7/(10.1)^7(10.1)^1$
$\qquad = (10.1)^7/(10.1)^7 \cdot 1/(10.1)^1 = 1/(10.1)^1 = 1/10.1.$

The above examples, which illustrate Definition 9, also motivate the following theorems.

THEOREM 8. If a is any real number and k and m are any positive integers, then $a^k \cdot a^m = a^{k+m}$.

THEOREM 9. If a is any nonzero real number and k and m are any positive integers such that $k < m$, then $a^m/a^k = a^{m-k}$.

THEOREM 10. If a is any nonzero real number and k and m are any positive integers such that $m < k$, then $a^m/a^k = 1/a^{k-m}$.

Theorems 8, 9, and 10 may be proved by means of the technique employed in Examples 5, 7, and 9, respectively.

The following examples illustrate the above theorems.

Example 11. $(8.2)^5(8.2)^8 = (8.2)^{5+8} = (8.2)^{13}$.

Example 12. $(2.71)^{11}/(2.71)^8 = (2.71)^{11-8} = (2.71)^3$.

Example 13. $(32.7)^6/(32.7)^5 = (32.7)^{6-5} = (32.7)^1 = 32.7$.

Example 14. $(91)^4/(91)^9 = 1/(91)^{9-4} = 1/91^5$.

Example 15. $a^5/a^8 = 1/a^{8-5} = 1/a^3$, provided $a \neq 0$.

As we would like to combine Theorem 9 and Theorem 10 into one theorem, regardless of whether $k < m$, $m < k$, or $m = k$, we make the following definition.

DEFINITION 10. For any real number $a \neq 0$ and any positive integer k,
   (a) $a^{-k} = 1/a^k$,
   (b) $a^0 = 1$.

According to Definition 10, $91^{-5} = 1/91^5$ and $(91)^0 = 1$.

Theorem 8 may now be extended, and Theorems 9 and 10 may be combined and extended as in the following theorems.

THEOREM 11. If a is any nonzero real number and k and m are any integers, then $a^k \cdot a^m = a^{k+m}$.

THEOREM 12. If a is any nonzero real number and k and m are any integers, then $a^m/a^k = a^{m-k}$.

You may prove the above theorems by considering the various cases. The following examples illustrate the theorems.

Example 16. $5^2 \cdot 5^{-3} = 5^{2+-3} = 5^{-1} = 1/5^1 = 1/5.$

Example 17. $(7.1)^{-6} \cdot (7.1)^6 = (7.1)^{-6+6} = (7.1)^0 = 1.$

Example 18. $(8.3)^2/(8.3)^3 = (8.3)^{2-3} = (8.3)^{-1} = 1/(8.3)^1 = 1/(8.3).$

Example 19. $(11.7)^5/(11.7)^{-3} = (11.7)^{5--3} = (11.7)^{5+3} = (11.7)^8.$

Example 20. $a^5/a^6 = a^{5-6} = a^{-1} = 1/a,$ provided $a \neq 0.$

The following theorems may be proved by use of a technique similar to that employed in Examples 4 and 1, respectively.

THEOREM 13. If a and b are any real numbers and k is any integer such that $ab \neq 0$ or $0 < k$, then $(ab)^k = a^k b^k$.

THEOREM 14. If a and b are any nonzero real numbers and k is any integer, then $(a/b)^k = a^k/b^k$.

The following definition of *square root* is based on exponents.

DEFINITION 11. The real number a is said to be a *square root* of the real number b if and only if $a^2 = b$.

For example, 3 is a square root of 9 because $3^2 = 9$ and $^-3$ is a square root of 9 because $(^-3)^2 = 9$. It follows directly from the sign property for multiplication and the Dedekind property that every positive real number has two square roots of equal absolute value—one negative and one positive. The positive square root of a positive real number is given a special name and notation.

DEFINITION 12. The positive square root of the positive real number b is called *the principal square root of b* (briefly, *the square root of b*) and is denoted by $\sqrt{b}$.

For example, $\sqrt{9} = 3$ (not -3) and $\sqrt{16} = 4$. If $b = 0$, then there is only *one* square root of b; $\sqrt{b} = 0$ if and only if $b = 0$. If $b < 0$, then there is no real number a such that $a^2 = b$; that is, $\sqrt{b}$ does not exist if $b < 0$. As the square root of 2 is *not* a rational number, the only exact expression for the square root of 2 is $\sqrt{2}$. Although $\sqrt{2}$ is not a rational number, Theorem 6 guarantees that $\sqrt{2}$ may be approximated by a rational number. In Section 8.8 we study approximations and approximate numbers, and in Section 8.9 we learn to compute with them. The following examples further illustrate the above definitions and theorems.

Example 21. $(\sqrt{2})^3 (\sqrt{5})^7/(\sqrt{2})^5 (\sqrt{5})^3 = (\sqrt{2})^3/(\sqrt{2})^5 \cdot (\sqrt{5})^7/$
$(\sqrt{5})^3 = (\sqrt{2})^{3-5} \cdot (\sqrt{5})^{7-3} (\sqrt{2})^{-2} \cdot (\sqrt{5})^4 = (\sqrt{5})^4/$
$(\sqrt{2})^2 = (\sqrt{5})^2(\sqrt{5})^2/(\sqrt{2})^2 = 5 \cdot 5/2 = 25/2.$

Example 22. $(1.6)^3 \ a^6 \ b^2/(1.6)^2ab^5 = (1.6)^{3-2} \ a^{6-1} \ b^{2-5} = 1.6a^5b^{-3}$
$= 1.6a^5/b^3.$

Example 23. $(\sqrt{2})^5(-b)^9c^2/(\sqrt{2})^5(-b)^3c^5 = (\sqrt{2})^{5-5} \ (-b)^{9-3} \ c^{2-5}$
$= (\sqrt{2})^0(-b)^6(c)^{-3} = (\sqrt{2})^0(-b)^6/c^3 = 1 \cdot (-b)^6/c^3$
$= b^6/c^3,$ provided $bc \neq 0.$

Example 24. $(a + b)^7(6 - c)^3/(a + b)^3(c - 6)^5 = (a + b)^7 \cdot {}^-(c$
$- 6)^3/(a + b)^3 \cdot (c - 6)^5 = (-1) \ (a + b)^7(c - 6)^3/$
$(a + b)^3(c - 6)^5 = (-1) \ (a + b)^4/(c - 6)^2 = {}^-(a$
$+ b)^4/(c - 6)^2,$ provided $(a + b)(c - 6) \neq 0.$

Example 25. $5a^2b^6/a^3b^6 = 5a^{-1}b^0 = 5a^{-1} = 5(1/a) = 5/a,$ provided $ab \neq 0.$

Notice that $5a^{-1} = 5/a$ and *not* $1/5a$.

Exercise 8.7

I. Apply Theorems 11 and 12 and Definition 10 to simplify each of the following.

(1) $5^5 \cdot 5^2/5^3$

(2) $6^6 \cdot 6^3/6^4$

(3) $2^2 \cdot 2^2 \cdot 3^2/2^5 \cdot 3^4$

(4) $3^4 \cdot 3^2 \cdot 4^3/3^6 \cdot 4^5$

(5) $8^0 \cdot 5 \cdot 6^2/5^2 \cdot 6$

(6) $7^0 \cdot 6 \cdot 8^3/6^3 \cdot 8^2$

(7) $[2\pi^2(\sqrt{2})^3] \cdot [2^4\pi^3]$

(8) $[2^2\pi^3(\sqrt{3})^5] \cdot [2^3\pi^2]$

(9) $a^3b^2c/a^4b^2c^5$

(10) a^2bc^5/a^7b^4c

II. Simplify each of the following.

(1) 8^0 (6) $(^-6)^0$

(2) 6^0 (7) $^-8^0$

(3) $(8\sqrt{2})^0$ (8) $^-6^0$

(4) $(5\sqrt{3})^0$ (9) $8(\sqrt{2})^0$

(5) $(^-8)^0$ (10) $5(\sqrt{3})^0$

III. Simplify each of the following.

(1) $(^-\sqrt{2})^2$ (6) $(b\sqrt{7})^2$

(2) $^-(\sqrt{3})^2$ (7) $b(\sqrt{7})^2$

(3) $^-(\sqrt{2})^2$ (8) $a(\sqrt{5})^3$

(4) $(^-\sqrt{3})^2$ (9) $(1.5a + 3.7b)^0$

(5) $(a\sqrt{5})^3$ (10) $(3.9a - 3.7b)^0$

IV. Apply Theorems 13 and 14 to each of the following.

(1) $(6ab)^3$ (6) $(9.1\,a/2.9b)^6$

(2) $(5ac)^2$ (7) $(\pi r^2/\pi ab)^2$

(3) $(bcd)^4$ (8) $(2\pi r/\pi r^2)^2$

(4) $(ack)^3$ (9) $(4\pi r^3/3a)^2$

(5) $(2 \cdot 6 \cdot a/3 \cdot 7 \cdot b)^5$ (10) $(4\pi r^2/ab)^3$

V. Write each of the following without a negative exponent.

(1) 2^{-3} (6) $3b^{-2}$

(2) 5^{-2} (7) $(2a)^{-3}$

(3) 4^{-2} (8) $(3b)^{-2}$

(4) 3^{-3} (9) $(2 + a)^{-2}$

(5) $2a^{-3}$ (10) $2 + a^{-2}$

VI. (1) Prove Theorem 11.

    (2) Prove Theorem 12.

    (3) Prove Theorem 13.

    (4) Prove Theorem 14.

8.8 Measurements and Approximate Numbers

Any number which is the result of *counting* discrete objects, such as the number of students in a class, is called an *exact* number. A so-called *approximate* number results from (1) a measurement, (2) an estimate or guess, (3) a computation, and (4) a rounding of an exact number. If you count the number of students in your mathematics class as 28, then 28 is used as an exact number. However, if the census officials publish the most recent census count of your city as 63,000, then

63,000 is used as an approximate number (estimated or rounded to the nearest thousand persons). If you measure the dimensions of your classroom as 19 ft by 26 ft, the numbers 19 and 26 are used as approximate numbers, probably measured to the nearest foot. If you estimate the number of students at an assembly as 4000, the number 4000 is used as an approximate number. Your estimate really means that the number of students at the assembly is probably between 3500 and 4500. If you compute the area (in square feet) of your classroom, the number of square feet is called an approximate number.

If you compute 1/7 and round the answer to 0.142857, the number 0.142857 is called an approximate number (an approximation of 1/7). However, the number 0.142857 as the decimal representation of the rational number 142,857/1,000,000 is called an exact number.

A clarification of the terminology *exact* and *approximate* is in order. Every real number is really an *exact* number. However, when we *say* that 0.142857 is an *approximate* number, we really mean that the *exact* number 0.142857 is an *approximation* of the *exact* number 1/7. In general, any terminating decimal is an approximation of some nonterminating decimal.

The number 100 in a $100 per plate political dinner is exact; however, the number 100 in a 100 pound sack of rice is an approximate number (that is, an approximation of the exact weight of each sack). The number 2.24 is an approximate number when it is used as $\sqrt{5}$, and an exact number when it is used as the decimal representation of 224/100.

The goodness of fit of an approximate number to the actual exact number which it approximates may be expressed by either the precision or the accuracy of the approximate number. In computation with approximate numbers, it is important to know the precision or the accuracy of the numbers involved. Before we discuss the techniques of computation with approximate numbers, we shall discuss the terms *precision* and *accuracy* and explain the technique of determining the precision and the accuracy of any approximate number.

The *greatest possible error* in any measurement is one-half of the smallest unit on the measuring scale. For example, the greatest possible error in the measurement 11.2 inches is (1/2)(0.1 in.) = 0.05 in. In this example, the smallest unit on the measuring scale is 0.1 unit. However, the greatest possible error in the measurement 11.20 in. is (1/2)(.01 in.) = 0.005 in., and the greatest possible error in the measurement 11 in. is (1/2)(1 in.) = 0.5 in.

In the former measurement the smallest unit on the measuring scale is 0.01 in.; in the latter measurement the smallest unit on the measuring scale is 1 in. When we approximate an exact number by the approximate number 3.62, we mean that the exact number lies between 3.615 and 3.625. Similarly, when we write 3.62000 as an approximation to an exact number r, we mean that $3.619995 \leq r < 3.620005$. The approx - imate number m_1 is said to be *more precise than* the approximate num - ber m_2 if and only if the greatest possible error in m_1 is less than the greatest possible error in m_2. By the *precision* of an approximate num - ber we mean the smallest unit in the approximate number. For example, the precision of 2.31 in. is 0.01 in., the precision of 4.0 ft is 0.1 ft, and the precision of 23 mm is 1 mm.

Thus the greatest possible error in a measurement determines the *precision* of the measurement. There are three common methods of expressing the greatest possible error of a measurement. These methods are exemplified for the measurement of the weight as follows:

(1) 2.2 pounds ± 0.05 pound,
(2) 2.2 pounds, correct to the nearest tenth of a pound,
(3) 2.2 pounds.

In all three methods, the same precision is expressed by the fact that the weight is measured to the nearest tenth of a pound; that is, by the fact that the greatest possible error is 0.05 pound.

Since the greatest possible error of the measurement 11.2 in. is 0.05 in. and the greatest possible error of the measurement 11.20 in. is 0.005 in., we see that the precision of 11.2 in. is less than that of 11.20 in.; that is, 11.20 in. is a more precise measurement than 11.2 in. Simi - larly, 9.0 in. is a more precise measurement than 15 in. In general, the precision of a measurement increases when the smallest unit of the measurement decreases; that is, the precision increases as the greatest possible error decreases.

It is easy to understand why an error of 500 miles in the distance from Boston to New Orleans is considered a rather large error, whereas an error of 500 miles in the distance from the earth to the sun is con - sidered a rather small error. Although the error is 500 miles in both cases, it is *relatively* large in the former case and *relatively* small in the latter case.

In order to have a method of comparing errors in measurements, we shall discuss relative error and percent error. The *relative error* in any measurement is equal to the greatest possible error divided by the measurement. For example, the *relative error* in the measurement 125.0 miles is $0.05/125.0 = 1/2500 = 0.0004$; the *percent error* is 0.04%. How - ever, the relative error in the measurement 5.0 miles is $0.05/5.0 = 1/10 = 0.1$; the percent error is 10%. Although the greatest possible error in both cases is 0.05 mile, the relative error in the former case is only 0.0004, whereas the relative error in the latter case is 0.1. We recognize this fact by saying that the former measurement is more *accurate* than the latter measurement. In general, a measurement is more *accurate* than a second measurement if and only if the relative error in the first measurement is less than the relative error in the second measurement. The *accuracy* of a measurement is designated by the number of *significant digits* of the measurement. The number of *significant digits* of a measurement is equal to the number of digits in that numeral which specifies the number of units in the measurement. The following examples will clarify the concept of *significant digits*.

Example 1. The distance from Lafayette to Opelousas is recorded as 26 miles. The unit of measurement is *one mile*. There are 26 units in the measurement. The number of digits in 26 is 2. Hence, the measurement contains 2 significant digits.

Example 2. Mr. Murray's odometer measures the distance from Lafayette to Opelousas as 26.4 miles. The unit of measurement is *one-tenth* of a mile. There are 264 units in the measurement. The number of digits in 264 is 3. Hence the measurement contains 3 significant digits.

Example 3. The thickness of a ream (500 sheets) of paper measures 2.000 in. The unit of measurement is *one-thousandth of an inch*. There are 2000 units in the measurement. The number of digits in 2000 is 4. Hence the measurement contains 4 significant digits.

Example 4. The thickness of one sheet of paper measures 0.004 in. The unit of measurement is *one-thousandth of an inch*. There are 4 units in the measurement. The number of digits in 4 is 1. Hence the measurement contains 1 significant digit.

Example 5. The thickness of 502 sheets of paper measures 2.008 in. The unit of measurement is *one-thousandth of an inch*. There are 2008 units in the measurement. The number of digits in 2008 is 4. Hence the measurement contains 4 significant digits.

Example 6. The distance from the earth to the sun is recorded as 93,000,000 miles, measured to the nearest million miles. The unit of measurement is *one million miles*. There are 93 units in the measurement. The number of digits in

93 is 2. Hence the measurement contains 2 significant digits. If the unit of measurement were *one thousand miles*, there would be 5 significant digits in the measurement. If the unit of measurement were *one mile*, there would be 8 significant digits in the measurement.

The above examples illustrate the following important rules concerning significant digits in any measurement.

Rule 1.   All nonzero digits of any approximate number are significant.

Rule 2.   In an approximate number whose absolute value is greater than 1, all zeros to the right of the decimal point are significant.

Rule 3.   In an approximate number whose absolute value is less than 1 all zeros to the right of the decimal point and to the left of the first nonzero digit are *not* significant, and all zeros to the right of a nonzero digit are significant.

Rule 4.   All zeros between two nonzero digits are significant.

Rule 5.   In an approximate number which is an integer, all terminal zeros are *not* significant unless it is indicated that they are.

The table in Figure 8.2 exhibits several measurements and their degrees of precision and accuracy.

Measurement	Unit of measurement	Greatest possible error (GPE)	Number of units	Accuracy (number of significant digits)
1278 pounds	1 pound	0.5 pound	1278	4
1260 pounds	10 pounds	5 pounds	126	3
1260.0 pounds	0.1 pound	0.05 pound	12,600	5
1206 pounds	1 pound	0.5 pound	1206	4
0.0009 Kg	0.0001 Kg	0.00005 Kg	9	1
0.0010 Kg	0.0001 Kg	0.00005 Kg	10	2
1.0009 Kg	0.0001 Kg	0.00005 Kg	10,009	5
10,500 Kg	100 Kg	50 Kg	105	3

FIGURE 8.2

If the unit of measurement in a measurement such as 10,500 Kg is not 100 Kg, then the unit must be specified. The usual procedure is to write the approximate number in *scientific notation*. A number is written in *scientific notation* if and only if it is written as the product of an exponential 10^m and a real number r such that $1 \le r < 10$. The following examples illustrate the procedure.

Example 7. 10,500 Kg correct to the nearest ten Kg is written in scientific notation as

1.050×10^4 Kg (4 significant digits).

Example 8. 10,500 Kg correct to the nearest Kg is written in scientific notation as

1.0500×10^4 Kg (5 significant digits).

Example 9. 100,000 miles correct to the nearest mile is written in scientific notation as

1.00000×10^5 miles (6 significant digits).

Example 10. 100,000 miles correct to the nearest 100 miles is written in scientific notation as

1.000×10^5 miles (4 significant digits).

Of course, other numbers can be written in scientific notation, and laboratory measurements taken by a physicist or chemist usually are. For example, the measurement 70.49 grams is usually written 7.049×10^1 grams; the mass of the electron is written 9.03×10^{-28} gram. The advantages of the scientific notation are clearly illustrated by this last application.

Frequently one has to *round off* approximate numbers to a desired degree of accuracy. If the left-end digit *dropped* is 0, 1, 2, 3, or 4, the remaining digits are unchanged. If the left-end digit *dropped* is 5, 6, 7, 8, or 9, the right-end digit retained is increased by 1. If an integral approximate number is rounded off, all digits dropped are replaced by zeros. The following examples illustrate the procedure.

Example 11. 23.456 rounded to 4 significant digits is 23.46, and rounded to 3 significant digits is 23.5.

Example 12. 23.446 rounded to 4 significant digits is 23.45, and rounded to 3 significant digits is 23.4.

Example 13. 2537 miles rounded to the nearest 10 miles (to 3 significant digits) is 2540 miles, and rounded to the nearest 100 miles (to 2 significant digits) is 2500 miles.

Example 14. 2967 miles rounded to the nearest 10 miles (to 3 significant digits) is 2970 miles, and rounded to the nearest 100 miles (to 2 significant digits) is 3000 miles. However, according to the convention, 3000 miles has only 1 significant digit. Thus we write 3.0×10^3 miles to indicate an accuracy of 2 significant digits. An alternate method is to underline the 0 to the right of the 3 or to write it in boldface type. Thus we could write **3000** or 300̲0 miles to indicate that the 0 to the right of the 3 is a significant digit.

Example 15. 0.00004973 rounded to 3 significant digits is 0.0000497, rounded to 2 significant digits is 0.000050, and rounded to 1 significant digit is 0.00005. In scientific notation these are written

$$4.97 \times 10^{-5},$$
$$5.0 \times 10^{-5},$$
$$5 \times 10^{-5}, \text{ respectively.}$$

Exercise 8.8

I. Classify each of the following numbers as exact or approximate.

(1) 23 students
(2) 30 students
(3) 560,000 citizens
(4) 649,000 teachers
(5) 29.83 inches of mercury

(6) 761 mm of mercury
(7) 10 home runs
(8) 6 singles
(9) 3.1416 (used for π)
(10) 3.1416 (used for the rational number 31,416/10,000)

II. Compute the greatest possible error in each measurement in Exercise I.

III. Write a compound inequality to indicate the exact numbers between which each of the following measurements lies. [For example, $27.25 < 27.3 < 27.35$.]

(1) 29.607
(2) 30.803
(3) 2.0630
(4) 1.0709
(5) 0.0709

(6) 0.1600
(7) 0.0700
(8) 470.0
(9) 470
(10) 5190

IV. Compute the relative error in each measurement in Exercise III.

V. Compute the percent error in each measurement in Exercise III.

VI. Determine the number of significant digits in each measurement in Exercise III.

VII. Round each measurement in Exercise III to two significant digits.

VIII. Write each of the following measurements in scientific notation to indicate the accuracy.

(1) 0.004700

(2) 0.074040

(3) 1.004700

(4) 3.074040

(5) 123.0

(6) 123.00

(7) 123

(8) 21

(9) 7500

(10) 690

(11) 7500.0

(12) 690.00

(13) 69.0

(14) 7.50

(15) 0.0000000005040

(16) 0.000000003270

(17) 30,000,000,000

(18) 93,000,000

(19) 650,003

(20) 400,090

IX. State the precision and accuracy of each measurement in Exercise III.

X. State the precision and accuracy of each measurement in Exercise VIII.

8.9 Computations with Approximate Numbers

Since all measurements involve approximate numbers, it follows that all sums, differences, products, and quotients of measurements also involve approximate numbers. Consequently, one is not justified in retaining so many digits in the answer that a false impression is thereby conveyed of the precision or accuracy of the answer. There are two basic rules of agreement for computation with approximate numbers.

Rule 1. We agree that the *precision* of a *sum* (or *difference*) of approximate numbers does not exceed the precision of any of the approximate numbers from which the sum (or difference) is formed.

Rule 2. We agree that the *accuracy* of a *product* (or *quotient*) of approximate numbers does not exceed the accuracy of any of the approximate numbers from which the product (or quotient) is formed.

The following examples illustrate the applications of Rule 1.

Example 1. Compute the total length of ribbon in four ribbons of lengths 4.6 in., 6.78 in., 3.67 in., and 9.232 in., respectively.

> 4.6   (precision: 0.1 in.)
> 6.78   (precision: 0.01 in.)
> 3.67   (precision: 0.01 in.)
> 9.232 (precision: 0.001 in.)

The least precise measurement is 4.6. By Rule 1 the precision of the sum does not exceed the precision of 4.6. Hence we round all measurements to the nearest tenth of an inch and add as follows:

> 4.6 in.
> 6.8 in.
> 3.7 in.
> 9.2 in.
> ‾‾‾‾‾‾‾‾
> 24.3 in. (approximately)

Example 2. Compute the difference 52.709 − 3.62 of the approximate numbers 52.709 and 3.62.

> 52.709 (precision: 0.001)
>   3.62 (precision: 0.01)

The less·precise approximate number is 3.62. By Rule 1 the precision of the difference does not exceed the precision of 3.62. Hence we round to the nearest hundredth and subtract as follows:

>   52.71
> − 3.62
> ‾‾‾‾‾‾‾‾
>   49.09 (approximately)

Example 3. Compute the sum of the measurements 11.03 and 8.72.

> 11.03
>   8.72
> ‾‾‾‾‾
> 19.75

Since both measurements are precise to the nearest hundredth, the sum is precise to the nearest hundredth, and no rounding is necessary.

The following examples illustrate the applications of Rule 2.

Example 4.   The dimensions of a room are 15.7 ft. by 13.2 ft. Compute the area of the room. If these measurements were exact, we would compute the product of 15.7 and 13.2 in the usual manner.

$$\begin{array}{r} 15.7 \\ 13.2 \\ \hline 31\,4 \\ 471\,0 \\ 1570\,0 \\ \hline 207.24 \end{array}$$

15.7 (3 significant digits)
13.2 (3 significant digits)

$207.24 \longrightarrow 207$ (3 significant digits)

The measurement 15.7 has 3 significant digits, and the measurement 13.2 has 3 significant digits. By Rule 2 the accuracy of the product does not exceed the accuracy of either measurement; that is, the product does not have more than 3 significant digits. Hence we round the answer to three significant digits and write the area as 207 square feet (approximately).

Example 5.   Compute the area of a heat-transfer slab whose dimensions are 11.03 cm. by 8.72 cm.

11.03 (4 significant digits)
8.72 (3 significant digits)

$$\begin{array}{r} 11.03 \\ 8.72 \\ \hline 22\,06 \\ 772\,10 \\ 8824\,00 \\ \hline 96.1816 \end{array}$$

$96.1816 \longrightarrow 96.2$ (3 significant digits)

There are 4 significant digits in 11.03 and 3 significant digits in 8.72. By Rule 2 the product does not have more than 3 significant digits; thus we round the answer to 3 significant digits and write the area as 96.2 square centimeters (approximately).

Observe that the sum (or difference) of 11.03 and 8.72 is not rounded. Although 11.03 and 8.72 have the same *precision*, they do not have the same *accuracy*. Even if they did have the same accuracy, it would still be necessary to round the product to the accuracy of the measurements as in Example 4.

Example 6.   Divide 12.05 by 21.

$$\begin{array}{r} .57 \\ 21\,\overline{)12.05} \\ 10\,5 \\ \hline 1\,55 \\ 1\,47 \\ \hline 8 \end{array}$$ $\longrightarrow$ 0.57 (2 significant digits)

By Rule 2 the quotient does not have more than 2 significant digits; thus it is rounded to 0.57.

Example 7.   Divide 12.05 by 0.02.

$$\begin{array}{r} 602. \\ .02\,\overline{)12.05} \\ 12 \\ \hline 05 \\ 4 \\ \hline 1 \end{array}$$ $\longrightarrow$ 600 (1 significant digit)

By Rule 2 the quotient does not have more than 1 significant digit; thus it is rounded to 600.

The following example illustrates the *necessity* for Rule 2.

Example 8.   Compute the area of a table top 5.3 ft by 2.4 ft.
Now $5.25 < 5.3 < 5.35$
and $2.35 < 2.4 < 2.45$.
Hence $(5.25)(2.35) < (5.3)(2.4) < (5.35)(2.45)$.

5.25	5.3	5.35
2.35	2.4	2.45
26 25	21 2	26 75
157 50	106 0	214 00
1050 00	12.72	1070 00
12.3375		13.1075

Since the actual product lies *somewhere* between 12.3375 and 13.1075, we are not justified in writing the product as 12.72. Thus we round the product to 2 significant digits and write 13.

Exercise 8.9

I. Compute each of the following approximate sums.

(1)	181.23	(4)	40
	4.67		21.0
	0.012		160.7

(2)	8.625	(5)	0.875
	210.000		0.946
	4.23		0.023

(3)	40.0	(6)	0.42
	21.2		0.40
	160.71		0.01

II. Compute each of the following approximate differences.

(1)	25.20	(6)	1.65200
	− 1.237		− 3.470

(2)	20.25	(7)	23
	− 2.167		− 67.4

(3)	100.0	(8)	23
	− 1.8		− 67.6

(4)	600.8	(9)	0.00008
	− 1.0		− 2.003

(5)	3.4560	(10)	7.0007
	− 5.23		− 5.00007

III. Compute each of the following products of approximate numbers.

(1) 8.002×2.3
(2) 2.008×8.3
(3) 6.1020×7.0
(4) 9.0110×3.0
(5) 12.05×1.25
(6) 7.93×18.10
(7) 0.0002×1.0002
(8) 0.0020×3.001
(9) $(2.30 \times 10^{-7}) \times (6.025 \times 10^{-3})$
(10) $(6.1 \times 10^{-2}) \times (7.03 \times 10^{-8})$

(11) $(4.20 \times 10^4) \times (1.23 \times 10^5)$
(12) $(1.51 \times 10^3) \times (8.92 \times 10^6)$
(13) $25,000 \times 410$
(14) $6,440 \times 1600$
(15) $(2.50 \times 10^4) \times (4.10 \times 10^2)$
(16) $(6.440 \times 10^3) \times (1.600 \times 10^3)$
(17) $1,050 \times 285$
(18) $1,050 \times 280$
(19) $1,500 \times 285$
(20) $1,510 \times 280$

IV. Compute each of the following quotients of approximate numbers.

(1) $8.002 \div 2.3$ (6) $1500 \div 285$
(2) $6.1020 \div 7.0$ (7) $0.0060 \div 2$
(3) $7.93 \div 18.10$ (8) $0.0060 \div 2.0$
(4) $0.0020 \div 3.001$ (9) $0.00010 \div 2.0$
(5) $1050 \div 280$ (10) $0.00010 \div 2$

V. (1) The volume of a box is measured as 564 cu. in. The height is measured as 4.0 in. Compute the area of the base.

(2) The approximate speed of sound is 1100 ft/sec (measured to the nearest 100 ft/sec). Compute the approximate number of seconds for the sound of a gun one mile (5280 ft) off-shore to reach the shore.

(3) The approximate speed of sound is 1090 ft/sec (measured to the nearest 10 ft/sec). Compute the approximate number of seconds for the sound of a gun one mile (5280 ft) off-shore to reach the shore.

(4) Compute the least possible area of a rectangular field whose dimensions are 509 ft by 125 ft.

(5) Compute the greatest possible area of a rectangular field whose dimensions are 509 ft by 125 ft.

(6) Compute the least possible sum of the measurements 9.5, 10.3, and 25.9.

(7) Compute the greatest possible sum of the measurements 9.5, 10.3, and 25.9.

(8) Explain why 19.70 and 3.06 have the same precision but not the same accuracy.

(9) Explain why 19.7 and 3.06 have the same accuracy but not the same precision.

(10) Explain why the correctly rounded answer to $64 \div 2$ is 30 if 64 and 2 are *measurements*, but the correct answer to $64 \div 2$ is 32 if 64 and 2 are exact numbers.

Chapter 9

FINITE NUMBER SYSTEMS

9.1 Clock Arithmetic

We began the study of arithmetic with the set of counting numbers, in Chapter 3 we defined the operations of addition and multiplication between counting numbers, and then we studied the properties of the counting number system $(C_0, +, \cdot)$. In Chapter 6 we continued the study of the counting number system by introducing the concept of $a \mid b$ and proved certain division theorems, the division algorithm, and the Euclidean algorithm. Now, we shall consider certain finite subsets of C_0, define the operations of addition and multiplication between numbers in *these subsets* to form finite *systems*, and then study the corresponding properties of these finite systems. We shall see that some finite number systems have all the properties of $(C_0, +, \cdot)$ and some do not. In fact, we shall discover that many of the finite number systems have all the field properties. At this time you should review the definitions and theorems of Chapter 6.

To introduce finite number systems we consider *clock arithmetic*. In clock arithmetic the only numbers are 1, 2, 3, . . . , 12, which we call *clock numbers*. In the definition of addition, we are guided by the clock. For example, if you have an appointment at 3:00 P.M. and you are 2 hours late, then you arrive for your appointment at 5:00 P.M. On the other hand, if you are 2 hours late for an 11:00 A.M. appointment, then you arrive at 1:00 P.M. Thus we define $a \oplus b$ so that $3 \oplus 2 = 5$ and $11 \oplus 2 = 1$. The binary operator $\oplus$, the operation of *clock addition*, and the *sum* $a \oplus b$ of any two clock numbers a and b are defined in Definition 1.

314

DEFINITION 1. The *sum* of any two clock numbers a and b is the number $a \oplus b$ defined as follows:

(a) $a \oplus b = a + b$ if and only if $a + b \leq 12$,
(b) $a \oplus b = (a + b) - 12$ if and only if $12 < a + b$.

Observe from Definition 1 that the sum of any two clock numbers is a clock number.

From Definition 1, we may compute the sum of any two clock numbers a and b by visualizing an initial clock reading of a o'clock and then visualizing a terminal clock reading b hours later; that is, we begin at a o'clock and move the hour hand clockwise b numbers. The addition of 9 and 5 is illustrated in Figure 9.1.

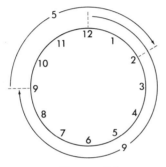

FIGURE 9.1

From Definition 1 (and Figure 9.1) we know that $9 \oplus 5 = 2$. From Definition 1, $5 \oplus 9 = (5 + 9) - 12 = 14 - 12 = 2$. In fact, if a and b are any clock numbers, then $a + b = b + a$ and hence $a \oplus b = b \oplus a$; that is, the commutative property for addition of clock numbers is true. Since the set of clock numbers is a finite set, we can list all of the addition facts in one table. The addition table is shown in Figure 9.2.

By Definition 1, the clock number system obeys the closure property for addition. Observe that the proof of the closure property for addition is contained also in Figure 9.2. In fact, although properties such as the commutative property and associative property for addition of clock numbers follow from Definition 1 and the corresponding properties for addition of counting numbers, we could prove these properties by actual *computation*. For example, to prove that $a \oplus b = b \oplus a$, for any clock numbers a and b, we could compute all 144 combinations of $a \oplus b$. If the clock number system were infinite rather than finite, we would not be able to compute all possible combinations; we would have to derive each property *in general*, as in Chapter 3.

From Figure 9.2 we see that the identity for addition is 12; that is,

⊕	12	1	2	3	4	5	6	7	8	9	10	11
12	12	1	2	3	4	5	6	7	8	9	10	11
1	1	2	3	4	5	6	7	8	9	10	11	12
2	2	3	4	5	6	7	8	9	10	11	12	1
3	3	4	5	6	7	8	9	10	11	12	1	2
4	4	5	6	7	8	9	10	11	12	1	2	3
5	5	6	7	8	9	10	11	12	1	2	3	4
6	6	7	8	9	10	11	12	1	2	3	4	5
7	7	8	9	10	11	12	1	2	3	4	5	6
8	8	9	10	11	12	1	2	3	4	5	6	7
9	9	10	11	12	1	2	3	4	5	6	7	8
10	10	11	12	1	2	3	4	5	6	7	8	9
11	11	12	1	2	3	4	5	6	7	8	9	10

FIGURE 9.2

for any clock number a, $a \oplus 12 = a$ and $12 \oplus a = a$. Of course, we could prove the identity property from Definition 1(b) as follows:

$a \oplus 12 = (a + 12) - 12 = (a + 12) + {}^-12 = a + (12 + {}^-12)$ $= a + 0 = a$, for any clock number a. Notice that the clock number system has a property that the counting number system does not have; namely, each clock number has a unique additive inverse which is a clock number. Since the additive identity is 12, the additive inverse of any clock number a is that unique clock number b such that $a \oplus b = 12$. Thus the additive inverse of 12 is 12, the additive inverse of 1 is 11, the additive inverse of 2 is 10, et cetera. Hence any open sentence of the form $a \oplus x = 12$, for any clock number a, can be converted to a true sentence by replacement of the variable x by a clock number. The fact that we could not convert any open sentence of the form $a + x = 0$, for any counting number a, to a true sentence by replacement of the variable x by a counting number led us to invent the negative integers. Consequently, although the *set* of clock numbers is a finite subset of the *set* of counting numbers, and the operators $\oplus$ and $+$ are related, the *system* of clock numbers has the above important property (that every clock number has a unique additive inverse) not possessed by the *system* of counting numbers.

We summarize this section by listing the properties of the clock number system considered thus far.

CLOSURE PROPERTY FOR ADDITION OF CLOCK NUMBERS
If a and b are any two clock numbers, then $a \oplus b$ is a unique clock number.

ASSOCIATIVE PROPERTY FOR ADDITION OF CLOCK NUMBERS
If a, b, and c are any clock numbers, then $(a \oplus b) \oplus c = a \oplus (b \oplus c)$.

IDENTITY PROPERTY FOR ADDITION OF CLOCK NUMBERS
If a and z are any clock numbers, then $a \oplus z = a$ if and only if $z = 12$.

INVERSE PROPERTY FOR ADDITION OF CLOCK NUMBERS
If a is any clock number, then there exists exactly one clock number a' (called the *additive inverse* of a) such that $a \oplus a' = 12$.

COMMUTATIVE PROPERTY FOR ADDITION OF CLOCK NUMBERS
If a and b are any clock numbers, then $a \oplus b = b \oplus a$.

Exercise 9.1

I. Verify the associative property for addition in each of the following.

(1) $a = 11, b = 1, c = 9$ (5) $a = 10, b = 4, c = 10$
(2) $a = 2, b = 8, c = 10$ (6) $a = 4, b = 12, c = 12$
(3) $a = 5, b = 10, c = 12$ (7) $a = 5, b = 5, c = 5$
(4) $a = 12, b = 4, c = 6$ (8) $a = 8, b = 7, c = 8$

II. Prove: If a, b, and c are any clock numbers such that $a + b + c \le 12$, then $(a \oplus b) \oplus c = a \oplus (b \oplus c)$.

III. Complete the following table.

Clock number	1	2	3	4	5	6	7	8	9	10	11	12
Additive inverse												

IV. Let the operation of addition of elements a and b of the set $A = \{0, 1, 2, 3\}$ be defined as follows:

$a \oplus b = a + b$ if and only if $a + b \leq 3$,

$a \oplus b = (a + b) - 4$ if and only if $3 < a + b$.

(1) Complete the addition table.

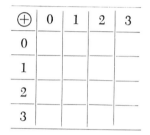

$\oplus$	0	1	2	3
0				
1				
2				
3				

(2) By use of the addition table, prove that this finite system possesses the closure, identity, inverse, and commutative properties.

(3) Justify the associative property for 6 examples.

V. Convert each of the following open sentences to a true sentence by replacing the variable by a clock number.

(1) $x \oplus 11 = 5$　　　　(6) $11 \oplus x = 1$
(2) $x \oplus 9 = 3$　　　　(7) $12 \oplus t = t$
(3) $x \oplus 5 = 11$　　　　(8) $u = u \oplus 12$
(4) $x \oplus 3 = 9$　　　　(9) $4 \oplus 10 = x$
(5) $7 \oplus x = 1$　　　　(10) $11 \oplus 5 = x$

VI. Convert each of the following open sentences to a true sentence by replacing the variable by an element of the set A of IV.

(1) $x \oplus 3 = 3$　　　　(6) $0 \oplus x = 3$
(2) $x \oplus 3 = 1$　　　　(7) $2 \oplus 3 = x$
(3) $2 \oplus x = 1$　　　　(8) $x = 3 \oplus 1$
(4) $2 \oplus x = 2$　　　　(9) $2 \oplus x = 0$
(5) $x \oplus 0 = 2$　　　　(10) $x \oplus 3 = 0$

9.2 Finite Number Systems

Recall that the additive identity of the clock number system is 12 and the additive identity of the system of counting numbers is 0. We now consider another finite number system consisting of the 12 elements 0, 1, 2, ..., 11 and an operation of addition similar to that of the clock numbers, and then we compare this finite number system with the clock number system. The binary operator $\oplus$, the operation *addition*, and the sum $a \oplus b$ of any two numbers of $\{0, 1, 2, \ldots, 11\}$ are defined in Definition 2.

DEFINITION 2. The *sum* of any numbers a and b of $\{0, 1, 2, \ldots, 11\}$ is the number $a \oplus b$ defined as follows:

(a) $a \oplus b = a + b$ if and only if $a + b \le 11$,
(b) $a \oplus b = (a + b) - 12$ if and only if $11 < a + b$.

By Definition 2, the sum of any two numbers of $\{0, 1, 2, \ldots, 11\}$ is a number of $\{0, 1, 2, \ldots, 11\}$, as shown in the addition table in Figure 9.3.

$\oplus$	0	1	2	3	4	5	6	7	8	9	10	11
0	0	1	2	3	4	5	6	7	8	9	10	11
1	1	2	3	4	5	6	7	8	9	10	11	0
2	2	3	4	5	6	7	8	9	10	11	0	1
3	3	4	5	6	7	8	9	10	11	0	1	2
4	4	5	6	7	8	9	10	11	0	1	2	3
5	5	6	7	8	9	10	11	0	1	2	3	4
6	6	7	8	9	10	11	0	1	2	3	4	5
7	7	8	9	10	11	0	1	2	3	4	5	6
8	8	9	10	11	0	1	2	3	4	5	6	7
9	9	10	11	0	1	2	3	4	5	6	7	8
10	10	11	0	1	2	3	4	5	6	7	8	9
11	11	0	1	2	3	4	5	6	7	8	9	10

FIGURE 9.3

By comparing the addition table in Figure 9.3 with the addition table in Figure 9.2, we see that these two different number systems are *abstractly identical;* that is, they are identical except for notation. In fact, the only difference in notation is that 0 in the new system plays the role of 12 in the clock number system. Since the new system is abstractly identical with the old system, it obviously possesses the five properties enumerated in the last section.

We now consider another finite number system suggested by the set {Sunday, Monday, Tuesday, Wednesday, Thursday, Friday, Saturday}. For simplicity, we designate the days in order, by 0, 1, 2, 3, 4, 5, 6 (called *calendar numbers*) as follows: 0 ↔ Sunday, 1 ↔ Monday, 2 ↔ Tuesday, 3 ↔ Wednesday, 4 ↔ Thursday, 5 ↔ Friday, 6 ↔ Saturday.

If you leave by car, on Friday, on a 4-day trip, when do you reach your destination? Looking at a calendar, you count 4 days from Friday; you reach your destination on Tuesday. You could count 4 days from 5 (for Friday): 6, 0, 1, 2. In this system $5 \oplus 4 = 2$. Similarly $2 \oplus 3 = 5$ and $5 \oplus 2 = 0$. Because of the above considerations, we define the binary operator $\oplus$, the operation of *addition*, and the sum of any two calendar numbers a and b as in Definition 3.

DEFINITION 3. The *sum* of any two calendar numbers a and b is the number $a \oplus b$ defined as follows:

(a) $a \oplus b = a + b$ if and only if $a + b \leq 6$,
(b) $a \oplus b = (a + b) - 7$ if and only if $6 < a + b$.

According to Definition 3, the sum of any two calendar numbers is a unique calendar number, as shown in Figure 9.4.

$\oplus$	0	1	2	3	4	5	6
0	0	1	2	3	4	5	6
1	1	2	3	4	5	6	0
2	2	3	4	5	6	0	1
3	3	4	5	6	0	1	2
4	4	5	6	0	1	2	3
5	5	6	0	1	2	3	4
6	6	0	1	2	3	4	5

FIGURE 9.4

From Definition 3 (and Figure 9.4) we see that the calendar number system defined above possesses the closure property for addition. We now state the five properties of the preceding section, all of which the calendar number system possesses.

CLOSURE PROPERTY FOR ADDITION OF CALENDAR NUMBERS

If a and b are any calendar numbers, then $a \oplus b$ is a unique calendar number.

ASSOCIATIVE PROPERTY FOR ADDITION OF CALENDAR NUMBERS

If a, b, and c are any calendar numbers, then $(a \oplus b) \oplus c = a \oplus (b \oplus c)$.

IDENTITY PROPERTY FOR ADDITION OF CALENDAR NUMBERS

If a and z are any calendar numbers, then $a \oplus z = a$ if and only if $z = 0$.

INVERSE PROPERTY FOR ADDITION OF CALENDAR NUMBERS

If a is any calendar number, then there exists exactly one calendar number a' (called the *additive inverse* of a) such that $a \oplus a' = 0$.

COMMUTATIVE PROPERTY FOR ADDITION OF CALENDAR NUMBERS

If a and b are any calendar numbers, then $a \oplus b = b \oplus a$.

The proofs of all but the associative property follow immediately from Definition 3. We can prove the associative property by either using Definition 3 and considering the various cases, or by using the addition table in Figure 9.4. However, there are 7^3 sums $(a \oplus b) \oplus c$ and 7^3 sums $a \oplus (b \oplus c)$ to compute if we use the table. In the exercises you will *verify* the associative property for a few of these sums and will *prove* the identity property, inverse property, and commutative property.

Since the additive inverse of each calendar number is a calendar number, the open sentence $a \oplus x = 0$, for any calendar number a, may be converted to a true sentence by replacement of the variable x by a calendar number. For example, the open sentence $5 \oplus x = 0$ may be converted to a true sentence by replacement of the variable x by the calendar number 2; that is, in classical terminology, the *solution* of the *equation* $5 \oplus x = 0$ is 2. The term *equation* is well known to you. Specifically, an equation is a sentence or open sentence which involves the relation $=$. Any replacement of the variable in an equation which converts that equation to a true sentence is called a *solution* or *root* of the equation. The set of all roots of an equation is called the *solution set* of the equation. Recall that no equation of the form $a + x = 0$, for any nonzero counting number a, has a root in the system of counting numbers. In fact, every equation $a \oplus x = b$, for any calendar numbers a and b, has a root which is a calendar number, but there are some equations $a + x = b$, for counting numbers a and b, which do not have roots.

However, since every integer has an additive inverse, we see that the equation $a + x = 0$, for any integer a, has a root which is an integer. Thus it appears that the calendar number system, which at first appeared to be more like the counting number system, is actually more like the system of integers. Does the system of integers possess the five properties of the calendar number system? In Chapter 5 we learned that the system of integers does possess these five properties. Although the calendar number system is a *finite* number system, it has these five properties in common with the *infinite* system of integers. In fact, the system of integers, the clock number system, and the calendar number system are three different number systems which all possess these same five properties. Because many other systems, some from the physical and social sciences, also possess these same five properties, it is advantageous to study an abstract (rather than a specific) system which has these five properties. Then any theorem which is provable from *these five properties* is immediately available for application to any one of the particular systems. Thus it is unnecessary to prove the same theorem in all of these systems; it is sufficient to prove it *once* in the abstract system.

Any abstract system $(G, \oplus)$ which possesses the above-mentioned properties is given a special name.

DEFINITION 4. A system $(G, \oplus)$ is called a *commutative group* if and only if it possesses all of the following properties.

  (a) If a and b are any elements of G, then $a \oplus b$ is a unique element of G (closure property).

  (b) If a, b, and c are any elements of G, then $(a \oplus b) \oplus c = a \oplus (b \oplus c)$ (associative property).

  (c) There exists a unique element i in G such that $a \oplus i = a$ for all a in G (identity property).

  (d) If a is any element of G, then there exists a unique element a' in G such that $a \oplus a' = i$ (inverse property).

  (e) If a and b are any elements of G, then $a \oplus b = b \oplus a$ (commutative property).

The following theorem, which states that the additive inverse of any sum is equal to the sum of the additive inverses, is an example of a theorem which may be proved from the definition of a commutative group. Observe that no properties other than the five properties of Definition 4 are used in the proof.

THEOREM 1.   If a and b are any elements of a commutative group $(G, \oplus)$, then $(a \oplus b)' = a' \oplus b'$.

Proof.
$$
\begin{aligned}
(a \oplus b) \oplus (a' \oplus b') &= (b \oplus a) \oplus [a' \oplus b'] \\
&= [(b \oplus a) \oplus a'] \oplus b' \\
&\quad \text{(by the associative property)} \\
&= [b \oplus (a \oplus a')] \oplus b' \\
&= [b \oplus i] \oplus b' \\
&= b \oplus b' \\
&= i.
\end{aligned}
$$

Thus $a' \oplus b'$ is the additive inverse of $a \oplus b$.

But $(a \oplus b)'$ is the additive inverse of $a \oplus b$.

Since the additive inverse is unique, it follows that
$$(a \oplus b)' = a' \oplus b'.\mathbin{/\!/}$$

According to the sign property for addition of integers given in Chapter 5, $^-(a + b) = {}^-a + {}^-b$ for any integers a and b. This property is an immediate consequence of Theorem 1. If Theorem 1 had been available in Chapter 5, it would have been unnecessary to prove the sign property. Moreover, since Theorem 1 applies to *any* commutative group, it applies, in particular, to the clock number system and to the calendar number system, and, in fact, to every particular commutative group regardless of the binary operator and the number of elements in the group.

Exercise 9.2

I. Prove that the calendar number system possesses each of the following properties.

   (1) Identity property for addition
   (2) Inverse property for addition
   (3) Commutative property for addition

II. Verify the associative property for addition of calendar numbers in each of the following cases.

   (1) $a = 3, b = 1, c = 4$
   (2) $a = 1, b = 4, c = 5$
   (3) $a = 6, b = 0, c = 6$
   (4) $a = 0, c = 5, c = 5$
   (5) $a = 6, b = 4, c = 4$
   (6) $a = 5, b = 5, c = 4$

III. Complete the following addition table so that the system will be commutative.

⊕	0	1	2	3	4
0	0	1	2	3	4
1		2	3	4	0
2			4	0	1
3				1	2
4					3

IV. (1) Complete the following table so that the system will be a commutative group. What is the identity of the group?

⊕	a	b	c
a	a	b	c
b		c	
c			b

(2) Complete the following table so that the system will be a commutative group. What is the identity of the group?

⊕	a	b	c	d
a	b		d	a
b	c			b
c			b	
d				d

V. Supply the reason for each step in the proof of Theorem 1.

9.3 Congruence Modulo m

In this and the following two sections we shall study a general method for generating a finite number system. First we define the *congruence relation modulo an integer m.*

DEFINITION 5. The integer a is said to be *congruent to* the integer b (modulo the integer m) if and only if m divides $a - b$. Symbolically, $a \equiv b \pmod{m}$ if and only if $m \mid (a - b)$.

By Definition 1 of Chapter 6, we see that $a \equiv b \pmod{m}$ if and only if there exists an integer k such that $a - b = km$. The following examples illustrate Definition 5.

Example 1. $47 \equiv 5 \pmod 7$ because $7 \mid (47 - 5)$; that is, $47 - 5$ $= 42 = 6(7)$. *Note.* $a = 47$, $b = 5$, $m = 7$, and $k = 6$.

Example 2. $47 \equiv 11 \pmod{12}$ because $12 \mid (47 - 11)$; that is, $47 - 11$ $= 36 = 3(12)$. *Note.* $a = 47$, $b = 11$, $m = 12$, and $k = 3$.

Example 3. $15 \equiv 1 \pmod 2$ because $2 \mid (15 - 1)$; that is, $15 - 1$ $= 14 = 7(2)$. *Note.* $a = 15$, $b = 1$, $m = 2$, and $k = 7$.

Example 4. $15 \equiv 1 \pmod 7$ because $7 \mid (15 - 1)$; that is, $15 - 1$ $= 14 = 2(7)$. *Note.* $a = 15$, $b = 1$, $m = 7$, and $k = 2$.

Example 5. $5 \equiv 47 \pmod 7$ because $7 \mid (5 - 47)$; that is, $5 - 47$ $= {}^-42 = {}^-6(7)$. *Note.* $a = 5$, $b = 47$, $m = 7$, and $k = {}^-6$.

Example 6. $5 \equiv 5 \pmod 7$ because $7 \mid (5 - 5)$; that is, $5 - 5 = 0$ $= 0(7)$. *Note.* $a = 5$, $b = 5$, $m = 7$, and $k = 0$.

As in any relation, we question whether congruence mod m is an equivalence relation. Examples 1 and 5 lead us to suspect that congruence mod m obeys the symmetric property, and Example 6 leads us to conjecture that congruence mod m obeys the reflexive property. The following theorem assures us that congruence mod m is an equivalence relation.

THEOREM 2.   The relation *congruence mod m* defined on I is an equivalence relation. That is,

(a) $a \equiv a \pmod m$ (reflexive property);
(b) If $a \equiv b \pmod m$, then $b \equiv a \pmod m$ (symmetric property);
(c) If $a \equiv b \pmod m$ and $b \equiv c \pmod m$, then $a \equiv c \pmod m$ (transitive property).

Proof.   (a) $a = a$.
$a - a = 0$.
$a - a = 0(m)$.
$a \equiv a \pmod m$.

(b) Let $a \equiv b \pmod{m}$.
   Then $m \mid (a - b)$.
   Hence $m \mid (b - a)$.
   Thus $b \equiv a \pmod{m}$.

(c) Let $a \equiv b \pmod{m}$ and $b \equiv c \pmod{m}$.
   Then $m \mid (a - b)$ and $m \mid (b - c)$.
   Thus $m \mid [(a - b) + (b - c)]$ (by Theorem 2 of Chapter 6)

   Hence $m \mid (a - c)$.
   Thus $a \equiv c \pmod{m}$.

Consequently, *congruence mod m* on the set of integers is an equivalence relation.//

Recall that an equivalence relation on a set S separates the elements of S into mutually exclusive subsets (called *equivalence classes*) of S as follows:

(1) Every element of S is in exactly one of the subsets;
(2) Any two elements which are in the same subset are related;
(3) No two elements which are in different subsets are related.

Since congruence mod m (and, in particular, congruence mod 7) on the set of integers is an equivalence relation, we know that congruence mod 7 separates the set of integers into mutually exclusive subsets (equivalence classes) as shown in Figure 9.5.

.	.	.	.	.	.	.
.	.	.	.	.	.	.
.	.	.	.	.	.	.
-14	-13	-12	-11	-10	-9	-8
-7	-6	-5	-4	-3	-2	-1
0	1	2	3	4	5	6
7	8	9	10	11	12	13
14	15	16	17	18	19	20
.	.	.	.	.	.	.
.	.	.	.	.	.	.
.	.	.	.	.	.	.

FIGURE 9.5

Similarly, congruence mod 4 separates the set of integers into equivalence classes as shown in Figure 9.6.

We shall employ the symbol a_7 to represent the equivalence class to which a belongs (mod 7). That is, $a_7 = \{x : x \equiv a \pmod{7}\}$. Similarly, $a_4 = \{x : x \equiv a \pmod{4}\}$. In general, $a_m = \{x : x \equiv a \pmod{m}\}$.

.	.	.	.
.	.	.	.
.	.	.	.
-8	-7	-6	-5
-4	-3	-2	-1
0	1	2	3
4	5	6	7
8	9	10	11
.	.	.	.
.	.	.	.
.	.	.	.

FIGURE 9.6

Thus the symbols 0_7, 1_7, 2_7, ..., 6_7 represent the equivalence classes (mod 7) to which 0, 1, 2, ..., 6, respectively, belong. Similarly, 0_4, 1_4, 2_4, 3_4 represent the equivalence classes (mod 4) to which 0, 1, 2, 3, respectively, belong. Similar notation is used for the equivalence classes (mod any integer m). Thus we refer to the equivalence classes (mod m) as 0_m, 1_m, 2_m, ..., $(m-1)_m$. However, you should realize that there are many other representations for a given equivalence class. For example, $10_4 = 6_4 = 2_4$, and $8_4 = 4_4 = 0_4$. In the following section we define the operations of addition and multiplication of equivalence classes (mod m).

Exercise 9.3

I. Label each of the following sentences as true or false.

(1) $65 \equiv 13 \pmod 5$ (6) $66 \equiv {}^-28 \pmod 2$

(2) $72 \equiv 12 \pmod 7$ (7) $27 \equiv 6 \pmod 3$

(3) $65 \equiv 13 \pmod{26}$ (8) $36 \equiv 12 \pmod 4$

(4) $72 \equiv 12 \pmod 5$ (9) ${}^-183 \equiv 6 \pmod 5$

(5) $79 \equiv {}^-17 \pmod 2$ (10) ${}^-178 \equiv 7 \pmod 7$

II. Separate the set of integers from $^-20$ to 20 into equivalence classes

(1) mod 5   (7) mod 10

(2) mod 7   (8) mod 8

(3) mod 6   (9) mod 15

(4) mod 4   (10) mod 20

(5) mod 2   (11) mod 1

(6) mod 3   (12) mod 0

III. Retrace the proof of Theorem 2 for the special case

(1) $m = 5$

(2) $m = 7$

IV. Convert each of the following open sentences to a true sentence by three different replacements of the variable.

(1) $x \equiv 7 \pmod 3$

(2) $x \equiv 3 \pmod 7$

(3) $x + 4 \equiv 6 \pmod 5$

(4) $x + 5 \equiv 4 \pmod 6$

(5) $x + 11 \equiv 11 \pmod 4$

(6) $x + 11 \equiv 11 \pmod{11}$

(7) $x + {}^-1 \equiv {}^-5 \pmod 3$

(8) $x + {}^-3 \equiv {}^-5 \pmod 1$

(9) $x + 10 \equiv 9 \pmod 2$

(10) $x + 9 \equiv 10 \pmod 2$

V. How are the three replacements in each part of Exercise IV related to each other?

VI. Give five representations of each of the following equivalence classes.

(1) 0_7

(2) 4_7

(3) 3_4

(4) 11_{12}

(5) $^-6_9$

(6) $^-3_5$

(7) 8_5

(8) 10_{10}

(9) 102_2

(10) 999_3

9.4 Addition and Multiplication of Equivalence Classes

If a, b, c, and d are any integers such that $a = b$ and $c = d$, then $a + c = b + d$. Is there a similar theorem for congruences? That is, if a, b, c, d, and m are any integers such that $a \equiv b \pmod m$ and $c \equiv d \pmod m$ can we conclude that $a + c \equiv b + d \pmod m$? The following examples suggest that we can.

Example 1. $25 \equiv 13 \pmod 3$ and $16 \equiv 1 \pmod 3$.
Is $25 + 16 \equiv 13 + 1 \pmod 3$?
$(25 + 16) - (13 + 1) = 27 = 9(3)$.
Hence $25 + 16 \equiv 13 + 1 \pmod 3$.

Example 2. $83 \equiv 28 \pmod 5$ and $71 \equiv 56 \pmod 5$.
Is $83 + 71 \equiv (28 + 56) \pmod 5$?
$(83 + 71) - (28 + 56) = 70 = 14(5)$.
Hence $83 + 71 \equiv 28 + 56 \pmod 5$.

The following theorem assures us that the above conjecture is true.

THEOREM 3.   If a, b, c, d, and m are any integers such that $a \equiv b \pmod m$ and $c \equiv d \pmod m$, then $a + c \equiv b + d \pmod m$.

Proof.   Let $a \equiv b \pmod{m}$ and $c \equiv d \pmod{m}$.

Then $m \mid (a - b)$ and $m \mid (c - d)$ (by Definition 5).

Hence $m \mid [(a - b) + (c - d)]$ (by Theorem 2 of Chapter 6).

Thus $m \mid [(a + c) - (b + d)]$.

Hence $a + c \equiv b + d \pmod{m}$ (by Definition 5).$/\!/$

It follows immediately from Theorem 3 that, if $a \equiv b \pmod{m}$, then $a + c \equiv b + c \pmod{m}$.

If a, b, c, and d are any integers such that $a = b$ and $c = d$, then $ac = bd$. Proceeding as above, we state and prove the following theorem.

THEOREM 4.   If a, b, c, d, and m are any integers such that $a \equiv b \pmod{m}$ and $c \equiv d \pmod{m}$, then $ac \equiv bd \pmod{m}$.

Proof.   Let $a \equiv b \pmod{m}$ and $c \equiv d \pmod{m}$.

Then $m \mid (a - b)$ and $m \mid (c - d)$.

Thus $a - b = k_1 m$ and $c - d = k_2 m$, for some integers k_1 and k_2.

$(a - b)c = k_1 mc$ and $b(c - d) = bk_2 m$

$ac - bc = k_1 mc$ and $bc - bd = k_2 mb$

$(ac - bc) + (bc - bd) = k_1 mc + k_2 mb$

$(ac - bd) = (k_1 c + k_2 b)m$

$ac - bd = km$, where $k = k_1 c + k_2 b$

$m \mid (ac - bd)$

Thus $ac \equiv bd \pmod{m}$.$/\!/$

It follows immediately from Theorem 4 that, if $a \equiv b \pmod{m}$, then $ac \equiv bc \pmod{m}$.

By Theorem 3, if a and b are in the same equivalence class, and c and d are in the same equivalence class, then $a + c$ and $b + d$ are in the same equivalence class. Now we define the sum of two *equivalence classes*.

DEFINITION 6.   The *sum* of the equivalence class a_m and the equivalence class c_m is the equivalence class $(a + c)_m$; that is, $a_m \oplus c_m = (a + c)_m$.

Because every equivalence class has many representations, we could not be certain that the sum does not depend on the particular representation used for each equivalence class if it were not for Theorem 3. The following theorem assures us that the sum defined in Definition 6 is well-defined.

THEOREM 5.   If $a_m, b_m, c_m,$ and d_m are equivalence classes (modulo m), and $a_m = b_m$ and $c_m = d_m$, then $a_m \oplus c_m = b_m \oplus d_m$.

Proof.   Let $a_m = b_m$ and $c_m = d_m$.

Thus a and b belong to the same equivalence class, and c and d belong to the same equivalence class.

Then $a \equiv b \pmod{m}$ and $c \equiv d \pmod{m}$.

Hence $a + c \equiv b + d \pmod{m}$ (by Theorem 3).

Thus $(a + c)_m = (b + d)_m$.

But $a_m \oplus c_m = (a + c)_m$ and $b_m \oplus d_m = (b + d)_m$
                                            (by Definition 6).

Hence $a_m \oplus c_m = b_m \oplus d_m.$//

Thus $\oplus$ is a well-defined binary operator between equivalence classes of integers modulo m.

The binary operator $\odot$, the binary operation *multiplication*, and the *product* of two equivalence classes is given in Definition 7.

DEFINITION 7.   The *product* of the equivalence class a_m and the equivalence class c_m is the equivalence class $(a \cdot c)_m$; that is, $a_m \odot c_m = (a \cdot c)_m$.

As in the sum of two equivalence classes, we want to be certain that the product does not depend on the particular representation of each equivalence class. The following theorem assures us that the product is well-defined.

THEOREM 6.   If $a_m, b_m, c_m,$ and d_m are equivalence classes (modulo m), and $a_m = b_m$ and $c_m = d_m$, then $a_m \odot c_m = b_m \odot d_m$.

Proof.   Similar to proof of Theorem 5, and based on Theorem 4.//

The following examples illustrate the computation of the sum and of the product of two equivalence classes.

Example 3. Compute the sum of the equivalence classes 5_7 and 6_7.
$5_7 \oplus 6_7 = (5+6)_7 = 11_7.$
Since $11 \equiv 4 \pmod 7$, it follows that $11_7 = 4_7$.
Hence $5_7 \oplus 6_7 = 4_7$.

Example 4. Compute the sum of the equivalence classes 11_{12} and 8_{12}.
$11_{12} \oplus 8_{12} = (11+8)_{12} = 19_{12}.$
Since $19 \equiv 7 \pmod{12}$, it follows that $19_{12} = 7_{12}$.
Hence $11_{12} \oplus 8_{12} = 7_{12}$.

Example 5. Compute the product of the equivalence classes 5_7 and 6_7.
$5_7 \odot 6_7 = (5 \cdot 6)_7 = 30_7.$
Since $30 \equiv 2 \pmod 7$, it follows that $30_7 = 2_7$.
Hence $5_7 \odot 6_7 = 2_7$.

Example 6. Compute the product of the equivalence classes 8_{12} and 6_{12}.
$8_{12} \odot 6_{12} = (8 \cdot 6)_{12} = 48_{12}.$
Since $48 \equiv 0 \pmod{12}$, it follows that $48_{12} = 0_{12}$.
Hence $8_{12} \odot 6_{12} = 0_{12}$.

Example 7. Compute $4_7 \odot (3_7 \oplus 5_7)$.
$$\begin{aligned}
4_7 \odot (3_7 \oplus 5_7) &= 4_7 \odot (3+5)_7 \\
&= 4_7 \odot 8_7 \\
&= 4_7 \odot 1_7 \\
&= (4 \cdot 1)_7 \\
&= 4_7.
\end{aligned}$$

Example 8. Compute $(4_7 \odot 3_7) \oplus (4_7 \odot 5_7)$.
$$\begin{aligned}
(4_7 \odot 3_7) \oplus (4_7 \odot 5_7) &= (4 \cdot 3)_7 \oplus (4 \cdot 5)_7 \\
&= 12_7 \oplus 20_7 \\
&= 5_7 \oplus 6_7 \\
&= (5+6)_7 \\
&= 11_7 \\
&= 4_7.
\end{aligned}$$

Exercise 9.4

I. Compute each of the following sums.

(1) $3_7 \oplus 2_7$
(2) $4_7 \oplus 2_7$
(3) $6_7 \oplus 1_7$
(4) $4_7 \oplus 3_7$
(5) $4_5 \oplus 3_5$

(6) $4_6 \oplus 3_6$
(7) $11_{12} \oplus 10_{12}$
(8) $8_{12} \oplus 9_{12}$
(9) $100_4 \oplus 72_4$
(10) $32_6 \oplus 72_6$

II. Compute each of the following products.

(1) $3_7 \odot 2_7$ (6) $0_8 \odot 3_8$
(2) $4_7 \odot 2_7$ (7) $3_7 \odot 0_7$
(3) $11_{12} \odot 10_{12}$ (8) $5_{10} \odot 6_{10}$
(4) $9_{12} \odot 8_{12}$ (9) $5_{10} \odot 8_{10}$
(5) $4_8 \odot 6_8$ (10) $5_{11} \odot 8_{11}$

III. Compute each of the following.

(1) $3_5 \odot (4_5 \oplus 2_5)$ (6) $4_8 \odot (5_8 \oplus 3_8)$
(2) $3_7 \odot (4_7 \oplus 2_7)$ (7) $(3_6 \odot 4_6) \oplus (3_6 \odot 2_6)$
(3) $(3_5 \odot 4_5) \oplus (3_5 \odot 2_5)$ (8) $(4_8 \odot 5_8) \oplus (4_8 \odot 3_8)$
(4) $(3_7 \odot 4_7) \oplus (3_7 \odot 2_7)$ (9) $(6_{12} \oplus 3_{12}) \oplus 2_{12}$
(5) $3_6 \odot (4_6 \oplus 2_6)$ (10) $6_{12} \oplus (3_{12} \oplus 2_{12})$

IV. Prove Theorem 6.

9.5   Properties of Equivalence Classes

In the preceding section we defined addition and multiplication of equivalence classes. In this section we study the important properties of any system of equivalence classes modulo any integer m. In addition, we compare the properties of any system of equivalence classes modulo any prime p with those of any system of equivalence classes modulo any composite c. One reason we study these systems is to gain a better understanding of the systems of counting numbers, integers, rationals, and reals. This is analogous to the study of a foreign language; after one has studied a foreign language, he has a better understanding of his native language. Another reason we study these systems is that they occasionally serve as mathematical models of physical problems.

Before we state and prove the properties of a given system of equivalence classes, we shall simplify the notation. Recall that $a_m \oplus b_m = c_m$ if and only if $a + b \equiv c \pmod{m}$. For this reason we write $a_m + b_m = c_m$ to mean that $a_m \oplus b_m = c_m$, and when no ambiguity results, we write $a + b = c$ to mean $a_m \oplus b_m = c_m$. For example, in the addition table mod 7 we write $5 + 6 = 4$ to mean $5_7 \oplus 6_7 = 4_7$. Frequently we shall refer to the equivalence classes modulo m as the integers modulo m. For example, we shall refer to the equivalence classes modulo 3 as the integers modulo 3.

Let m be any integer and consider the system of equivalence classes modulo m. We shall prove that the system $(I_m, +)$ of equivalence classes mod m is a commutative group; that is, the system $(I_m, +)$ possesses the following properties.

(1) If a_m and b_m are any elements of I_m, then $a_m + b_m$ is a unique element of I_m (closure property for addition).

(2) If a_m, b_m, and c_m are any elements of I_m, then $(a_m + b_m) + c_m = a_m + (b_m + c_m)$ (associative property for addition).

(3) There exists a unique element 0_m of I_m such that $a_m + 0_m = a_m$ for all a_m in I_m (identity property for addition).

(4) If a_m is any element of I_m, then there exists a unique element a_m' of I_m such that $a_m + a_m' = 0_m$ (inverse property for addition).

(5) If a_m and b_m are any elements of I_m, then $a_m + b_m = b_m + a_m$ (commutative property for addition).

It follows immediately from Definition 6 that the sum of any two equivalence classes is a unique equivalence class; that is, the closure property for addition of equivalence classes is true.

Since $(a + b) + c \equiv a + (b + c) \pmod{m}$ for any integers a, b, c, it follows that for any equivalence classes a_m, b_m, and c_m, $(a_m + b_m) + c_m = a_m + (b_m + c_m)$. Hence the associative property for addition of equivalence classes is true.

Since $a + 0 \equiv a \pmod{m}$, for any integer a, it follows that $a_m + 0_m = a_m$ for any equivalence class a_m.

To prove that the class 0_m is unique, we let z_m be an equivalence class mod m such that $a_m + z_m = a_m$.

Then $a + z \equiv a \pmod{m}$.

By Definition 5, $m \mid (a + z) - a$; that is, $m \mid z - 0$.

By Definition 5, $z \equiv 0 \pmod{m}$.

Thus $z_m = 0_m$.

Hence there exists a unique equivalence class 0_m such that $a_m + 0_m = a_m$ for any equivalence class a_m. Thus the identity property for addition of equivalence classes is true.

If a is any integer, then $a + (m - a) \equiv 0 \pmod{m}$. Thus $a_m + (m - a)_m = 0_m$ for any equivalence class a_m.

To prove that the equivalence class $(m - a)_m$ is unique, we let q_m be an equivalence class such that $a_m + q_m = 0_m$.

Then $a + q \equiv 0 \pmod{m}$.

By Definition 5, $a + q = km$, for some integer k.

Hence $a + q = m + (k - 1)m$.

$q + {^-m} + a = (k - 1)m$,

$q - (m - a) = (k - 1)m$,

$q \equiv m - a \pmod{m}$.

Thus $q_m = (m - a)_m$; that is, the equivalence class $(m - a)_m$ is unique.

Hence if a_m is any equivalence class mod m, then there exists a unique equivalence class $(m - a)_m$ such that $a_m + (m - a)_m = 0_m$. Thus the inverse property for addition of equivalence classes is true.

Since $a + b \equiv b + a \pmod{m}$ for any integers a and b, it follows that $a_m + b_m = b_m + a_m$ for any equivalence classes a_m and b_m containing a and b, respectively. Hence the commutative property for addition of equivalence classes is true.

Thus every system of equivalence classes modulo any integer m, with operation addition, is a commutative group.

We shall follow the customary procedure of designating an equivalence class by the smallest counting number in the class. For example, if $m = 7$, we designate the 7 equivalence classes by 0_7, 1_7, 2_7, 3_7, 4_7, 5_7, 6_7 or simply by 0, 1, 2, 3, 4, 5, 6, whenever there is no ambiguity. Then we may write the addition table as shown in Figure 9.7.

+	0	1	2	3	4	5	6
0	0	1	2	3	4	5	6
1	1	2	3	4	5	6	0
2	2	3	4	5	6	0	1
3	3	4	5	6	0	1	2
4	4	5	6	0	1	2	3
5	5	6	0	1	2	3	4
6	6	0	1	2	3	4	5

FIGURE 9.7

As we have already proved that the system $(I_m, +)$, for any integer m, is a commutative group, we know that the system $(I_7, +)$ is a commutative group. Observe that the identity element is 0_7 and that the inverse of any element a_7 is $(7 - a)_7$. The system $(I_7, +)$ is abstractly identical with the calendar number system of Figure 9.4. The advantage of the present development is that we can generate a finite system consisting of any desired number of elements and we know, in advance, that this system is a commutative group with operation addition.

The system $(I_m, +)$, for any integer m, is a commutative group. Recall that $a_m \odot b_m = c_m$ if and only if $ab \equiv c \pmod{m}$. For this reason, we shall write $a_m \cdot b_m$ or $a_m b_m$ to mean $a_m \odot b_m$, and whenever there is no ambiguity, we shall write ab to mean $a_m \odot b_m$. Since we have defined multiplication of equivalence classes modulo m, we might suspect that the system $(I_m, +, \cdot)$ is a field. In order to decide whether or not $(I_m, +, \cdot)$ is a field, we must check each of the 11 field properties. As we have already proved that the system $(I_m, +, \cdot)$ possesses the first five of the field properties (the five properties of a commutative group with the operation addition), we must check the remaining properties F6 to F11. We can prove that, for any integer m, the system $(I_m, +, \cdot)$ possesses not only properties F1 through F5 but also the following properties.

F6. If a_m and b_m are any elements of I_m, then $a_m \cdot b_m$ is a unique element of I_m (closure property for multiplication).

F7. If a_m, b_m, and c_m are any elements of I_m, then $(a_m \cdot b_m) \cdot c_m = a_m \cdot (b_m \cdot c_m)$ (associative property for multiplication).

F8. There exists a unique element 1_m of I_m such that $a_m \cdot 1_m = a_m$ for all a_m in I_m (identity property for multiplication).

F10. If a_m and b_m are any elements of I_m, then $a_m \cdot b_m = b_m \cdot a_m$ (commutative property for multiplication).

F11. If a_m, b_m, and c_m are any elements of I_m, then $a_m \cdot (b_m + c_m) = a_m \cdot b_m + a_m \cdot c_m$ (distributive property).

As the proofs of F6, F7, F8, and F10 are similar to the proofs of F1, F2, F3, and F5, respectively, they are assigned to you in the exercises. Since $a \cdot (b + c) \equiv a \cdot b + a \cdot c \pmod{m}$ for any integers a, b, and c, it follows that $a_m \cdot (b_m + c_m) = a_m \cdot b_m + a_m \cdot c_m$ for any equivalence classes a_m, b_m, and c_m. Hence the distributive property is true.

Hence the system $(I_m, +, \cdot)$, for any integer m, possesses all field properties except F9. For example, the system $(I_4, +, \cdot)$ possesses all field properties except F9. Why does $(I_4, +, \cdot)$ not have the property F9? To answer this question, we consider the elements 0_4, 1_4, 2_4, 3_4 of $(I_4, +, \cdot)$ and show that the element 2_4 does not have a multiplicative inverse. If 2_4 has a multiplicative inverse b_4, then $2_4 b_4 = 1_4$. However, since $2_4 \cdot 0_4 = 0_4$, $2_4 \cdot 1_4 = 2_4$, $2_4 \cdot 2_4 = 0_4$, and $2_4 \cdot 3_4 = 2_4$, we see that there is no element b_4 such that $2_4 b_4 = 1_4$. Hence 2_4 has no multiplicative inverse. In the next section we prove that $(I_m, +, \cdot)$ possesses property F9 if and only if m is a prime. That is, if m is a prime, then $(I_m, +, \cdot)$ does possess F9 and is, therefore, a field; and inversely, if m is not a prime, then $(I_m, +, \cdot)$ does not possess F9.

Exercise 9.5

I. Prove that each of the following systems possesses field property
F9, and exhibit the multiplicative inverse of each nonzero element.

(1) $(I_2, +, \cdot)$ (4) $(I_7, +, \cdot)$

(2) $(I_3, +, \cdot)$ (5) $(I_{11}, +, \cdot)$

(3) $(I_5, +, \cdot)$ (6) $(I_{13}, +, \cdot)$

II. Prove that each of the following systems does *not* possess field
property F9, and exhibit all nonzero elements which do not have
multiplicative inverses.

(1) $(I_6, +, \cdot)$ (4) $(I_{10}, +, \cdot)$

(2) $(I_8, +, \cdot)$ (5) $(I_{12}, +, \cdot)$

(3) $(I_9, +, \cdot)$ (6) $(I_{14}, +, \cdot)$

III. Determine which of the following systems is a commutative group
with operation addition.

(1) $\{0, 3, 6\}$ (mod 7)   (5) $\{0, 2\}$ (mod 3)

(2) $\{0, 2, 4, 6\}$ (mod 7)   (6) $\{0, 3\}$ (mod 4)

(3) $\{0, 2, 4\}$ (mod 6)   (7) $\{0, 2, 4, 6\}$ (mod 8)

(4) $\{0, 3\}$ (mod 6)   (8) $\{0, 5, 10\}$ (mod 15)

IV. (1) Prove that *congruence mod* 0 is equality and hence defines
the system of integers.

(2) Prove that *congruence mod* 1 yields a single equivalence
class which contains all integers.

(3) Prove that *congruence mod* 2 separates the integers into two
equivalence classes—one consisting of the odd integers and
the other consisting of the even integers.

(4) Prove property F6 in $(I_m, +, \cdot)$.

(5) Prove property F7 in $(I_m, +, \cdot)$.

(6) Prove property F8 in $(I_m, +, \cdot)$.

(7) Prove property F10 in $(I_m, +, \cdot)$.

9.6 Properties of the System of Integers Modulo a Prime

Recall that the system $(I, +, \cdot)$ of integers possesses all field properties except F9, and recall also that the system $(I_m, +, \cdot)$, for any
composite integer m, possesses all field properties except F9. Do all of
the properties of $(I, +, \cdot)$ follow from F1–F8, F10, F11? If they do, then
for every property of $(I, +, \cdot)$ there is a corresponding property of
$(I_m, +, \cdot)$. For example, under this assumption, since $(I, +, \cdot)$ has the
multiplication property of 0, then the system $(I_m, +, \cdot)$ must also have

this property. However, we shall prove that $(I_m, +, \cdot)$ does not have the multiplication property of 0. As a consequence, we shall see that the multiplication property of zero does not follow from the properties F1–F8, F10, F11.

THEOREM 7.   If m is any composite number, then the system $(I_m, +, \cdot)$ does not possess the multiplication property of 0.

Proof.   Let m be any composite number.

Then there exist integers a and b such that $1 < a < m$, $1 < b < m$, and $ab = m$.

Then $ab \equiv 0 \pmod{m}$.

Hence $a_m \cdot b_m = 0_m$; that is, the product of the two *nonzero* equivalence classes a_m and b_m is equal to the equivalence class 0_m.

Consequently, $(I_m, +, \cdot)$ does not possess the multiplication property of 0.$/\!/$

For example, consider the equivalence classes mod 6. Although $2_e \neq 0_6$ and $3_6 \neq 0_6$, we see that $2_6 \cdot 3_6 = 0_6$. In $(I, +, \cdot)$, $(ab = 0) \rightleftarrows (a = 0 \lor b = 0)$. However, in $(I_m, +, \cdot)$, $(a_m b_m = 0_m) \rightleftarrows (a_m = 0_m \lor b_m = 0_m)$ *is a false sentence,* provided m is a composite number.

Recall the cancellation property for multiplication of integers: if a, b, and c are any integers such that $a \neq 0$ and $ab = ac$, then $b = c$. If m is a composite, is the cancellation property for multiplication true in $(I_m, +, \cdot)$? To answer this question, we observe that $5_{10} \cdot 2_{10} = 5_{10} \cdot 4_{10}$ and $5_{10} \neq 0_{10}$, but $2_{10} \neq 4_{10}$.

The following theorem assures us that $(I_m, +, \cdot)$, for any composite m, does not possess the cancellation property for multiplication.

THEOREM 8.   If m is any composite number, then the system $(I_m, +, \cdot)$ does not possess the cancellation property for multiplication.

Proof.   Follows from Theorem 7.$/\!/$

We know that the system $(I_m, +, \cdot)$ does not possess property F9 if m is composite. Now we wish to prove that $(I_m, +, \cdot)$ does possess property F9 if m is a prime p. That is, we wish to prove that every equation of the form $a_p x_p = 1_p$, for any $a_p \neq 0_p$, has a unique solution. The following examples illustrate the method of proof.

Example 1.   Solve the equation $6_7 x_7 = 1_7$.

Of course, we can solve the given equation by actually replacing the variable x_7 by each of the equivalence classes 0_7, 1_7, 2_7, 3_7, 4_7, 5_7, 6_7. By this method, we see that $6_7 \cdot 6_7 = 1_7$ and hence that the equation $6_7 x_7 = 1_7$ has the unique solution 6_7; that is, the multiplicative inverse of 6_7 is 6_7.

Example 2.   Solve the equation $4_{11} x_{11} = 1_{11}$.

Replacing the variable successively by 1_{11}, 2_{11}, 3_{11}, ... , 10_{11}, we see that $4_{11} \cdot 3_{11} = 1_{11}$ and, moreover, that 3_{11} is the only solution.

Thus if $4 \cdot 3 \equiv 1 \pmod{11}$ and, moreover, if $4 \cdot s \equiv 1 \pmod{11}$, then $s \equiv 3 \pmod{11}$. More generally, if $4r \equiv 1 \pmod{11}$ and $4s \equiv 1 \pmod{11}$, then $4r \equiv 4s \pmod{11}$. Moreover, if $4r \equiv 4s \pmod{11}$, then $r \equiv s \pmod{11}$. Thus we are assured that the congruence $4x \equiv 1 \pmod{11}$ has a unique solution in the set $\{0, 1, 2, \ldots, 10\}$.

THEOREM 9.   If p is any prime and a is any positive integer less than p, then there exists a unique positive integer $b < p$ such that $ab \equiv 1 \pmod{p}$.

Proof.   Let p be a prime, let a be a positive integer less than p, , and let $ar \equiv as \pmod{p}$.

Then $(p, a) = 1$ and $p \mid (ar - as)$.

Thus $p \mid a(r - s)$.

But $p \nmid a$.

Hence $p \mid (r - s)$ (by Theorem 8 of Chapter 6).

Thus $r \equiv s \pmod{p}$ (by Definition 5).

Hence $ar \equiv as \pmod{p} \to r \equiv s \pmod{p}$.

Conversely, $r \equiv s \pmod{p} \to ar \equiv as \pmod{p}$ (by Theorem 4).

Hence $ar \equiv as \pmod{p} \rightleftarrows r \equiv s \pmod{p}$.

Now $a \in \{0, 1, 2, \ldots, p - 1\}$.

Let $r \in \{0, 1, 2, \ldots, p - 1\}$.

Thus r is one of p distinct elements less than p.

Hence ar is congruent to one of p distinct elements less than p.

For exactly one choice b of r, ab must be congruent to 1; that is, $ab \equiv 1 \pmod{p}$ for some $b \in \{0, 1, 2, \ldots, p - 1\}$.//

By Theorem 9, if p is a prime and a_p is any equivalence class, then there exists a unique equivalence class b_p such that $a_p b_p = 1_p$. That is, if p is any prime, then $(I_p, +, \cdot)$ possesses field property F9. Since $(I_p, +, \cdot)$ possesses all other field properties, we see that $(I_p, +, \cdot)$ is a field. For reference, we state this result as a theorem.

THEOREM 10. If p is any prime, then $(I_p, +, \cdot)$ is a field.

Since $(I_p, +, \cdot)$ is a field, we can solve any equation of the form $a_p x_p = b_p$. For example, to solve the equation $3_7 x_7 = 4_7$, we multiply both sides by 5_7 (the multiplicative inverse of 3_7). Thus $5_7 (3_7 x_7) = 5_7 (4_7)$; that is, $x_7 = 6_7$. You should realize that this means that the product of the equivalence class containing 3 and the equivalence class containing 6 is the equivalence class containing 4. In general, we solve $a_p x_p = b_p$ by multiplying both members by the multiplicative inverse $a^\#{}_p$ of a_p as follows:

$$a^\#{}_p (a_p x_p) = a^\#{}_p b_p, \text{ and } x_p = a_p b_p.$$

In summary we observe the following:

In $(I, +, \cdot)$, every equation $a + x = b$ has a solution.
In $(I_m, +, \cdot)$ every equation $a_m + x_m = b_m$ has a solution.
In $(I, +, \cdot)$, not every equation $ax = b$ has a solution (even if $a \neq 0$).
In $(I_m, +, \cdot)$, not every equation $a_m x_m = b_m$ has a solution (even if $a_m \neq 0_m$).
In $(F, +, \cdot)$, every equation $ax = b$ has a solution if $a \neq 0$.
In $(I_p, +, \cdot)$, every equation $a_p x_p = b_p$ has a solution if $a_p \neq 0_p$.

Exercise 9.6

I. Solve each of the following congruences.

(1) $2x \equiv 1 \pmod 3$	(6) $5x \equiv 1 \pmod{17}$
(2) $2x \equiv 1 \pmod 5$	(7) $10x \equiv 3 \pmod{17}$
(3) $3x \equiv 1 \pmod 5$	(8) $8x \equiv 3 \pmod{17}$
(4) $4x \equiv 1 \pmod 5$	(9) $4x \equiv 10 \pmod{11}$
(5) $6x \equiv 1 \pmod{17}$	(10) $6x \equiv 10 \pmod{11}$

II. Solve each of the following equations.

(1) $2_3 x_3 = 1_3$	(6) $3_{11} x_{11} = 2_{11}$
(2) $2_5 x_5 = 1_5$	(7) $9_{11} x_{11} = 10_{11}$
(3) $8_{17} x_{17} = 4_{17}$	(8) $10_{11} x_{11} = 9_{11}$
(4) $8_{17} x_{17} = 6_{17}$	(9) $3_{13} x_{13} = 11_{13}$
(5) $2_{11} x_{11} = 3_{11}$	(10) $4_{13} x_{13} = 11_{13}$

III. Discuss the difference between the congruence $ax \equiv b \pmod{p}$ and the equation $a_p x_p = b_p$.

IV. Illustrate Theorem 8 in each of the following.

(1) $(I_8, +, \cdot)$ (6) $(I_{15}, +, \cdot)$

(2) $(I_6, +, \cdot)$ (7) $(I_{21}, +, \cdot)$

(3) $(I_9, +, \cdot)$ (8) $(I_{25}, +, \cdot)$

(4) $(I_{10}, +, \cdot)$ (9) $(I_{49}, +, \cdot)$

(5) $(I_{14}, +, \cdot)$ (10) $(I_{81}, +, \cdot)$

9.7 Applications

In this section we study some of the applications of modular number systems. One of the applications is to a well-known divisibility test which states that an integer is divisible by 9 if and only if the sum of its digits is divisible by 9. The following examples illustrate the test.

Example 1.   Does $9 \mid 603$?
$9 \mid (6 + 0 + 3)$.
Hence $9 \mid 603$.

Example 2.   Does $9 \mid 654{,}327$?
$9 \mid (6 + 5 + 4 + 3 + 2 + 7)$.
Hence $9 \mid 654{,}327$.

Example 3.   Does $9 \mid 754{,}327$?
$9 \nmid (7 + 5 + 4 + 3 + 2 + 7)$
Hence $9 \nmid 754{,}327$.

Why does this test work? Before we answer this question in general, we shall analyze the test for the integer 567.

$$567 = 5(10^2) + 6(10) + 7(1)$$
$$7(1) \equiv 7 \pmod 9$$
$$10 \equiv 1 \pmod 9$$
$$6(10) \equiv 6 \pmod 9 \quad \text{(by Theorem 4)}$$
$$10(10) \equiv 1(1) \pmod 9 \quad \text{(by Theorem 4)}$$
$$5(10^2) \equiv 5 \pmod 9 \quad \text{(by Theorem 4)}$$
$$5(10^2) + 6(10) + 7(1) \equiv 5 + 6 + 7 \pmod 9 \quad \text{(by Theorem 3)}$$

Hence $567 \equiv 5 + 6 + 7 \pmod 9$
If $567 \equiv 0 \pmod 9$, then $5 + 6 + 7 \equiv 0 \pmod 9$ (by transitive property for $\equiv$)
Conversely, if $5 + 6 + 7 \equiv 0 \pmod 9$, then $567 \equiv 0 \pmod 9$ (transitive property for $\equiv$)

Hence if $9 \mid 567$, then $9 \mid (5 + 6 + 7)$.
Conversely, if $9 \mid (5 + 6 + 7)$, then $9 \mid 567$.
Consequently $9 \mid 567 \rightleftarrows 9 \mid (5 + 6 + 7)$.

We now state a preliminary theorem which will enable us to give the general proof of the test.

THEOREM 11.   If a and k are any counting numbers, then $a \cdot 10^k \equiv a$ (mod 9).

Proof. $10 \equiv 1 \pmod{9}$
$10 \cdot 10 \equiv 1 \cdot 1 \pmod{9}$
$10 \cdot 10 \cdot 10 \equiv 1 \cdot 1 \cdot 1 \pmod{9}$

$$\underbrace{10 \cdot 10 \cdot 10 \cdot \ldots \cdot 10}_{k \text{ factors}} \equiv \underbrace{1 \cdot 1 \cdot 1 \cdot \ldots \cdot 1}_{k \text{ factors}} \pmod{9}$$

$10^k \equiv 1 \pmod{9}$
However $a \equiv a \pmod{9}$
Hence $a \cdot 10^k \equiv a \pmod{9}.\,/\!/$

We now state and prove the general theorem that any integer is divisible by 9 if and only if the sum of its digits is divisible by 9.

THEOREM 12.   The integer $a_k(10^k) + a_{k-1}(10^{k-1}) + \ldots + a_1(10^1) + a_0(1)$ is divisible by 9 if and only if $(a_k + a_{k-1} + \ldots + a_1 + a_0)$ is divisible by 9.

Proof. $a_0(1) \equiv a_0 \pmod{9}$
$a_1(10^1) \equiv a_1 \pmod{9}$ (by Theorem 11)
$a_2(10^2) \equiv a_2 \pmod{9}$ (by Theorem 11)
$\vdots$
$a_{k-1}(10^{k-1}) \equiv a_{k-1} \pmod{9}$ (by Theorem 11)
$a_k(10^k) \equiv a_k \pmod{9}$ (by Theorem 11)
Hence $a_k(10^k) + a_{k-1}(10^{k-1}) + \ldots + a_1(10^1) + a_0(1)$
$\equiv a_k + a_{k-1} + \ldots + a_1 + a_0 \pmod{9}$ (by Theorem 3).
Thus $a_k(10^k) + a_{k-1}(10^{k-1}) + \ldots + a_1(10^1) + a_0(1) \equiv 0$
$\pmod{9} \rightleftarrows a_k + a_{k-1} + \ldots + a_1 + a_0 \equiv 0 \pmod{9}$
(by transitive property for $\equiv$).
Consequently, $9 \mid [a_k(10^k) + a_{k-1}(10^{k-1}) + \ldots + a_1(10^1)$
$+ a_0(1)]$ if and only if $9 \mid [a_k + a_{k-1} + \ldots + a_1 + a_0].\,/\!/$

A second application of modular number systems is to a well-known addition check called *casting out nines*. According to this check, we may check the sum of integers by adding the digits of each integer, casting out nines, adding the remainders, casting out nines, and so on until a remainder less than 9 is obtained. Then we add the digits of the sum, cast out nines, and retain the remainder. If the arithmetic contains no errors, the latter remainder is equal to the remainder after nines have been cast from the sum of the remainders. The following example illustrates the method of casting out nines.

Example 4.   Compute the following sum and check by casting out nines.

$$547 \to 5 + 4 + 7 = 1(9) + 7 \equiv 7$$
$$(\bmod 9) \to 7 \; | \; 7 + 8 + 3$$
$$89 \to 8 + 9 = 1(9) + 8 \equiv 8 \;(\bmod 9) \to 8 \; \} = 2(9) + 0 \equiv \textcircled{0}$$
$$930 \to 9 + 3 + 0 = 1(9) + 3 \equiv 3 \qquad | \quad (\bmod 9)$$
$$(\bmod 9) \to 3$$
$$1566 \to 1 + 5 + 6 + 6 = 2(9) + 0 \equiv 0 \;(\bmod 9) \to \textcircled{0}$$

Hence the computed sum is probably correct. If the computed sum is incorrect, the error in the computed sum is a multiple of 9.

Observe that $547 \equiv 7 \;(\bmod 9)$, $89 \equiv 8 \;(\bmod 9)$, and $930 \equiv 3 \;(\bmod 9)$.

Hence $547 + 89 + 930 \equiv 7 + 8 + 3 \;(\bmod 9)$. That is, $1566 \equiv 18 \;(\bmod 9)$. Consequently, when 1566 is divided by 9, it leaves the same remainder as 18 does when it is divided by 9. We see, then, that checking addition by casting out nines is based on Theorem 12 and the fact that $a \equiv r \;(\bmod 9)$ and $b \equiv s \;(\bmod 9) \to a + b \equiv r + s \;(\bmod 9)$.

We usually abbreviate the procedure for casting out nines as in the following example.

Example 5.   Compute the following sum and check by casting out nines.

$$9877 \to 9 + 8 + 7 + 7 \to 4$$
$$5746 \to 5 + 7 + 4 + 6 \to 4$$
$$8097 \to 8 + 0 + 9 + 7 \to 6 \quad \} \to 4 + 4 + 6 + 5 \to \textcircled{1}$$
$$1202 \to 1 + 2 + 0 + 2 \to 5$$
$$24922 \to 2 + 4 + 9 + 2 + 2 \to \textcircled{1}$$

Hence the computed sum is probably correct.

The checking of multiplication by casting out nines is based on Theorem 12 and the fact that $a \equiv r \pmod 9$ and $b \equiv s \pmod 9$ → $ab \equiv rs \pmod 9$. The following example illustrates the method.

Example 6. Compute the product of 678 and 83, and check by casting out nines.

$$678 \rightarrow 6 + 7 + 8 \rightarrow 3 \left.\begin{matrix} \\ \\ \end{matrix}\right\} \ 3 \cdot 2 \rightarrow \textcircled{6}$$
$$83 \rightarrow 8 + 3 \rightarrow 2$$

$$\overline{}$$
$$2034$$
$$5424$$
$$\overline{56274} \rightarrow 5 + 6 + 2 + 7 + 4 \rightarrow \textcircled{6}$$

Another computational check is called the method of *casting out elevens*. This check is based on the fact that $10 \equiv {}^-1 \pmod{11}$. If the numeration system is the base five numeration system, the corresponding checks are *casting out fours* and *casting out sixes*, respectively.

Exercise 9.7

I. Determine which of the following are divisible by 9.

(1) 27,638   (6) 37,894
(2) 78,362   (7) 173,287
(3) 85,419   (8) 771,382
(4) 93,645   (9) 654,723
(5) 26,893   (10) 465,372

II. Compute $a + b$ in each of the following, and check by casting out nines.

(1) $a = 673, b = 93$ (4) $a = 583, b = 768$
(2) $a = 795, b = 88$ (5) $a = 6359, b = 7286$
(3) $a = 876, b = 538$ (6) $a = 9365, b = 2876$

III. Compute $a - b$ in each part of Exercise II and check by casting out nines.

IV. Compute ab in each part of Exercise II and check by casting out nines.

V. Devise a method of checking long division by casting out nines. (*Hint.* Recall that $a = bq + r$ and, consequently, $a - r = bq$.)

VI. Compute q and r in each of the following.

(1) $23\overline{)653}$ (4) $68\overline{)9630}$

(2) $32\overline{)536}$ (5) $837\overline{)29{,}367}$

(3) $73\overline{)6390}$ (6) $783\overline{)37{,}926}$

VII. (1) Devise a check for divisibility by 11.

(2) Devise a method for checking addition by casting out elevens.

(3) Devise a method for checking multiplication by casting out elevens.

(4) Devise a method for checking division by casting out elevens.

VIII. Check each sum in Exercise II by casting out elevens.

IX. Check each product in Exercise IV by casting out elevens.

X. Check each division in Exercise VI by casting out elevens.

XI. In base $b(2 \le b)$, the corresponding checks are casting out $b - 1$ and casting out $b + 1$. Compute each of the following sums and check (the subscript indicates the *base*).

(1) $627_8 + 533_8$ (4) $344_5 + 232_5$

(2) $375_8 + 643_8$ (5) $t0te_{12} + t39_{12}$

(3) $413_5 + 342_5$ (6) $tete_{12} + 931_{12}$

9.8 Applications (continued)

A third application of modular number systems and the congruence relation is to the solution of a certain type of equation called a *linear Diophantine equation*, named for the Greek mathematician Diophantos, who lived in Alexandria during the middle of the third century A.D. Any equation of the form $ax + my = b$ (or $mx + ay = b$) in two variables x and y is called a *linear Diophantine equation* in two variables if and only if the universe is the set of integers. Thus the solution set of a linear Diophantine equation is a subset of I. The numbers a, b, and m are integers; a and m are called *coefficients* of the variables x and y.

Example 1.   Solve the linear Diophantine equation $7x + 16y = 40$; that is, compute $\{(x, y): x \in I \wedge y \in I \wedge 7x + 16y = 40\}$.

$7x + 16y = 40$ ($x \in I$ and $y \in I$)
$16y - 40 = 7(^-x)$
$16y \equiv 40 \pmod 7$
$2y \equiv 5 \pmod 7$

Since 7 is a prime, we know that 2 has a multiplicative inverse. By inspection, we see that the inverse of 2 is 4.

$4(2y) \equiv 4(5) \pmod 7$

$y \equiv 6 \pmod 7$

$y = 6 + 7k \ (k \in I)$

$7x + 16y = 40 \ (x \in I \text{ and } y \in I)$

$7x + 16(6 + 7k) = 40$

$7x + 96 + 16(7k) = 40$

$7x = {}^-56 - (16k)7$

$x = {}^-8 - 16k \ (k \in I)$

$y = 6 + 7k \ (k \in I)$

For any integer k, the integers x and y given by $x = {}^-8 - 16k$ and $y = 6 + 7k$ satisfy the given linear Diophantine equation; that is, $\{(x, y): 7x + 16y = 40 \ \wedge \ x \in I \wedge y \in I\} = \{(x, y): (x = {}^-8 - 16k) \wedge (y = 6 + 7k) \wedge (k \in I)\}$.

The accompanying table exhibits some of the pairs (x, y) which satisfy the given equation.

k	x	y
⁻2	24	⁻8
⁻1	8	⁻1
0	⁻8	6
1	⁻24	13
2	⁻40	20

The following example illustrates the type of problem which can be solved by means of a linear Diophantine equation.

Example 2.   An electrical appliance dealer placed an order for some transistor radios at \$31 each and for some cheaper ones at \$28 each. The total order amounted to \$1460. How many of each type did he order?

Let x represent the number of \$28 radios and let y represent the number of \$31 radios.

Then $28x + 31y = 1460 \ (x \in C_0 \text{ and } y \in C_0)$

$28x - 1460 = 31({}^-y)$

$28x \equiv 1460 \pmod{31}$

$28x \equiv 3 \pmod{31}$

Since 31 is a prime, we know that 28 has a multiplicative
inverse.
By inspection we compute the inverse to be 10.
Hence $10(28x) \equiv 10(3) \pmod{31}$
$x \equiv 30 \pmod{31}$
$x - 30 = 31k$
$x = 30 + 31k$
$28x + 31y = 1460$ ($x \in C_0$ and $y \in C_0$)
$28(30 + 31k) + 31y = 1460$
$840 + 28(31)k + 31y = 1460$
$31y = 620 - (28k)(31)$
$y = 20 - 28k$ ($k \leq 0$, since $y \in C_0$)
$x = 30 + 31k$ ($0 \leq k$, since $x \in C_0$)
Hence $k = 0$.
Thus $x = 30$ and $y = 20$.
Hence the dealer ordered 20 radios at \$31 each and 30
radios at \$28 each.

The essential point in Examples 1 and 2 is that one of the coefficients
is an odd prime and the other coefficient is different from it. In Example
1, the coefficient of x is 7; in Example 2, the coefficient of y is 31. The
procedure in the above examples can be used whenever one of the
coefficients is an odd prime and the two coefficients are not equal. Is
there a procedure which can be used when neither coefficient is prime?
To answer this question, we consider the general Diophantine equation
$ax + my = b$, in which $(a, m, b) = 1$; that is, the greatest common
divisor of a, m, and b is equal to 1. If a, m, and b have a common factor
larger than 1, we first divide by this common factor and consider the
resulting equation. For example, in lieu of $75x + 20y = 50$, we write
$15x + 4y = 10$. The following example illustrates the fact that a linear
Diophantine equation may be solvable even if neither coefficient is
prime.

Example 3.   Solve the linear Diophantine equation $15x + 4y = 10$.

$15x + 4y = 10$ ($x \in I, y \in I$)
$15x - 10 = 4(^-y)$
$15x \equiv 10 \pmod{4}$
$3x \equiv 2 \pmod{4}$
To solve this congruence for x, we need to compute a
multiplicative inverse of 3 $\pmod{4}$, if one exists.
By inspection, we see that a multiplicative inverse of 3
is 3; that is, $3(3) \equiv 1 \pmod{4}$.

$3(3x) \equiv (3)(2) \pmod 4$
$x \equiv 6 \pmod 4$
$x \equiv 2 \pmod 4$
$x = 2 + 4k \ (k \in I)$
$15x + 4y = 10 \ (x \in I, y \in I)$
$15(2 + 4k) + 4y = 10$
$30 + 15(4k) + 4y = 10$
$4y = {}^-20 - 15(4)k$
$y = {}^-5 - 15k \ (k \in I)$
For any integer k,
$x = 2 + 4k,$
$y = {}^-5 - 15k.$

The above example illustrates an important point in the solution of a linear Diophantine equation. Although 4 (the modulus) is not prime, 3 has a multiplicative inverse. If 3 had no multiplicative inverse (mod 4), the above procedure would have failed. We have already learned that every integer $a \neq 0 \pmod p$ has a multiplicative inverse (mod p); however, we have learned that this is not true if the modulus is composite. Under what conditions can we be assured that an integer $a \not\equiv 0 \pmod m$, for an integer m, has a multiplicative inverse?

The following theorem answers this question.

THEOREM 13.   If a and m are any integers and $(a, m) = 1$, then there is an integer $a^{\#}$ such that $a^{\#} \cdot a \equiv 1 \pmod m$.

Proof.   Similar to the proof of Theorem 9.//

THEOREM 14.   (a) If $(a, m) = 1$, then the solution set of the linear Diophantine equation $ax + my = b$ is infinite.

(b) If $(a, m) \neq 1$, and $(a, m, b) = 1$, then the solution set of the linear Diophantine equation $ax + my = b$ is empty.

Proof.   (a) Let $ax + my = b$ and $(a, m) = 1$.
Then $ax \equiv b \pmod m$, and $(a, m) = 1$.
Hence there exists $a^{\#}$ such that $a^{\#}a \equiv 1 \pmod m$
(by Theorem 13).

$a^{\#}ax \equiv a^{\#}b \pmod m$
$x \equiv a^{\#}b \pmod m$
$x = a^{\#}b + km \ (k \in I)$
$ax + my = b$

$a(a^\#b + km) + my = b$

$aa^\#b + akm + my = b$

$my = b - aa^\#b - akm$

$y = b(1 - aa^\#)/m - ak$

Since $1 - aa^\# \equiv 0 \pmod{m}$, it follows that $(1 - aa^\#)/m$ is an integer v.

Hence $y = bv - ak$.

Thus $\{(x, y): ax + my = b \land (a, m) = 1 \land x \in I \land y \in I\} = \{(x, y): x = a^\#b + km \land y = bv - ak \land k \in I\}$.

(b) Let $(a, m) \neq 1$ and $(a, m, b) = 1$.

Then $(a, m) = d \neq 1$, and $a = a_1 d$, and $m = m_1 d$ for some integers a_1 and m_1.

Assume that there exists a pair of integers x and y such that $ax + my = b$.

Then $a_1 dx + m_1 dy = b$; that is, $d(a_1 x + m_1 y) = b$.

Hence $d \mid b$ (by Definition 1 of Chapter 6).

But $(a, m, b) = 1$.

Hence $d \nmid b$.

Thus $d \mid b \land d \nmid b$.

Hence there are no integers x and y such that $ax + my = b$; that is, $\{(x, y): ax + my = b \land (a, m) \neq 1 \land (a, b, m) = 1 \land U = I\} = \phi.\!/\!/$

Example 4. Carol has \$5.42 worth of stamps in 4 cent stamps and 15 cent stamps. What are the possible combinations of 4 cent stamps and 15 cent stamps?

Let x represent the number of 4 cent stamps and y represent the number of 15 cent stamps.

Then $4x + 15y = 542$

Thus $15y - 542 = 4(^-x)$

$15y \equiv 542 \pmod{4}$

$3y \equiv 2 \pmod{4}$

$3(3y) \equiv 3(2) \pmod{4}$

$y \equiv 6 \pmod{4}$

$y \equiv 2 \pmod{4}$

$y = 2 + 4k \ (k \in C_0)$

$4x + 15y = 542$

$4x + 15(2 + 4k) = 542$

$4x + 30 + 15(4k) = 542$

$4x = 512 - 15(4k)$

$$x = 128 - 15k$$
$$y = 2 + 4k$$

Since x cannot be negative, we see that $k \leq 8$. Since y cannot be negative, we see that $0 \leq k$.

Hence $0 \leq k \leq 8$.

The results are shown in the accompanying table.

k	No. of 4 cent stamps	No. of 15 cent stamps
0	128	2
1	113	6
2	98	10
3	83	14
4	68	18
5	53	22
6	38	26
7	23	30
8	8	34

We have seen that a multiplicative inverse $a^{\#}$ of a exists whenever $(a, m) = 1$. If m is small, it is easy to compute $a^{\#}$ by inspection. If m is large, it may be easier to apply the Euclidean algorithm, as in the following example.

Example 5. Solve the congruence $24x \equiv 1 \pmod{35}$.

$$35 = 24(1) + 11$$
$$24 = 11(2) + 2$$
$$11 = 2(5) + 1$$
$$1 = 11 - 2(5)$$
$$= 11 - [24 - 11(2)](5)$$
$$= 11 - 5(24) + 11(10)$$
$$= 11(11) - 5(24)$$
$$= 11[35 - 24(1)] - 5(24)$$
$$= 11(35) - 11(24) - 5(24)$$
$$= 11(35) - 16(24)$$
$$1 = 11(35) + {}^{-}16(24)$$

$$11 = 35 - 24(1)$$
$$2 = 24 - 11(2)$$
$$1 = 11 - 2(5)$$

$24(^-16) - 1 = ^-11(35)$

$24(^-16) \equiv 1 \pmod{35}$

Thus $^-16$ is a solution of $24x \equiv 1 \pmod{35}$.

But $^-16 \equiv 19 \pmod{35}$.

Hence 19 is a solution of the congruence $24x \equiv 1$ (mod 35).

Consequently 19 is a multiplicative inverse of 24 (mod 35).

Occasionally we wish to solve a system of congruences. Usually we are not interested in the complete solution but only in a particular solution. The following example illustrates a method by which some solutions may be computed.

Example 6. Solve the system $\begin{bmatrix} x \equiv 1 \pmod{4} \\ x \equiv 4 \pmod{7} \\ x \equiv 7 \pmod{9} \end{bmatrix}$ for $0 \le x \le 40$; that

is, compute the solution set $\{x: x \equiv 1 \pmod{4} \wedge x \equiv 4 \pmod{7} \wedge x \equiv 7 \pmod{9} \wedge 0 \le x \le 40\}$.

The solution set is equal to $\{x: x \equiv 1 \pmod{4}\} \cap \{x: x \equiv 4 \pmod{7}\} \cap \{x: x \equiv 7 \pmod{9}\} \cap \{x: 0 \le x \le 40\}$.

Now $\{x: x \equiv 1 \pmod{4} \wedge 0 \le x \le 40\} = \{1, 5, 9, 13, 17, 21, 25, 29, 33, 37\}$.

$\{x: x \equiv 4 \pmod{7} \wedge 0 \le x \le 40\} = \{4, 11, 18, 25, 32, 39\}$.

$\{x: x \equiv 7 \pmod{9} \wedge 0 \le x \le 40\} = \{7, 16, 25, 34\}$.

Hence the solution of the system is 25; that is, $\{x: x \equiv 1 \pmod{4} \wedge x \equiv 4 \pmod{7} \wedge x \equiv 7 \pmod{9} \wedge 0 \le x \le 40\} = \{25\}$.

The following example illustrates an application of systems of congruences.

Example 7. The driver of a sightseers' bus takes his passengers into a small shop which has only 4 rows of seats and notices that the sightseers exactly fill all seats. At the lunch stop, they fill 5 tables and one person sits at the counter. At the third and final stop, they occupy 7 rows of chairs and one person stands. The bus accommodates 50 passengers. How many persons did the driver take on the tour?

Let x represent the number of sightseers.

Then $\begin{bmatrix} x \equiv 0 \ (\text{mod } 4) \\ x \equiv 1 \ (\text{mod } 5) \\ x \equiv 1 \ (\text{mod } 7) \\ 0 \leq x \leq 50 \end{bmatrix}$

The solution set is $\{x: x \equiv 0 \ (\text{mod } 4)\} \cap \{x: x \equiv 1 \ (\text{mod } 5)\} \cap \{x: x \equiv 1 \ (\text{mod } 7)\} \cap \{x: 0 \leq x \leq 50\}$.

Now $\{x: x \equiv 0 \ (\text{mod } 4) \wedge 0 \leq x \leq 50\} = \{0, 4, 8, 12, 16, 20, 24, 28, 32, 36, 40, 44, 48\}$.

$\{x: x \equiv 1 \ (\text{mod } 5) \wedge 0 \leq x \leq 50\} = \{1, 6, 11, 16, 21, 26, 31, 36, 41, 46\}$.

$\{x: x \equiv 1 \ (\text{mod } 7) \wedge 0 \leq x \leq 50\} = \{1, 8, 15, 22, 29, 36, 43, 50\}$.

Hence the solution of the system is 36; that is, the number of passengers is 36.

We have considered only some elementary topics of congruences and their applications. The standard texts on number theory include more advanced topics and general theorems. For example, the conditions under which any system of linear congruences has a solution are stated in a general theorem, called the *Chinese Remainder Theorem*. This theorem also prescribes the general procedure for solving the system. In the exercises you will have an opportunity to test your skill on some of the simpler applications.

Exercise 9.8

I. Solve each of the following linear Diophantine equations.

(1) $x + 3y = {}^-21$ (4) $7x - 6y = {}^-25$
(2) $3x + y = 21$ (5) $9x - 8y = 10$
(3) $5x - 6y = 20$ (6) $10x - 9y = 10$

II. Compute the solution set of each of the following systems.

(1) $\begin{bmatrix} x \equiv 2 \ (\text{mod } 3) \\ x \equiv 3 \ (\text{mod } 5) \\ x \equiv 1 \ (\text{mod } 4) \\ 0 \leq x \leq 30 \end{bmatrix}$ (3) $\begin{bmatrix} 2x \equiv 3 \ (\text{mod } 5) \\ 5x - 3 \equiv 2 \ (\text{mod } 4) \\ 0 \leq x \leq 100 \end{bmatrix}$

(2) $\begin{bmatrix} x \equiv 1 \ (\text{mod } 3) \\ x \equiv 2 \ (\text{mod } 5) \\ x \equiv 3 \ (\text{mod } 4) \\ 0 \leq x \leq 30 \end{bmatrix}$ (4) $\begin{bmatrix} 3x \equiv 2 \ (\text{mod } 7) \\ 3x - 5 \equiv 4 \ (\text{mod } 8) \\ 0 \leq x \leq 100 \end{bmatrix}$

III. Formulate a mathematical model of each of the following problems and solve.

(1) Rene has $5.12 worth of 4 cent stamps and 15 cent stamps. What are the possible combinations of 4 cent stamps and 15 cent stamps?

(2) James has $7.25 worth of 5 cent stamps and 8 cent stamps. What are the possible combinations of 5 cent stamps and 8 cent stamps?

(3) Joe asked his mathematics professor for his grade on the last test. The professor told Joe, "If you divide your grade by 3, the remainder is 2; if you divide your grade by 13, the remainder is 1; and if you divide your grade by 5, the remainder is 2. What was Joe's grade on the test? (Assume that the total possible score is 100).

(4) A stock clerk who is assigned to stacking boxes stacks the boxes in three stacks. When the manager notices that the stacks are too high, he orders the clerk to restack the boxes in more stacks. The clerk then restacks the boxes into 7 stacks, with two boxes left over. The manager then tells the clerk that the new arrangement is taking up too much floor space. So the clerk restacks once more, this time into 5 stacks. Later the manager wants to know how many boxes the clerk stacked. Not wishing to leave his air-conditioned office to count them himself or to ask the unreliable clerk to count them, he decided to compute the number of boxes. How many boxes were there?

IV. Prove Theorem 13.

ANSWERS TO EXERCISES

CHAPTER 1

Exercise 1.1 (page 5)

I. (1) Sentence
   (3) Sentence
   (5) Open sentence
   (7) Sentence
   (9) Neither
   (11) Open sentence
   (13) Open sentence
   (15) Open sentence

   (17) Open sentence
   (19) Open sentence
   (21) Neither
   (23) Open sentence
   (25) Neither
   (27) Neither
   (29) Open sentence

Exercise 1.2 (page 7)

I. (1) All
   (3) Some (there exists)
   (5) Some (there exists)
   (7) All

   (9) All
   (11) Some (there exists), no (none)
   (13) All
   (15) Some (there exists)

II. (1) No quantifier
    (3) Implied
    (5) No quantifier

    (7) No quantifier
    (9) No quantifier

III. (3) All

IV. (1) Sentence
    (3) Open sentence
    (5) Sentence

    (7) Sentence
    (9) Sentence

V. (1) For all x, $x + x = 2x$ (true); for some x, $x + x = 2x$ (true); for no x, $x + x = 2x$ (false)
   (3) For all t, $t + 5 = 5$ (false); for some t, $t + 5 = 5$ (true); for no t, $t + 5 = 5$ (false)

(5) for all y, $7 + y = y$ (false); for some y, $7 + y = y$ (false); for no y, $7 + y = y$ (true)

(7) For all t, $t + 6 = 6$ (false); for some t, $t + 6 = 6$ (true); for no t, $t + 6 = 6$ (false)

(9) For all a, $a + 7 = 3$ (false); for some a, $a + 7 = 3$ (false); for no a, $a + 7 = 3$ (true)

Exercise 1.3 (page 10)

I.
(1) Simple
(3) Compound, not
(5) Compound, or, not
(7) Compound, and
(9) Compound, and, not

(11) Simple
(13) Compound, if ... then ...
(15) Compound, if ... then ...
(17) Compound, if and only if
(19) Compound, or, not

Exercise 1.4 (page 13)

I.
(1) Sentence, compound, p: Bill is in jail. q: Bill is a nuisance to his family. $\sim q$: Bill is not a nuisance to his family. $p \to \sim q$

(3) Sentence, simple, p: $(2 + 3) + 7 = 2 + (3 + 7)$, p

(5) Sentence, compound, p: 7 is larger than 3. q: 3 is smaller than 7. $p \lor q$

(7) Sentence, simple, p: 2 is smaller than $2 \cdot 3$. p

(9) Sentence, compound, p: 8 is larger than 1. q: $8 + 3$ is smaller than 5. $p \land q$

(11) Sentence, simple, p

(13) Sentence, compound, $p \lor q$

(15) Sentence, compound, $p \to q$

(17) Sentence, compound, $p \lor q$

(19) Sentence, compound, $p \lor \sim q$

(21) Sentence, compound, $p \land q$

Exercise 1.5 (page 15)

I.
(1) $\sim$(Uranus is a star.) Uranus is not a star.

(3) $\sim$(George Washington lived before Abraham Lincoln.) George Washington did not live before Abraham Lincoln.

(5) $\sim$($6 + 2 = 9$), $6 + 2 \neq 9$

(7) $\sim$($2 + 3 = 3$), $2 + 3 \neq 3$

(9) $\sim$(Some numbers are odd.) No numbers are odd.

(11) $\sim$(Some numbers are not odd.) All numbers are odd.

(13) $\sim$(No numbers are perfect squares.) Some numbers are perfect squares.

(15) $\sim$(All numbers are primes.) Some numbers are not prime.

(17) ~(There is at least one number larger than 100.) There is no number larger than 100.

(19) ~(Not all numbers are divisible by 2.) All numbers are divisible by 2.

II. (1) F, T   (11) T, F
     (3) T, F   (13) F, T
     (5) F, T   (15) F, T
     (7) F, T   (17) T, F
     (9) T, F   (19) T, F

Exercise 1.6 (page 19)

I. (1) True   (11) True
    (3) True   (13) True
    (5) False   (15) False
    (7) True   (17) True
    (9) False   (19) True

II. (1)

p	$\sim p$	$p \vee \sim p$
T	F	T
F	T	T

(3)

p	q	$(p \vee q)$	$\sim(p \vee q)$
T	T	T	F
T	F	T	F
F	T	T	F
F	F	F	T

(5)

p	$\sim p$	$\sim(\sim p)$
T	F	T
F	T	F

(7)

p	$p \vee p$
T	T
F	F

(9)

p	$\sim p$	$(p \vee \sim p)$	$\sim(p \vee \sim p)$
T	F	T	F
F	T	T	F

(11)

p	q	$\sim p$	$\sim p \vee q$
T	T	F	T
T	F	F	F
F	T	T	T
F	F	T	T

(13)

p	q	$\sim p$	$\sim q$	$(\sim p \vee \sim q)$	$\sim(\sim p \vee \sim q)$
T	T	F	F	F	T
T	F	F	T	T	F
F	T	T	F	T	F
F	F	T	T	T	F

III. (1) (*1*) $(2+3=5) \lor (2+3 \neq 5)$ True
     (*3*) ${\sim}[(2+3=5) \lor (2 \cdot 3 = 6)]$ False
     (*5*) ${\sim}(2+3 \neq 5)$ True
     (*7*) $(2+3=5) \lor (2+3=5)$ True
     (*9*) ${\sim}[(2+3=5) \lor (2+3 \neq 5)]$ False
     (*11*) $(2+3 \neq 5) \lor (2 \cdot 3 = 6)$ True
     (*13*) ${\sim}[(2+3 \neq 5) \lor (2 \cdot 3 \neq 6)]$ True
   (3) (*1*) $(2+3=6) \lor (2+3 \neq 6)$ True
     (*3*) ${\sim}[(2+3=6) \lor (2 \cdot 3 = 6)]$ False
     (*5*) ${\sim}(2+3 \neq 6)$ False
     (*7*) $(2+3=6) \lor (2+3=6)$ False
     (*9*) ${\sim}[(2+3=6) \lor (2+3 \neq 6)]$ False
     (*11*) $(2+3 \neq 6) \lor (2 \cdot 3 = 6)$ True
     (*13*) ${\sim}[(2+3 \neq 6) \lor (2 \cdot 3 \neq 6)]$ False

Exercise 1.7 (page 23)

I. (1) False   (13) True if p is false and
    (3) True   false if p is true
    (5) False   (15) True
    (7) True   (17) True
    (9) False   (19) True
    (11) True

II. (1)

p	q	$p \lor q$	$p \to p \lor q$
T	T	T	T
T	F	T	T
F	T	T	T
F	F	F	T

(5)

p	q	$(p \land q)$	$(p \land q) \to q$
T	T	T	T
T	F	F	T
F	T	F	T
F	F	F	T

(9)

p	${\sim}p$	$p \to {\sim}p$
T	F	F
F	T	T

(13)

p	q	$(p \to q)$	$[p \wedge (p \to q)]$	$[p \wedge (p \to q)] \to q$
T	T	T	T	T
T	F	F	F	T
F	T	T	F	T
F	F	T	F	T

(17)

p	q	$\sim p$	$\sim q$	$(p \to q)$	$[\sim p \wedge (p \to q)]$	$[\sim p \wedge (p \to q)] \to \sim q$
T	T	F	F	T	F	T
T	F	F	T	F	F	T
F	T	T	F	T	T	F
F	F	T	T	T	T	T

III. (1) Yes (3) No (5) No (7) Yes (9) No

Exercise 1.8 (page 26)

I. (1)

p	$(p \vee p)$	$p \leftrightarrows (p \vee p)$
T	T	T
F	F	T

(3)

p	$p \leftrightarrows p$
T	T
F	T

(5)

p	q	$\sim p$	$\sim q$	$(p \wedge q)$	$\sim(p \wedge q)$	$(\sim p \vee \sim q)$	$\sim(p \wedge q) \leftrightarrows (\sim p \vee \sim q)$
T	T	F	F	T	F	F	T
T	F	F	T	F	T	T	T
F	T	T	F	F	T	T	T
F	F	T	T	F	T	T	T

(7)

p	q	$\sim q$	$(p \vee \sim q)$	$\sim(p \vee \sim q)$	$(p \to q)$	$\sim(p \vee \sim q) \leftrightarrows (p \to q)$
T	T	F	T	F	T	F
T	F	T	T	F	F	T
F	T	F	F	T	T	T
F	F	T	T	F	T	F

(9)

p	q	$\sim p$	$\sim q$	$(p \vee \sim q)$	$\sim(p \vee \sim q)$	$(\sim p \wedge q)$	$\sim(p \vee \sim q) \leftrightarrows (\sim p \wedge q)$
T	T	F	F	T	F	F	T
T	F	F	T	T	F	F	T
F	T	T	F	F	T	T	T
F	F	T	T	T	F	F	T

(11)

p	q	$\sim p$	$\sim q$	$(p \rightarrow q)$	$(\sim q \rightarrow \sim p)$	$(p \rightarrow q) \leftrightharpoons (\sim p \rightarrow \sim q)$
T	T	F	F	T	T	T
T	F	F	T	F	F	T
F	T	T	F	T	T	T
F	F	T	T	T	T	T

II. (1) Logical-truth   (7) Not a logical-truth
     (3) Logical-truth   (9) Logical-truth
     (5) Logical-truth   (11) Logical-truth

Exercise 1.9 (page 29)

III. (1) $\sim p$, $\sim[\sim(\sim p)]$ (7) $\sim[\sim(p \wedge \sim q)]$, $p \wedge \sim q$
      (3) $\sim(p \vee q)$, $\sim p \wedge \sim q$ (9) $\sim(p \rightarrow q)$, $p \wedge \sim q$
      (5) $\sim[\sim(p \vee q)]$, $p \vee q$ (11) $\sim[p \rightarrow (q \vee r)]$, $p \wedge (\sim q \vee \sim r)$

Exercise 1.10 (page 32)

I. (1) If John and Mary have the same birthday, then John and
        Mary are twins.
    (3) If Mary makes an A, then John does Mary's homework.
    (5) If John and Mary have exactly 9 apples, then John has
        exactly 5 apples and Mary has exactly 4 apples.
    (7) $(q \wedge r) \rightarrow p$
    (9) $r \rightarrow (p \vee q)$
    (11) $(p \wedge q) \rightarrow (p \vee q)$
    (13) $p \rightarrow (p \vee q)$
    (15) $(q \vee \sim p) \rightarrow (\sim p \vee q)$

II. (1) If John and Mary are not twins, then John and Mary do not
         have the same birthday.
     (3) If John does not do Mary's homework, then Mary will not
         make an A.
     (5) If John does not have exactly 5 apples or Mary does not
         have exactly 4 apples, then John and Mary do not have
         exactly 9 apples.
     (7) $\sim p \rightarrow (\sim q \vee \sim r)$
     (9) $(\sim p \wedge \sim q) \rightarrow \sim r$
     (11) $(\sim p \wedge \sim q) \rightarrow (\sim p \vee \sim q)$
     (13) $(\sim p \wedge \sim q) \rightarrow \sim p$
     (15) $(p \wedge \sim q) \rightarrow (\sim q \wedge p)$

III. (1) If John and Mary do not have the same birthday, then John
          and Mary are not twins.

(3) If Mary did not make an A, then John did not do Mary's homework.

(5) If John and Mary do not have exactly 9 apples, then John does not have exactly 5 apples or Mary does not have exactly 4 apples.

(7) $(\sim q \vee \sim r) \rightarrow \sim p$

(9) $\sim r \rightarrow (\sim p \wedge \sim q)$

(11) $(\sim p \vee \sim q) \rightarrow (\sim p \wedge \sim q)$

(13) $\sim p \rightarrow (\sim p \wedge \sim q)$

(15) $(\sim q \wedge p) \rightarrow (p \wedge \sim q)$

Exercise 1.11 (page 38)

I. (1) Invalid (3) Invalid (5) Invalid

III. (1) All (implied)   (17) All (implied)
   (3) No quantifier   (19) All (implied)
   (5) All (implied)   (21) All (implied)
   (7) All (implied)   (23) Some (implied)
   (9) All (implied)   (25) No quantifier
   (11) All (implied)   (27) All (implied)
   (13) None (implied)   (29) All (implied)
   (15) All (implied)

CHAPTER 2

Exercise 2.1 (page 43)

III. (1) $0 \in A, 0 \notin B, 0 \notin C, 0 \notin D, 0 \notin E, 0 \notin F, 0 \in G.$

(3) $5 \notin A, 5 \in B, 5 \notin C, 5 \in D, 5 \notin E, 5 \notin F, 5 \in G.$

(5) $9 \notin A, 9 \in B, 9 \in C, 9 \in D, 9 \notin E, 9 \in F, 9 \notin G.$

(7) $5/2 \notin A, 5/2 \notin B, 5/2 \notin C, 5/2 \notin D, 5/2 \notin E, 5/2 \notin F, 5/2 \notin G.$

(9) $24600000 \in A, 24600000 \notin B, 24600000 \in C, 24600000 \notin D, 24600000 \notin E, 24600000 \notin F, 24600000 \notin G.$

V. All of the elements of E are also elements of A.

VII. The set D and the set F have the element 9 in common.

IX. All of the elements of F are also elements of B.

Exercise 2.2 (page 44)

I. $\{10\}, \{10, 12\}, \{10, 12, 14\}.$

V. (1) The set of all counting numbers greater than 100.

(3) The set of all numbers such that 5 times the number equals 10.
(5) The set of all odd numbers greater than 9.

Exercise 2.3 (page 47)

I. (1) 0   5   10   15
        $\updownarrow$ $\updownarrow$ $\updownarrow$ $\updownarrow$
        a b x y

(3) $w \leftrightarrow 11$

(5) 0   4   8   12   16   ... $4n$ ...
     $\updownarrow$ $\updownarrow$ $\updownarrow$ $\updownarrow$ $\updownarrow$ $\updownarrow$
     0   1   2   3   4   ... n ...

III. (1) C, D, H, L

Exercise 2.4 (page 49)

I. (1) Subset of A (9) Subset of A
    (3) An element of A (11) Subset of A
    (5) An element of A (13) Subset of A
    (7) Subset of A (15) Subset of A

III. (1) {2, 6, 10}   (7) { } or ϕ
     (3) {0, 4, 6, 8}   (9) {2}
     (5) {2, 4, 6, 8, 10}

V. (1) {x: x is a male}   (5) {x: x is a female}
    (3) {x: x is a single person}

Exercise 2.5 (page 51)

I. (1) {2, 4, 6, 8, 9}   (5) {0, 1, 2, 3, ... }
    (3) {0, 1, 2, 3, 4, 5}   (7) {0, 1, 2, 3, ... }
    (9) {Jessie, May, Bea, Janice, Craig, Lise, Inez}

III. (1) {0, 1, 2}, {0, 1}   (7) {1, 2, 3, 4, 5}, { }
     (3) {1, 2, 3, 4, 5, 6}, { } or ϕ (9) {0, 1, 2, 3, ... }, {100}
     (5) {1, 2, 3, 4, ... }, ϕ (11) {0, 1, 2, 3, ... }, { }.

V. $A \cap B = B \cap A$

Exercise 2.6 (page 54)

V. (1) The set of all students of mathematics or chemistry.
    (3) The set of all students of mathematics and chemistry.
    (5) The set of all students of chemistry or speech.
    (7) The set of all students of mathematics, and chemistry, and speech.

Exercise 2.7 (page 62)

I.   (1) {0, 1, 2, 4, 6, 8}
     (3) {4, 6}
     (5) {1}
     (7) {0, 1, 2, 4, 6, 8}
     (9) {1}
    (11) {1, 4, 6, 8}
    (13) {4, 6}
    (15) {0, 1, 2, 3, 4, 5, 6, 8, 9}
    (17) ϕ

    (19) ϕ
    (21) {0, 2, 3, 4, 5, 6, 7, 9}
    (23) {0, 1, 2, 3, 5, 7, 8, 9}
    (25) U
    (27) ϕ
    (29) {7}
    (31) {0, 1, 2, 4, 6, 7, 8}
    (33) U
    (35) {4, 6}

V.   (1) {0, 6, 12, 18, . . .}
     (3) { }
     (5) {0, 2, 4, . . . , 98}
     (7) {0, 2, 4, . . .} or {x: x is even} or B
     (9) C
    (11) D
    (13) {1, 3, 5, . . . , 99, 105, 111, . . .}
    (15) {101, 103, 105, . . .}
    (17) {0, 2, 4, . . . , 98}
    (19) {0, 2, 4, 6, . . .}

Exercise 2.8 (page 67)

I.   (1) {(2, 0)}
     (3) {(2, 1), (2, 2)}
     (5) {(0, 1), (0, 2), (0, 3), (1, 1), (1, 2), (1, 3)}
     (7) {(0, 0), (0, 1), (0, 2), (0, 3)}
     (9) {(10, 1), (10, 2), (10, 3), (10, 4), . . .
         (11, 1), (11, 2), (11, 3), (11, 4), . . .
         (12, 1), (12, 2), (12, 3), (12, 4), . . .}

V.   (1) $A = \{1, 5\}, B = \{1, 2, 3\}$
     (3) $A = \{0\}, B = \{0, 1, 2\}$

Exercise 2.9 (page 70)

I.   (1) Equivalence relation
     (3) Equivalence relation
     (5) Equivalence relation
     (7) Equivalence relation
     (9) Equivalence relation

III. (1) Symmetric property fails

CHAPTER 3

Exercise 3.1 (page 77)

I. (1) $\{2, 5, 8\}$ (3) $\{a, b, 6, 8, 10\}$ (5) $\{3, 6, 9\}$
       $\updownarrow \;\updownarrow \;\updownarrow$ $\updownarrow \;\updownarrow \;\updownarrow \;\updownarrow \;\;\updownarrow$ $\updownarrow \;\updownarrow \;\updownarrow$
      $\{1, 2, 3\}$ $\{1, 2, 3, 4, \;\; 5\}$ $\{1, 2, 3\}$

    (7) $\{0, 3, 6, 9, 12, 15\}$ (9) $\{21, 22, 23, 24, 25\}$
       $\updownarrow \;\updownarrow \;\updownarrow \;\updownarrow \;\;\updownarrow \;\;\updownarrow$ $\updownarrow \;\;\updownarrow \;\;\updownarrow \;\;\updownarrow \;\;\updownarrow$
      $\{1, 2, 3, 4, \;\; 5, \;\; 6\}$ $\{ \;1, \;\; 2, \;\; 3, \;\; 4, \;\; 5\}$

III. (1) 2   (3) 6   (5) 15

V. (1) Yes   (3) No   (5) Yes

Exercise 3.2 (page 83)

II. (1) Definition of addition
    (5) Definition of addition
    (9) Commutative property for addition
  (13) Identity property for addition and definition of addition
  (17) Associative property for addition and definition of addition

VIII. (1) Yes   (7) Yes
    (3) Yes   (9) Yes
    (5) Yes

Exercise 3.3 (page 96)

I. (1) Definition of multiplication
    (5) Definition of multiplication
    (9) Commutative property for multiplication
  (13) Commutative property for multiplication and identity property for multiplication
  (17) Associative property for multiplication and definition of multiplication

VIII. (1) Yes   (7) Yes
    (3) Yes   (9) No
    (5) Yes

Exercise 3.4 (page 101)

V. (1) $3a + 3b + 3x$ (7) $2(3a + b + 2c + 4d)$
    (3) $2a + ab + ac + ax$ (9) $4a(2b + 3c + 4d + 7x)$
    (5) $a(x + y + z)$

CHAPTER 4

Exercise 4.1 (page 114)

I. (1) | | | | | | |
    (3) ∩ ∩ ∩ ∩ ∩ ∩ ∩ ∩ ∩ | | | | | | | | |
    (5) | | | | | | | | | |
    (7) ⌐𝕐 ◉ | |
    (9) ⟨⟩ ⟨⟩ ⟨⟩ ⟨⟩ ⟨⟩ | | |

II. (1) ∩ ∩ ∩ ∩ | | (3) ◉ | (5) ∩ ∩ ∩ ∩

Exercise 4.2 (page 116)

I. (1) XLIV   (7) MCMXCIX
    (3) XC   (9) LI
    (5) CDXCVII

II. (1) XLII   (3) XL   (5) MCCXV

Exercise 4.3 (page 119)

I. (1) 2 tens and 7 ones
    (3) 4 tens and 0 ones
    (5) 1 ten thousand, 0 thousands, 1 hundred, 0 tens, and 3 ones
    (7) 1 thousand, 0 hundreds, 2 tens, and 0 ones
    (9) 1 ten million, 1 million, 8 hundred thousands, 2 ten thousands, 6 thousands, 8 hundreds, 9 tens, and 1 one.

III. (1) 7   (3) 227   (5) 1,000,407

IV. (1) (10)(10)(10)(10)(10)(10)(10)
    (3) (10)(10)(10)(10)(10)(10)(10)(10)(10)
    (5) (10)(10)

V. (1) 99999   (3) 9999999   (5) 9

Exercise 4.4 (page 123)

I. (1) 2^4 (9) 7^3
    (3) 5^3 (11) 4^3
    (5) 8^2 (13) a^2
    (7) 10^7 (15) 6^2

II. (1) 27   (11) 35
    (3) 25   (13) 32
    (5) 100   (15) 64
    (7) 144   (17) 9
    (9) 343   (19) 100000

III.　(1) $7(10) + 1(1)$
　　(3) $6(10^3) + 1(10^2) + 0(10) + 5(1)$
　　(5) $1(10^4) + 0(10^3) + 1(10^2) + 0(10) + 0(1)$
　　(7) $1(10^6) + 1(10^5) + 2(10^4) + 0(10^3) + 9(10^2) + 0(10)$
　　　　$+ 0(1)$
　　(9) $2(10^8) + 0(10^7) + 0(10^6) + 0(10^5) + 0(10^4) + 0(10^3)$
　　　　$+ 0(10^2) + 1(10) + 0(1)$

IV.　(1) a^8　　　　　　　　　(7) 10^8
　　(3) 10^5　　　　　　　　　(9) $7^{(b+c)}$
　　(5) b^{20}

V.　(1) $7b^2$
　　(3) $10c^7$
　　(5) $5b^2 + 5b + 4$
　　(7) $2(10^4) + 7(10^3) + 9(10^2) + 1(10^1) + 12$
　　(9) $15a^3 + a^2 + 5a + 10$

Exercise 4.6 (page 129)

I.　(1) $2a + 2b$
　　(3) $7 + 49a + 14b$
　　(5) $ac + 2a + 2bc + 4b$
　　(7) $a^2 + 2ab + b^2$
　　(9) $a^2(10^2) + 7a(10^2) + ab(10) + 7b(10) + 28(1) + 4a(1)$

Exercise 4.7 (page 135)

I.　(1) $\{\boxdot\,\square\,\boxplus,\ \boxdot\,\square\,\boxplus, \ldots, \boxdot\,\boxplus\,\square\}$
　　(3) $\{\boxplus\,\boxplus\,\boxplus\,\boxplus,\ \boxplus\,\boxplus\,\boxplus\,\boxplus, \ldots, \boxdot\,\square\,\square\,\boxdot\,\boxdot\}$

II.　(1) $1(25) + 1(5) + 0(1)$
　　(3) $1(25) + 1(5) + 3(1)$
　　(5) $3(125) + 0(25) + 0(5) + 0(1)$
　　(7) $1(125) + 2(25) + 0(5) + 1(1)$
　　(9) $3(3125) + 0(625) + 2(125) + 0(25) + 1(5) + 0(1)$

III.　(1) 30　　　　　　　　　(7) 176
　　(3) 33　　　　　　　　　(9) 9630
　　(5) 375

VIII.　(1) ⊡ ⊡　　　　　　　(7) ⊡ □ ⊡ ⊡
　　(3) ⊡ □ ⊡　　　　　　　(9) ⊡ □ □ □ ⊡
　　(5) ⊞ ⊞ ⊡

IX.　(1) ⊞ ⊡　　　　　　　　(7) ⊡ □ □ ⊡
　　(3) ⊞ □　　　　　　　　(9) ⊞ ⊞ ⊡ ⊞
　　(5) ⊞ ⊡ ⊡

Exercise 4.8 (page 140)

I. (1) $\{43_5, 44_5, \ldots, 102_5\}$ (3) $\{4444_5, 10000_5, 10001_5\}$

III. (1) 51   (7) 8220
    (3) 89   (9) 11925
    (5) 148

VII. (1) 20_5 (7) 1001_5
    (3) 102_5 (9) 4444_5
    (5) 1020_5

VIII. (1) 413_5 (7) 1110_5
    (3) 21_5 (9) 10340_5
    (5) 103_5

XI. (1) 442_5 (7) 321004_5
    (3) 424_5 (9) 2204303_5
    (5) 140032_5

XII. (1) 44444_5 (5) 777_8
    (3) 10_5

Exercise 4.9 (page 147)

I. (1) $\{10101, 10110, 10111, 11000, 11001, 11010, 11011, 11100,$ $11101, 11110, 11111, 100000, 100001, 100010\}$

III. (1) 1101   (3) 100000   (5) 11001100

V. (1) 1111   (3) 10101   (5) 110001

VI. (1) $1e$ (3) 702   (5) 300

VIII. (1) $4t$ (3) 350   (5) 26920

XII. (1) 57   (3) 111   (5) 525

XIV. (1) 36   (3) 714   (5) 37603

CHAPTER 5

Exercise 5.1 (page 158)

I. (1) -7   (5) -14
    (3) -10

II. (1) 0   (7) 2
    (3) 3   (9) 0
    (5) 10

IV. (1) ⁻8
   (3) ⁻12
   (5) *b*
   (7) 0

   (9) 3
   (11) 4
   (13) ⁻10

VI. (1) ⁻5
   (3) 0
   (5) 1
   (7) 4

   (9) 7
   (11) 1
   (13) 2
   (15) 0

Exercise 5.2 (page 163)

I. (1) ⁻7
  (3) 0
  (5) 9

  (7) ⁻1
  (9) $^-a + {}^-b$

VI. (1) 7
   (3) 4
   (5) ⁻4
   (7) 7
   (9) 8

  (11) 2
  (13) 7
  (15) ⁻1 or 1
  (17) ϕ
  (19) ϕ

Exercise 5.3 (page 171)

I. (1) ⁻15
  (3) ⁻15
  (5) 15
  (7) ⁻42
  (9) 8
  (11) 56
  (13) 21

  (15) ⁻7
  (17) 9
  (19) ⁻9
  (21) ⁻3
  (23) 2
  (25) ⁻6*a*

Exercise 5.5 (page 177)

II. (1) 1104
   (3) 3023

  (5) 1040

IV. (1) 110
   (3) 120

  (5) 1
  (7) 30E

VI. (1) 1000
   (3) 10

  (5) 111

VIII. (1) ⁻1320 (base 5)
    (3) ⁻110 (base 2)
    (5) ⁻4146 (base 12)

  (7) 51236 (base 8)
  (9) ⁻15651 (base 7)

CHAPTER 6

Exercise 6.1 (page 184)

VI. (1) 3, 6, 9, 12, 15, 18, 21, 24, 27, 30
     (3) 1, 2, 3, 4, 5, 6, 7, 8, 9, 10, 11, 12, 13, 14, 15
     (5) 5, 10, 15, 20, 25, 30, 35, 40, 45, 50

VII. (1) 1, ⁻1
     (3) 1, 2, 4, ⁻1, ⁻2, ⁻4
     (5) 1, 3, 9, ⁻1, ⁻3, ⁻9
     (7) 1, 2, 11, 22, ⁻1, ⁻2, ⁻11, ⁻22
     (9) 1, 2, 4, 7, 14, 28, ⁻1, ⁻2, ⁻4, ⁻7, ⁻14, ⁻28
    (11) I

X.   (1) $2k$ where $k \in I$ (3) $3k$ where $k \in I$

Exercise 6.2 (page 189)

I.   (1) $q = 3, r = 1$ (7) $q = 4, r = 4$
     (3) $q = 10, r = 0$ (9) $q = 33, r = 26$
     (5) $q = 21, r = 0$

V.   (1) $23 = 7(q) + r$ (5) $25 = 23(q) + r$
     (3) $97 = 30(q) + r$

Exercise 6.3 (page 194)

I.   (1) 2, 3, 5, 7, 11, 13, 17, 19, 23, 29, 31, 37, 41, 43, 47, 53, 59, 61,
         67, 71, 73, 79, 83, 89, 97
     (3) 2

III. (1) 2
     (3) 9, 21, 25, 33, 45, 49, 57, 65, 69, 77, 81, 85, 93

V.   (1) 1 and ⁻1   (5) 9, 25, 49, 121, 169
     (3) 2, 3, 5, 7

VII. (1) $j = 1, k = ⁻3$ (7) $j = 2, k = ⁻1$
     (3) $j = ⁻1, k = 4$ (9) $j = ⁻1, k = 1$
     (5) $j = 32, k = ⁻43$

Exercise 6.4 (page 200)

I.   (1) $2 \cdot 3 \cdot 3 \cdot 7$ or $2 \cdot 3^2 \cdot 7$
     (3) $2 \cdot 2 \cdot 5 \cdot 5 \cdot 5$ or $2^2 \cdot 5^3$
     (5) $2 \cdot 2 \cdot 2 \cdot 2 \cdot 3 \cdot 5$ or $2^4 \cdot 3 \cdot 5$
     (7) $5 \cdot 7 \cdot 89$
     (9) $2 \cdot 2 \cdot 2 \cdot 2 \cdot 2 \cdot 2 \cdot 3 \cdot 5$ or $2^6 \cdot 3 \cdot 5$

III.   (1) 15   (5) 1
       (3) 5   (7) 6

Exercise 6.5 (page 204)

  I.   (1) 5, 10, 15, 20, 25, 30, 35, 40, 45, 50, 55, 60, 65, 70, 75, 80, 85,
           90, 95, 100
       (3) 2, 4, 6, 8, 10, 12, 14, 16, 18, 20, 22, 24, 26, 28, 30, 32, 34, 36,
           38, 40, 42, 44, 46, 48
       (5) 10, 20, 30, 40, 50, 60, 70, 80, 90

III.   (1) 1   (7) 42
       (3) 3   (9) 11
       (5) 42

 VI.   (1) 660   (5) 5929
       (3) 924

CHAPTER 7

Exercise 7.1 (page 220)

  I.   (1) yes   (9) no
       (3) yes   (11) yes
       (5) yes   (13) yes
       (7) yes

Exercise 7.2 (page 225)

  I.   (1) True   (7) False
       (3) True   (9) True
       (5) False

III.   (1) True   (7) True
       (3) True   (9) False
       (5) True

Exercise 7.3 (page 231)

  I.   (1) 41/35   (7) 50/7
       (3) 567/400   (9) 1/1
       (5) 215/126

III.   (1) 8   (7) 3
       (3) 8   (9) 3
       (5) 10

  V.   (1) 1/2 + 1/7   (3) 3/2 + 2/3

Exercise 7.4 (page 235)

I. (1) -11/15   (7) -1/1
    (3) -2/35   (9) -1/4
    (5) -5/72

III. (1) -1/2   (7) 5/1
     (3) 1/3   (9) 0/1
     (5) 1/10

V. (1) 7/20   (5) 721/2640
    (3) 3/20

Exercise 7.5 (page 240)

I. (1) 2/9   (7) 1/3, 8
    (3) 21/32   (9) 8/5 bu.
    (5) 1/2

III. (1) -6/35   (11) 1/1
     (3) 1/35   (13) 1/1
     (5) -6/7   (15) 1/1
     (7) 4/25   (17) -1/1
     (9) -5/13   (19) 8/1

Exercise 7.6 (page 246)

I. (1) 8/9   (7) 7/8
    (3) 0/1   (9) 90/121
    (5) 7/6

V. (1) 57/10   (11) 96/35
    (3) -80/21   (13) 96/35
    (5) -89/36   (15) -14/3
    (7) -5/3   (17) $(b-a)/(a-b)$ or $\frac{-1}{1}$
    (9) -19/105   (19) $1/b$

VII. (1) 5/27
     (3) 56
     (5) 58
     (7) Lucille 668/23 min. or
         29¹⁄₂₃ min., Rita 501/17
         min. or 29⁸⁄₁₇ min.
     (9) 75 children, 2/5 lb.

Exercise 7.7 (page 254)

III. (1) Yes   (7) No
     (3) Yes   (9) Yes
     (5) Yes

Exercise 7.8 (page 258)

  I. (1) $2/3 < 4/5$ (7) $653/277 < 538/169$
     (3) $^-98/11 < ^-89/10$ (9) $^-100/16 < ^-100/17$
     (5) $115/^-19 < 117/^-21$

  V. (1) $9\%_5$ (7) $231/290$
     (3) $1^{34}\!/_{75}$ (9) $^-488/1655$
     (5) $1^{91}\!/_{96}$

VII. (1) 4   (7) 1
     (3) 3   (9) 15
     (5) 18

Exercise 7.9 (page 265)

  I. (1) True   (11) False
     (3) False   (13) True
     (5) False   (15) True
     (7) True   (17) True
     (9) True   (19) False

CHAPTER 8

Exercise 8.3 (page 279)

  I. (1) .4   (7) .375
     (3) $.\overline{6}$ (9) $1.1\overline{3}$
     (5) $.\overline{428571}$

  V. (1) $5.7\overline{56}$ (7) $17.\overline{161}$
     (3) $0.050\overline{41}$ (9) $3.\overline{3}$
     (5) $11.1\overline{2}$

Exercise 8.4 (page 284)

  I. (1) $5699/990$ (7) $17144/999$
     (3) $4991/99000$ (9) $10/3$
     (5) $367/33$

Exercise 8.5 (page 295)

I. (1) $49.\overline{95}$ (3) $11.2\overline{78}$

III. (1) $.0\overline{3}$

Exercise 8.7 (page 300)

I. (1) 5^4 (7) $2^6 \cdot \pi^5 \cdot \sqrt{2}$
   (3) $1/(2 \cdot 3^2)$ (9) $1/ac^4$
   (5) $6/5$

III. (1) 2   (7) $7b$
    (3) $^-2$ (9) 1
    (5) $5a^3\sqrt{5}$

V. (1) $1/2^3$ (7) $2/a^3$
   (3) $1/4^2$ (9) $1/(2 + a)^2$
   (5) $2/a^3$

Exercise 8.8 (page 303)

I. (1) Exact   (7) Exact
  (3) Approximate   (9) Approximate
  (5) Approximate

V. (1) .002%   (7) .07%
  (3) .002%   (9) 1.06%
  (5) .07%

Exercise 8.9 (page 312)

I. (1) 185.91   (5) 1.844
  (3) 221.9

III. (1) 18   (11) 5.17×10^9
   (3) 43   (13) 10,000,000
   (5) 15.1   (15) 1.03×10
   (7) .0002   (17) 299,000
   (9) 1.39×10^{-9} (19) 430,000

V. (1) 140 cu. inches   (5) 63,942.25 sq. ft.
  (3) 4.84 sec.   (7) 45.85

CHAPTER 9

Exercise 9.1 (page 317)

III.

Clock number	1	3	5	7	9	11
Additive inverse	11	9	7	5	3	1

V. (1) 6   (7) true for all t
    (3) 6   (9) 2
    (5) 6

Exercise 9.3 (page 327)

I. (1) False   (7) True
    (3) True   (9) False
    (5) True

Exercise 9.4 (page 331)

I. (1) 5_7 (7) 9_{12}
    (3) 0_7 (9) 0_4
    (5) 2_5

III. (1) 3_5 (7) 0_6
     (3) 3_5 (9) 11_{12}
     (5) 0_6

Exercise 9.5 (page 336)

III. (1) Not a commutative group
     (3) Commutative group
     (5) Not a commutative group
     (7) Commutative group

Exercise 9.6 (page 339)

I. (1) $x \equiv 2 \pmod 3$ (7) $x \equiv 2 \pmod{17}$
    (3) $x \equiv 2 \pmod 5$ (9) $x \equiv 8 \pmod{11}$
    (5) $x \equiv 3 \pmod{17}$

Exercise 9.7 (page 343)

I. (1) $9 \nmid 27{,}638$ (7) $9 \nmid 173{,}287$
    (3) $9 \mid 85{,}419$ (9) $9 \mid 654{,}723$
    (5) $9 \nmid 26{,}893$

Exercise 9.8 (page 351)

I. (1) $\{(x, y): x = 3k \wedge y = -7 - k \wedge k \in I\}$;
    (3) $\{(x, y): x = 4 + 6k \wedge y = 5k \wedge k \in I\}$;
    (5) $\{(x, y): x = 2 + 8k \wedge y = 1 + 9k \wedge k \in I\}$

III. (1)

4¢	15¢
128	0
113	4
98	8
83	12
68	16
53	20
38	24
23	28
8	32

(3) 92

INDEX

D E F G H I J   0 6 9 8 7

Printed in the United States of America.

ABOUT THE AUTHORS

MERLIN M. OHMER received his B.S. and M.S. degrees from Tulane University and his Ph.D. degree in mathematics from the University of Pittsburgh. In 1948 he joined the staff of the mathematics department at the University of Southwestern Louisiana, where he became full professor in 1956. Since 1959 he has been an associate director and lecturer in National Science Foundation summer and in-service institutes at the University. His lectures on the changing mathematical curricula in the elementary and secondary schools have reached wide audiences throughout the U. S. and Canada. Professor Ohmer is a member of the Mathematical Association of America, the National Council of Teachers of Mathematics, the Louisiana Academy of Sciences, the Louisiana Teachers Association, the American Association of University Professors, and is active in civic, church, and school affairs. He is a commander in the U. S. Naval Reserve and commanding officer of a Naval Reserve Officers' School. Dr. Ohmer is a visiting lecturer for the Mathematical Association of America, a visiting scientist for the Louisiana Academy of Sciences, and a member of the advisory board to the Louisiana State Department of Education. He conducts a state-wide television program in mathematics for elementary school teachers and parents.

CLAYTON V. AUCOIN received his B.S. degree from Louisiana College and his M.S. and Ph.D. degrees in mathematics from Auburn University. Subsequently, he spent a year at Stanford University on an N.S.F. faculty fellowship studying operations research and stochastic processes. From 1959 to 1963 he was a member of the mathematics department at the University of Southwestern Louisiana, where he was promoted to Associate Professor in 1962. In 1963 he joined the staff of the mathematics department at Clemson University and became department chairman in 1964. While he was at the University of Southwestern Louisiana, Professor Aucoin lectured in N.S.F. summer and in-service institutes. Dr. Aucoin is a member of the Mathematical Association of America, the Society for Industrial and Applied Mathematics, and the Association for Computing Machinery.

MARION J. CORTEZ received his B.S. and M.Ed. degrees from the University of Southwestern Louisiana. In 1959 he became mathematics teacher at Lafayette High School. Presently, as mathematics teacher at Northside High School and supervising teacher for the University, he is responsible for supervising student teachers of mathematics. His lectures on mathematics in the elementary schools have reached wide audiences throughout Louisiana. Mr. Cortez is a member of the Mathematical Association of America, the National Council of Teachers of Mathematics, the National Education Association, and the Louisiana Teachers Association.